Recent Advancements in Geotechnical Engineering
NCRAG'21

Eighth National Conference on Recent Advancements in Geotechnical Engineering NCRAG'21, March 26, 2021, Department of Civil Engineering, Bannari Amman Institute of Technology Sathyamangalam, India

Editors
B. Soundara
M. Vasudevan
V. Jeevanantham
V. Preetha

Department of Civil Engineering, Bannari Amman Institute of Technology Sathyamangalam, Tamil Nadu, India

Peer review statement

All papers published in this volume of "Materials Research Proceedings" have been peer reviewed. The process of peer review was initiated and overseen by the above proceedings editor. All reviews were conducted by expert referees in accordance to Materials Research Forum LLC high standards.

Published under License by **Materials Research Forum LLC**
Millersville, PA 17551, USA

Published as part of the proceedings series
Materials Research Proceedings
Volume 19 (2021)

ISSN 2474-3941 (Print)
ISSN 2474-395X (Online)

ISBN 978-1-64490-160-1 (Print)
ISBN 978-1-64490-161-8 (eBook)

This book contains information obtained from authentic and highly regarded sources. Reasonable efforts have been made to publish reliable data and information, but the author and publisher cannot assume responsibility for the validity of all materials or the consequences of their use. The authors and publishers have attempted to trace the copyright holders of all material reproduced in this publication and apologize to copyright holders if permission to publish in this form has not been obtained. If any copyright material has not been acknowledged please write and let us know so we may rectify in any future reprint.

Distributed worldwide by

Materials Research Forum LLC
105 Springdale Lane
Millersville, PA 17551
USA
http://www.mrforum.com

Manufactured in the United States of America
10 9 8 7 6 5 4 3 2 1

Table of Contents

Preface

Geotechnical engineering has become an important and inevitable discipline of civil engineering due to its rapid advancements and the growing needs in the present. This field has taken a huge leap forward in the last 8 decades. Geotechnical engineers face difficult environment and fresh challenges every day.

This Eighth National Conference on Recent Advancements in Geotechnical Engineering NCRAG'21 organized by the Department of Civil Engineering, Bannari Amman Institute of Technology Sathyamangalam, India, aims at bringing students, researchers, and experts together on a single platform to discuss and interact with the materials involved and day to day challenges faced by geotechnical engineers. The presentation made by the participants will motivate young researchers to come up with new problem identification and new methodologies which will help in finding solutions to current and future problems. In the conference, emphasis is made on the topics such as innovative materials in the fields of geotechnical engineering, pavement engineering, health monitoring of structures and sustainability.

This conference proceedings book will be a valuable reference material. It will be highly beneficial not only to the academicians and scholars, but also to industrial researchers and policy makers who are keen in observing the latest trends in engineering and technology towards product/service/policy formulation. In this regard, we anticipate a good welcoming opportunity for this title to get exposed and popularized, especially through the banner of MRP Publications.

On behalf of the organizing committee and the host institute, we thank all the contributing authors, members of various committees, technical reviewers, and co-editors for making this attempt a grant success. We apologize for any inadvertent mistakes occurred in this edition.

Department of Civil Engineering, Bannari Amman Institute of Technology Sathyamangalam, Tamil Nadu, India

Editorial Note

The ongoing pandemic situation has forced us to opt for virtual mode of conference presentations. This is based on the realization that the participants (and the organizers too) will not be able to travel and or assemble physically at a common place due to the prevailing Covid-19 restrictions.

Conference model

One day program with two keynote lectures followed by technical presentation sessions. Conference paper presentation, totally 10 panels were planned and about 120 selected papers were presented by the participants during the Conference Day. Eminent academic persons from various institutions were invited for chairing the panels. Conference presentations gave the opportunity to share their research ideas.

The participants were given 15 minutes time covering 10 minutes' presentation and 5 minutes interaction with the session chair. Each presentation was evaluated by the session chair and co-chair for a maximum score of 30 (technical content-10, presentation-10, and communication/interaction-10). 10 Best Paper Awards were selected by the Panel chairs

The conference was delivered using Google Meet application (https://meet.google.com/)

This Conference Proceedings consist of total 166 abstracts is available at conference website with other details. (https://sites.google.com/bitsathy.ac.in/ncrag21/proceedings)

Department of Civil Engineering, Bannari Amman Institute of Technology Sathyamangalam, Tamil Nadu, India

Technical Review Committee Members,

Dr. PL Meyyappan, Kalasalingam Academy of Research and Education, Krishnan kovil
Dr. M. Kalaivani   , K.S.Rangasamy College of Technology, Tiruchengode
Dr. K. Murali, Sri Ramakrishna Institute of Technology, Coimbatore
Dr. S.V.Sivapriya, SSN College of Engineering, Chennai
Dr. Sujatha Unnikrishnan, CHRIST(Deemed to be University), Bangalore
Dr. A. THIRUMURUGAN , JCT College of Engineering and Technology, Coimbatore
Dr. P.S. Kothai, Kongu Engineering College, Perundurai
Dr. N. Ramu, IFIM College, Bangalore
Dr. Naresh K Sharma, Kalasalingam Academy of Research and Education, Krishnan kovil
Dr. M. Kaarthik, Coimbatore Institute of Technology, Coimbatore
Dr. R. Jagadeesan, K.S. Rangasamy College of Technology, Tiruchengode
Dr. N. Karthiga Shenbagam, Bannari Amman Institute of Technology, Sathyamangalam
Dr. M.Vasudevan, Bannari Amman Institute of Technology, Sathyamangalam
Dr. Prakash Chinnaiyan, Amrita vishwa vidyapeetham, Coimbatore Campus
Dr. G. Kumaresan, Bannari Amman Institute of Technology, Sathyamangalam
Dr. L. Andal, Vellamal College of Engineering and Technology, Madurai
Dr. N. Saranya, TLC-CIT, Coimbatore
Dr. M. Jemimah Carmichael, Vignan's Lara Institute of Technology and Science, Vadlamudi, Andhra
Pradesh
Dr. M. Karthikeyan, Vignan's Foundation for Science and Technology, Vadlamudi, Andhra Pradesh
Dr. SM Suneeth Kumar, ATME College of Engineering, Mysore
Dr. B. Vijaya, Dr.MGR Educational and Research Institute University
Dr. Malathy R, Sona College of Technology, Salem
Dr. Sathish Reddy, VEMU Institute of Technology, Tirupathi
Dr. Subash, Guru Nanak Institute of Technology,Hyderabad
Dr. V. Vijayakumar, Bannari Amman Institute of Technology, Sathyamangalam
Dr. S. Thenmozhi, St. Joseph's Institute of Technology, Chennai
Ms. M. Hannah Angelin, Coimbatore Institute of Technology, Coimbatore
Ms. S. Brindha ,Coimbatore Institute of Technology, Coimbatore
Dr. V. Senthilkumar, Shakthi Institute of Engineering and Technology, Coimbatore
Dr. M. Devasena, PSG Institute of Technology and Applied Research, Coimbatore
Dr. Subramanyam Busetty, SASTRA Deemed University, Thanjavur
Dr. Sathyamoorthy G L, Kumaraguru College of Technology, Coimbatore
Dr M. ARUN, PSG Institute of Technology and Applied Research, Coimbatore
Dr. Jayachandran K., National Institute of Technology Calicut (NIT Calicut)
Dr. G. Venkatesan, Anna University, University College of Engineering (BIT campus), Tiruchirappalli
Dr. K Nirmalkumar, Kongu Engineering College, Perundurai
Dr. L.K. REX, Agni College of Technology, Chennai
Dr. K. Ramadevi, Kumaraguru College of Technology, Coimbatore
Dr. J. Premalatha, Kumaraguru College of Technology, Coimbatore
Dr. S. Ramakrishnan, Sri Krishna College of Engineering and Technology, Coimbatore
Dr. S. Selvakumar, Vel Tech Rangarajan Dr.Sagunthala R & D Institute of Science & Technology,
Chennai
Dr. K.G. Elangovan, University College of Engineering, Thirukkuvalai
Dr. P. Muthupriya, Dr.N.G.P Institute of Technology, Coimbatore
Dr. S. Boopathi, Mechanical Engineering, Department, Muthayammal Engineering College, Rasipuram
Dr. S.Ramesh, K.S.Rangasamy College of Technology, Tiruchengode
Dr. D. Ambika, Kongu Engineering College, Perundurai
Dr. M. Saravanan, Marri Laxman Reddy Institute of Technology and Management, Telangana

BIT Organising Committee

Recent Advancements in Geotechnical Engineering - NCRAG'21   Materials Research Forum LLC
Materials Research Proceedings **19** (2021) 1-8   https://doi.org/10.21741/9781644901618-1

Broad-Spectrum of Sustainable Living Management Using Green Building Materials- An Insights

R. Sivarethinamohan[1,a] *, S. Sujatha[2,b]

[1]CHRIST (Deemed to be University), Bangalore, Karnataka

[2]K.Ramakrishnan College of Technology, Trichy, Tamilnadu

[a]mohan.dimat@gmail.com, [b]sujalalit@gmail.com

Keywords: Life Cycle Assessment, Environmental Benefit, Economic Benefit, Sustainable Construction

Abstract. Owing to the recurrent modifications in the lifestyle and demands of humans the regular life of buildings is decreasing whereas the demolition or renovation of the buildings increases. Building materials and their components ingest just about 40 percent of world-wide vigour per annum in their life segments such as fabrication and procurement of building materials, construction and demolition. The development of the construction industry completely relies on the deployable resources. To abate the consumption of construction materials in current years, the construction industry has established an environmental track, which wishes to use naturally available materials. Reviving such technology, further developing this technology green building materials are paramount for constructing green buildings. Such a green-building constructional model does not require energy contributions frequently for production. The advantage of reducing the energy used in manufacturing, increases strength. Green Building material is one which utilizes less water, optimizes energy efficiency, conserves natural resources, generates less waste, produces less carbon dioxide emissions and provides improved space for inhabitants as compared to conventional buildings. It includes environmental, economic, and social benefits as well. This paper aims to provide knowledge about some of the green building materials that help for sustainable living. These elucidations can obligate a significant influence in contemporary construction owed to the escalation in the charges of traditional construction materials.

Introduction

Growth in the construction industry is influenced on depletable resources. Producing the conventional building materials lead to impact on environment that is irreversible. Traditional and conventional construction of buildings involves high usage of water, energy [1], carbon emissions and so on. Mainly it has a greater impact on environment. At this juncture using the eco-friendly material is a best way to construct the building.Eco-friendly exactly means earth-friendly or not harmful to the environment. This refers to products that that help in conserving resources which are depletable in nature and GO GREEN is a crux for all production arena. Eco-friendly produces prevent contributions to air, water and land pollution. Its benefits [2] may not be easily recognizable tangibly, but through design, construction and operations buildings that are constructed with green building materials reducing carbon emissions, energy and waste, conserving   water   and   lowering   humans   exposure   to   toxins.In building, environmentally-friendly materials [3] (also identified as green building materials) are those which, perform actions of low environmental impact [4]. The green building material [3] actually either partially replacing the conventional building materials or completely replacing the conventional one. The rationale behind this paper is to highlight how sustainable building material

Recent Advancements in Geotechnical Engineering - NCRAG'21   Materials Research Forum LLC
Materials Research Proceedings **19** (2021) 1-8   https://doi.org/10.21741/9781644901618-1

can contribute to minimize the impact of environmental degradation, and produce healthy buildings which can be sustainable to the inhabitant as well as our environment

Existing scenario of using conventional building material
The materials used for constructing the building generally take various forms of challenges. The discharge or the emission from the building materials is given much consideration and the fabrication of building materials entails employ high energy and resources in relationship with building processes. Some environmental concerns are prominent among the by-products of construction material used in buildings. Several restrictions are also there in extracting the resources which are the main ingredients in the manufacturing of many materials. In addition to it, one should think about the infrastructure that supports the built environment. Lot more advancements pertains to the technology, are there that need to be addressed [5] to resolve the hitches of exhaustion of resources, corrosion, durability, lifespan of the materials, pollution and so on. Figure 1 shows the techno edge for the conventional building materials.

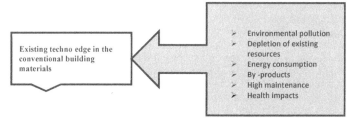

Fig.1 Current techno edge in the conventional building materials

Properties of green building materials
A green material is introverted that does the most with the smallest amount, fits most amicably surrounded by ecosystem processes, assists in eliminating the use of other materials and energy, and gives to the accomplishment of a service-based financial system. The advantages of using green building materials [6] over traditional materials are
- To achieve material efficiency which are everlasting, recyclable and reusable
- To design buildings in a conduct that consents for the use of smaller amount materials
- To take up processes that exploits less water, raw materials, and energy

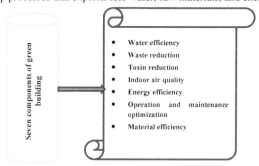

Fig. 2 Seven components of green building

Fig. 3 *Properties of green building materials*

Green expertise in the construction business engages brings into being new buildings that integrate one or more characteristics of environmentally friendly way out [7] . Building green has upstretched the bar for the construction industry entirety by launching new standards for sustainability and at the same time liveability. It is particularly clear when we observe structures that are now being premeditated to allow buildings to be easily dismantled rather than demolished. Seven components of green building are shown in the figure 2. Properties of green building materials are elucidated in the figure 3.

Evaluation of building materials for its sustainability

The general categories of available material resources, and its performance and pollution analysis is based on

- Kinds of energy sources are used in producing the material [8]
- Kinds of pollution and waste used for production and transport generate, and how much harm will its disposal generate and could it obtainable locally.
- Recyclable throughout its entire product life and its durability.

The evaluation of green building materials is likely to [9] begin with conventional materials that are mostly used. However, in an evolution to sustainability, the process of evaluation must commence to consider more and more of materials that fit within environment [5]. To Evaluate the building products, it is essential the evaluation process should start from gathering of raw materials to their eventual clearance which could give us a better insight about the enduring costs of materials. During the production and selection of materials three stages of appraisal [10] could be done. The first and foremost stage is prior to constructing the building that is meant as pre building stage. Second stage is during the execution of the construction that is meant as ongoing building stage and the third stage is termed as post building stage. The first stage starts in finding unprocessed materials in nature and ends in transportation those materials to a building site. In between these two there exist manufacturing and packaging too. There is a much possibility of environmental destruction in the first stage. Second stage involves in assembling of material, maintaining and repairing the materials. This stage hangs on throughout the lifetime of the materials. In this second stage also waste generation is considered. The last and the least acknowledged stage is the third stage which is meant as post building stage. In this stage the performance of the materials will be low and it is the stage in which these materials should undergo recycling process. They could be reused into other goods or less can be thrown away.

Green building materials (eco- friendly materials) for construction

Some of the green building materials have been discussed below (source:https://www.dumpsters.com/blog/green-building-materials) and have been displayed in the figures from figure 4 to figure 8.

Bamboo

Bamboo plant grows easily and bamboo produces more oxygen than carbon dioxide as a consequence creating it a very eco-friendly and cost-effective construction material. It has a great durability as well.

Fig.4 Bamboo(source:https://www.dumpsters.com/blog/green-building-materials)

Engineered Wood

Lot of wood gets wasted during the making of wooden boards from raw timber. This waste be capable of making engineered wood (which includes layers of wood and fillers similar to wood scraps and fibres). This is further used to make walls, doors and so on and which is in turn a eco-friendly material.

Fig. 5 Engineered Wood (source: https://www.dumpsters.com/blog/green-building-materials)

Earthen Materials

Earthen materials are in use since the beginning of the construction. These include adobe bricks and rammed earth. Adobe bricks are fabricated from earth, comprising mainly of clay and straw or cow dung. Load bearing walls can be constructed using adobe bricks. Rammed earth is a kind of artificial rock that's formed by compacting ingredients such as dirt, gravel, sand, clay and silt. This kind of earth is fire resistant and rammed earth walls do not require periodical maintenance. Termite attach could be reduced by the usage of earthen material in building construction.

Straw Bale

Straw bale is one of the green building materials consisting of baled straw from rice, oats, wheat, barley, rye and so on. It possesses great insulating properties and acoustic properties. Since it has acoustic properties the wall that is built with straw bale will be completely soundproof.

Fig. 6 Straw bale (source: https://www.dumpsters.com/blog/green-building-materials)

Reclaimed Wood

Those building that are constructed using reclaimed wood is the most environmentally friendly and have high accountability towards reducing the amount landfills and saving trees. It is a qualitative wood which could be obtained from sources like manufacturing units, old ships, withdrawn ships, godowns, warehouses and so on. The usage of reclaimed wood diminishes the demand for virgin wood which will eventually preserve the forests and thereby safeguards forest ecosystem.

Cork

In modern years, flooring with cork has happened to be more prevailing in residential and commercial areas. Cork is one among the sustainable building materials that does not hurt or injure trees. The tree bark could be stripped up to twenty times all through its life phase. Apart from the sustainable nature the cork has fire resistant quality as well. It also has resistant towards the liquids. Figure 7 portrays the cork.

Figure 7.Cork(source:https://www.dumpsters.com/blog/green-building-materials)

Mycelium

It is fibrous material which resembles root of a tree. Mycelium are the root like fibres found on mushrooms and it is a vegetative part of fungus-like bacterial colony. Mycologist Philip Ross formerly tested with fungi and mycelium for his art fittings. This mushroom-based building material is able to hold up extreme temperatures, and degradable which is a better alternative to home insulation. Now days this kind of bio fabrication is ruling the sustainable construction world. Bricks that are prepared from mycelium are even act a bullet proof and even absorb carbon di oxide. Figure 8 indicating the wall made up of mycelium.

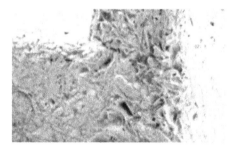

Fig.8. Mycelium wall(source:https://www.dumpsters.com/blog/green-building-materials)
Ferrock and Recycled steel

In the context of manufacturing the concrete a material called as ferrock is fabricated by incorporating steel dust or ferrous rock which will be otherwise sent to the landfill. This additive produces iron carbonate with carbon dioxide. This alternative can be used to lay pathways, drive ways and even staircases. It is well known that 2,000 square-foot house entails up to 50 trees to build, whereas a frame made from recycled steel involves steel, equivalent of six crumbed cars. Above all steel has high recyclable value which can eventually

Trees could be saved and durability can be increased against earthquakes and high winds if steel beams are used for the framing process instead of wood. According to the Steel Recycling organization, since steel is 100 percent recyclable, it can significantly shrink the ecological shock of new construction.

Precast concrete also plays a major role in this context [11]. Light-emitting cement, Martian Concrete, Self-healing of cracked concrete using bacteria, Wood foam, Transparent wood are all newly created green building material [12].

Economic benefits of green construction using green building materials and risk in constructing green buildings

Green construction can end up with considerable economic savings by getting better employee yield, escalating benefits from up gradation in health and safety [2]. The cost components are manufacturing wages, office wages, utilities, building maintenance, equipment maintenance and initial investment are also reduced. It was found that "negligence of constructability in green designs" is the most severe risk factor. Design-related risk factors include the inexperience of designers in green projects, limited creativity and innovation in green designs, slow response to change orders, negligence of constructability in green designs, and negligence of material waste in green designs [13,14].

Conclusion

Sustainability is a substitute measure for building materials and are usually preferred through some specifications related to functionality. It is also chosen based on technical and economical specifications. On the other hand, with sustainability as a vital dispute in the past few decades, predominantly in developed nations, the environmental stack of building materials as well happen to a more noteworthy prerequisite. The construction segment is directly or possibly indirectly generates a sizeable portion of the destruction on environment, which has become the key point to support sustainable development. It is finding more environmental friendly movements to construction and building. A building material which is said to be sustainable in nature needs to be exercised appropriately and contextually in each and every community growth. The purpose of sustainable building materials is not just lessening the transport costs, carbon emissions, and in most of the cases costs of the materials. It also recommends service and skills development opportunities for community members. In this paper how to find a better green material for the construction has been described. The risk that involves in constructing a green building using go green materials is also analysed here. Ultimately a thorough and steady action is needed today to protect our surroundings from further damage and to control the exhaustive usage of energy for the sustainable future.

References

[1] R.M.Pulselli, E. Simoncini, F.M.Pulselli and S.Bastianoni, Energy analysis of building manufacturing, maintenance and use: building indices to evaluate housing sustainability, Energy Build. 39 5 (2007) 620–8. https://doi.org/10.1016/j.enbuild.2006.10.004

[2] R.Ries, M. Bilec and N.M.Gokhan and K.L.Needy, The economic benefits of green buildings: a comprehensive case study , Eng. Eco. 51 3 (2006) 259–95. https://doi.org/10.1080/00137910600865469

[3] J.E.Fernandez, Material Architecture: Emergent Materials for Innovative Buildings and Ecological Construction ,Architectural Press: Amsterdam, Boston, Elsiever, 2006

[4] A.Karolides, Green Building Approaches Green Building: Project Planning and Cost Estimating,W iley, E-Book, Third Edition, 2002.

Materials Research Forum LLC
https://doi.org/10.21741/9781644901618-1

[5] D.Sherwin, Reducing the cost of green, J. Green Build. 11 (2006) 46–54.
https://doi.org/10.3992/jgb.1.1.46

[6] G.Polat and A.P. Gurgun ,Identification of Material-related Risks in Green, Building
Procedia Eng. 196 (2017) 956-963. https://doi.org/10.1016/j.proeng.2017.08.036

[7] I.Cooper, Which focus for building assessment methods: Environmental performance or
sustainability?, Build. Res. Inf. 27 4-5 (1999) 321-331.
https://doi.org/10.1080/096132199369435

[8] B.V. Venkatarama Reddy and K.Jagadish, Embodied energy of common and alternative
building materials and technologies, Energy Build. 35 2 (2003) 129–37.
https://doi.org/10.1016/S0378-7788(01)00141-4

[9] A.Muse and J.M. Plaut, 2006 An inside look at LEED: experienced practitioners reveal the
inner workings of LEED, J. Green Build. 1 1 (2006) 3–8. https://doi.org/10.3992/jgb.1.1.1

[10] L.Bourdeau, Agenda 21 on sustainable construction, CIB Report Publication, 237,1999

[11] P.Wu and S.P.Low, Barriers to Achieving Green Precast Concrete Stock Management–a
Survey of Current Stock Management Practices in Singapore, J. Constr. Manag. 14 (2014) 78-89.
https://doi.org/10.1080/15623599.2014.899126

[12] P.De.Luca, I. Carbone and J.B.Nagy, Green building materials: a review of state Of the art
studies of innovative materials, J. Green Build. 12 4 (2017) 141 -161.
https://doi.org/10.3992/1943-4618.12.4.141

[13] B.Ashuri and A.Durmus-Pedini, An Overview of the Benefits and Risk Factors of Going
Green in Existing Buildings, J. Facil. Manag. 1 (2020) 1-15

[14] H.Ali and S.Alnusairat, Developing a Green Building Assessment Tool for Developing
Countries–Case of Jordan, Build Environ . 44 5 (2009) 1053-1064.
https://doi.org/10.1016/j.buildenv.2008.07.015

Recent Advancements in Geotechnical Engineering - NCRAG'21   Materials Research Forum LLC
Materials Research Proceedings **19** (2021) 9-17   https://doi.org/10.21741/9781644901618-2

Study on Strength and Behaviour of Cold-Formed Steel Built-up Columns

K. Sivasathya[1,a*], S. Vijayanand[2,b], M. Merlin Prabha[3,c] and I. Paarvendhan[4,d]

[1*]PG Student, Department of Civil Engineering, Kongu Engineering College, Perundurai, Erode, Tamil Nadu, India

[2]Assistant Professor, Department of Civil Engineering, Kongu Engineering College, Perundurai, Erode, Tamil Nadu, India

[3,4]UG Students, Department of Civil Engineering, Kongu Engineering College, Perundurai, Erode, Tamil Nadu, India

[a*]sivasathyacivil97@gmail.com, [b]atmvijay.anand@gmail.com, [c]merlin141999@gmail.com, [d]impaari143@gmail.com

Keywords: Cold-Formed Steel, Compression Elements, Built-Up Columns, Open and Closed Sections

Abstract. Cold-formed Steel (CFS), a sort of steel weighing lesser, suits to be a wise choice of material in the construction of steel structures. It has more benefits that indeed make CFS get famous. Effortless installation can be accomplished with the CFS. It also renders a factor that only a few materials show, that is, longevity. Corrosion does not affect the CFS. Employing under moderate loads, CFS finds to be economically feasible when compared with hot-rolled steel. It can be used as compression members comprising single or built-up members. Since a single member cannot sustain the heavy load, the built-up members can be utilized. Open and closed sections are the two sorts of built-up profiles and these profiles show diverse buckling characteristics. This paper lays out a clear outline of the research works done on providing design recommendations to the codes by employing diverse built-up sections. It is reviewed by categorizing the investigated research works based on the kind of CFS sections chosen by each researcher. It was evident from the study that after validation, many researchers have done parametric study on CFS built-up columns to assess the accuracy of the design strength prediction by code specifications. Many codes failed to estimate the section's ultimate capacity accurately as there are no specific design equations.

Introduction

CFS members are used in industries, office buildings (low-rise), houses with steel frames, etc., [1, 2]. CFS single section's capacity to take large compressive loads is minimum. Connection of two or more single sections like the hat, C, Z, etc., give rise to built-up sections [3-5] that show greater load carrying capacity than individuals [6-8]. Lacings and battens are used to assemble them [9]. The built-up members are made of two geometries i.e., open and closed. Higher torsional rigidity is shown by closed sections in contrary to open sections [2, 5, 10-12]. These elements show unique behaviors of buckling. The demerit is that specific provisions in codes are not available for designing a built-up member [6]. Thus, investigators on designing the built-up sections, have recommended new equations for the codes to calculate the bearing capacity of the columns. Their works are consolidated and presented in this paper.

Recent Advancements in Geotechnical Engineering - NCRAG'21   Materials Research Forum LLC
Materials Research Proceedings **19** (2021) 9-17   https://doi.org/10.21741/9781644901618-2

Closed built-up sections
Fig.1 shows the typical built-up closed sections.

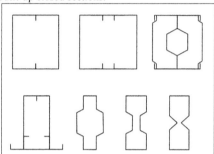

Figure 1. Built-up closed sections

Usage of web stiffeners
Research works employing stiffeners in the web of a section were presented in [2, 4, 13-16]. Web stiffeners are generally said to give better resistance to local buckling [1, 2]. Young and Chen [2], on connecting two open profiles with screws (self-tapping) in their flange portion, formed a closed section. Inclination of 45° was made on the web. By testing the 17 fixed-ended columns under axial force, the Direct Strength Method (DSM) in North American Specification (NAS 2004) and Australian/New Zealand Standard (AS/NZS 2005) was checked for its aptness in calculating the ultimate strength of web stiffened built-up columns. There was a determination of unsuitability of the DSM. Later, Zhang and Young [4] done quality work on two different web-stiffened (inwardly and outwardly) built-up sections formed by connecting two open profiles with screws (self-tapping). The column ends were fixed and loaded axially. Here, the DSM was good for the sections having a nominal thickness at the area of contact. But, the same sections after validating by ABAQUS software in [13] and on doing an extensive study with 252 columns, modified DSM was seen to be a suitable one. On studying welded and screwed stub columns (made of plain and lipped channels), higher load carrying capacity was observed in the columns with stiffeners at webs [14].

Two lipped C-sections connected face-to-face
Closed sections were assembled by welding in [10, 17], screws in [3], battens in [18]. There were only scanty research works in columns with welding connectivity. Whittle and Ramseyer [17] tested 150 welded closed columns and came up with many conclusions regarding the appropriateness of the modified slenderness ratio approach. It was exceedingly conservative. Followingly, 48 seam welded closed sections were tested between the two support conditions - fixed or flexible. Ultimate strength was not reduced for all the columns except with maximum spacing of weld and so for those, it was concluded that there was no need to apply modified slenderness ratio in American Iron and Steel Institute (AISI S100-2007). Muftah et al. [3], conducting investigations on the capacity of closed columns of various lengths with screw connection through tests and on comparing with Eurocode specifications (EC3), observed an 80% difference in load values. Kherbouche and Megnounif [18] compared the numerical results (ANSYS) of closed columns with battens connectivity with theoretical results obtained from a new

Materials Research Forum LLC
https://doi.org/10.21741/9781644901618-2

approach using DSM, AISI and EC3 specifications. It was evident from the study that the column's strength was influenced by the ratio of channel spacing to the length of the web.

Assembling four angle sections
Four angle sections were connected by battens [19-21] and lacings [12, 22, 23] to form a closed section and investigations were carried out. Pin-ended laced columns with bolt connectivity were tested under monotonic axial loading experimentally. A parametric study was further carried out using ABAQUS software. Limitations on parameter varied were suggested and also as the effect of slenderness ratio of lacing was not included in codes, NAS and EC3 were not appropriate [22, 23]. Similarly, Anbarasu and Dar [12] investigated battened four lipped angle sections by varying the parameters like angle section's sectional compactness, global column slenderness and batten's spacing by ABAQUS. New design provisions were put forward as the current rules were not satisfactory. Yet another research on closed section with four lipped angles connected by battens was presented in [20]. It was clear that the capacity of the section increased with the lower slenderness of the chord. The design expressions proposed by El Aghoury et al. (2013) gave safe results but not the provisions of NAS and EC3.

Connecting C and U-shaped elements
Single C and U-shaped sections were connected by screws and investigated in [24-30]. Various parameters on multi-limbs stub columns were analyzed by ANSYS. Reduction in the maximum width-thickness ratio increased the capacity of columns. Recently, single box [28] and double box [27] columns were investigated compressing concentrically and eccentrically by experimental, numerical and theoretical means. Some other recent research on box columns was to estimate the fire-resistant capacity [29, 30]. Findings on the effect of connector spacing were given in [25, 26].

Assemblage of single innovative sections
There were innovative columns investigated in [5, 11, 31, 32]. Georgieva et al. [11] compared DSM predictions with experimental buckling capacities of two sections formed by Σ, Z, channel and track profiles using CUFSM software. If the DSM was added with the global-distortional buckling interaction provision, DSM could be easily used. New design expression was provided in [5] to predict the CFS built-up lipped sigma channel's strength. Usually, local buckling stress and torsional rigidity were seen to get increased with closed sections formed by sigma shape.

Open built-up sections
Fig.2 shows the typical built-up open sections.

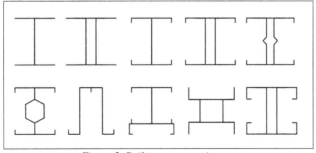

Figure 2. Built-up open sections

Lipped channels connected back-to-back
Investigations on back-to-back connectivity in lipped channels were carried out in [3, 33-41]. Thirty-two columns with screw connectivity were experimentally investigated in [33]. Five stub columns were tested experimentally under axial compression in [40] and numerically by LUSAS software in [41]. With EWM, better results were obtained than DSM. Local buckling was the major type of failure seen in stub columns. Muftah et al. [3] on conducting tests and comparing the results of open section columns with the EC3 approach, a 20% difference was seen. Then, Abu-Hamd et al. [34] on doing a parametric study, found AISI's prediction was safe for medium and long but for not short columns. Roy et al. [36] studied the thickness effect by using 204 models and as it was found that AISI and AS/NZS gave unsafe results for the columns undergoing local buckling, new rules of the design were given. Ting et al. [37] studied the screw spacing effect on 144 columns. The strength of intermediate and short columns depended on screw numbers but not stub columns. Chen et al. [38] found that holes (edge-stiffened) in the built-up open section rendered an increase in axial strength.

Lipped channels connected back-to-back with gap
Using this section, researches were done in [6, 7, 18, 42-46]. Roy et al. [42] found 53% appropriateness in AISI and AS/NZS strength predictions of columns with link-channels at intermediate. Kherbouche and Megnounif [18], with battened open columns, numerically studied and compared with the results of EC3, a new approach using DSM and AISI. Then, Vijayanand and Anbarasu [7] on investigating the strength of columns with battens found DSM and EWM were appropriate only under specific buckling behavior. Further, 228 models were taken for parametric study and the adequacy of EC3 and AISI specifications were checked [45]. Followingly, Anbarasu and Adil Dar [43] found that the resistance to local buckling could be achieved by incorporating spacers in open built-up columns. Recently, Muthuraman et al. [44] found safe predictions of DSM with the battened columns having a slenderness ratio less than 60.

Plain channels connected back-to-back
Experimental work was done in cold-formed stainless steel columns without any interval in between in [47]. Researches falling under the sections with intervals inbetween were presented in [25, 26, 48, 49]. NAS, AS/NZS and EC3 predictions were found unsafe for the battened columns that had locally buckled [48, 49]. Recently, two channels were connected by plates and an investigation was done in [25, 26]. It was revealed that the spacing of connectors and the component's interaction with one another influenced the column's ultimate capacity.

Employing stiffeners
Stiffeners were employed in built-up sections and investigated in [9, 14, 34, 50-52]. Anbarasu et al. [9] connected two lipped channels with web stiffeners using battens, studied 30 models and came up with the conclusion that there was no sight of local buckling due to stiffeners. A simple expression for the design was proposed then. In [50], with 40 hinged-hinged built-up sigma columns, a parametric study was conducted. AISI was found to give results conservatively of about 5% for long, medium and short columns. Beulah and Ashvini [14] found an increase in the axial capacity of the back-to-back connected channel column with stiffeners at both webs and flanges. Laim et al. [51] came up with the fact that the fire resistance for built-up sections was greater when compared to single sections. This was evident from the study on fire resistance behavior of edge and web stiffened sigma single and built-up open columns. There was also the

incapability of existing methods to find the behavior of such columns under fire. Deepak et al. [52] found an increase in load carrying capacity of lipped back-to-back connected columns with stiffeners on comparing with seven other configurations.

Assemblage of single innovative sections
Innovative sections were investigated in [11, 25, 26, 53-55]. Georgieva et al. [11], comprising Σ, channel and track profiles formed a closed section and the suitability of DSM was assessed with the experimental results. Yet another research in this category was on bolted double Z members with rolled spacers in between [53]. Single Z profiles generally have low torsional rigidity and so the built up sections made of it could overcome this demerit. For such a section, there was a proposal of an approach based on DSM which seemed to be appealing. Liu and Zhou [54] tested 18 T-sections (long, intermediate and stub columns) formed by three lipped channels with screw connectivity and the study was conducted by varying parameters with 90 models. Anbarasu and Venkatesan [55] proposed an equation for accurate prediction of strength for an open section formed by four U-shaped sections. Recently, two different geometries formed by plain and lipped channels connected by screw were experimentally investigated [25, 26].

Conclusions
A clear sum up was given on the research works in CFS built-up sections. Each section was uniquely designed to carry the loads. Higher resistance to torsion was shown by CFS built-up closed sections. Stiffeners have shown good control against the local instabilities of the section. There was also an improvement of load carrying capacity with stiffeners. It was clear from the review that due importance should be given to various factors like connector spacing, number of connectors, slenderness of battens, etc., as they may affect the ultimate capacity of the column. Since the current design codes do not hold the provisions for the built-up sections, many investigators came up with new provisions to be adopted in those codes. Emerging software made their research works very easier. Though there were many pieces of research, not many innovative single sections were assembled to create a built-up section. Thus, there is a wide scope for investigating many innovative built-up sections that may serve to be economical. This paper may help the upcoming researchers to know more about the different CFS built-up sections investigated.

References

[1] B. Young, Research on cold-formed steel columns, Thin-Walled Structures. 46 (2008) 731-740. https://doi.org/10.1016/j.tws.2008.01.025

[2] B. Young, J. Chen, Design of cold-formed steel built-up closed sections with intermediate stiffeners, Journal of Structural Engineering. 134 (2008) 727-737. https://doi.org/10.1061/(ASCE)0733-9445(2008)134:5(727)

[3] F. Muftah, M. Sani, S. Mohammad, M.M. Tahir, Ultimate load of built-up cold-formed steel column, ARPN J. of Eng. and Appl.. Sciences. 9 (2014) 2095-2101.

[4] J.-H. Zhang, B. Young, Experimental investigation of cold-formed steel built-up closed section columns with web stiffeners, Journal of Constructional Steel Research. 147 (2018) 380-392. https://doi.org/10.1016/j.jcsr.2018.04.008

[5] M. Anbarasu, Numerical investigation on behaviour and design of cold-formed steel built-up column composed of lipped sigma channels, Advances in Structural Engineering. 22 (2019) 1817-1829. https://doi.org/10.1177/1369433218824499

[6] S. Vijayanand, M. Anbarasu, Effect of Spacers on Ultimate Strength and Behavior of Cold-Formed Steel Built-up Columns, Procedia engineering. 173 (2017) 1423-1430. https://doi.org/10.1016/j.proeng.2016.12.205

[7] S. Vijayanand, M. Anbarasu, Strength and behavior of cold-formed steel built-up battened columns: tests and numerical validation, Journal of Structural Engineering. 46 (2019) 154-164.

[8] K. Sivasathya, S. Vijayanand, Review of Cold-Formed Steel Columns, in: S. Mohan, S. Shankar, G. Rajeshkumar (Eds.) Materials, Design, and Manufacturing for Sustainable Environment, Springer 2021, pp. 289-300. https://doi.org/10.1007/978-981-15-9809-8_24

[9] M. Anbarasu, K. Kanagarasu, S. Sukumar, Investigation on the behaviour and strength of cold-formed steel web stiffened built-up battened columns, Materials and Structures. 48 (2015) 4029-4038. https://doi.org/10.1617/s11527-014-0463-8

[10] W. Reyes, A. Guzmán, Evaluation of the slenderness ratio in built-up cold-formed box sections, Journal of Constructional Steel Research. 67 (2011) 929-935. https://doi.org/10.1016/j.jcsr.2011.02.003

[11] I. Georgieva, L. Schueremans, L. Vandewalle, L. Pyl, Design of built-up cold-formed steel columns according to the direct strength method, Procedia Engineering. 40 (2012) 119-124. https://doi.org/10.1016/j.proeng.2012.07.066

[12] M. Anbarasu, M.A. Dar, Improved design procedure for battened cold-formed steel built-up columns composed of lipped angles, Journal of Constructional Steel Research. 164 (2020) 105781. https://doi.org/10.1016/j.jcsr.2019.105781

[13] J.-H. Zhang, B. Young, Finite element analysis and design of cold-formed steel built-up closed section columns with web stiffeners, Thin-walled Structures. 131 (2018) 223-237. https://doi.org/10.1016/j.tws.2018.06.008

[14] G. Beulah Gnana Ananthi, B. Ashvini, Experimental theoretical and numerical studies on cold-formed steel stub channel columns with stiffeners, Asian Journal of Civil Engineering. 20 (2018) 171-185. https://doi.org/10.1007/s42107-018-0096-2

[15] G. Aruna, S. Sukumar, V. Karthika, Behaviour of cold-formed steel built-up closed columns composed by angle profiles, Asian Journal of Civil Engineering. 20 (2019) 1037-1048. https://doi.org/10.1007/s42107-019-00164-8

[16] G. Aruna, Stub Column Tests of Cold-Formed Steel Built-Up Square Sections with Intermediate Stiffeners, Strength of Materials. 52 (2020) 281-290. https://doi.org/10.1007/s11223-020-00176-9

[17] J. Whittle, C. Ramseyer, Buckling capacities of axially loaded, cold-formed, built-up C-channels, Thin-Walled Structures. 47 (2009) 190-201. https://doi.org/10.1016/j.tws.2008.05.014

[18] S. Kherbouche, A. Megnounif, Numerical study and design of thin walled cold formed steel built-up open and closed section columns, Engineering Structures. 179 (2019) 670-682. https://doi.org/10.1016/j.engstruct.2018.10.069

[19] M. El Aghoury, A. Salem, M. Hanna, E. Amoush, Strength of cold formed battened columns subjected to eccentric axial compressive force, Journal of Constructional Steel Research. 113 (2015) 58-70. https://doi.org/10.1016/j.jcsr.2015.04.008

[20] M. Anbarasu, Behaviour of cold-formed steel built-up battened columns composed of four lipped angles: Tests and numerical validation, Advances in Structural Engineering. 23 (2020) 51-64. https://doi.org/10.1177/1369433219865696

[21] M.A. El Aghoury, A.H. Salem, M.T. Hanna, E.A. Amoush, Ultimate capacity of battened columns composed of four equal slender angles, Thin-Walled Structures. 63 (2013) 175-185. https://doi.org/10.1016/j.tws.2012.07.019

[22] M.A. Dar, D.R. Sahoo, S. Pulikkal, A.K. Jain, Behaviour of laced built-up cold-formed steel columns: Experimental investigation and numerical validation, Thin-Walled Structures. 132 (2018) 398-409. https://doi.org/10.1016/j.tws.2018.09.012

[23] M.A. Dar, D.R. Sahoo, A.K. Jain, Axial compression behavior of laced cold-formed steel built-up columns with unstiffened angle sections, Journal of Constructional Steel Research. 162 (2019) 105727. https://doi.org/10.1016/j.jcsr.2019.105727

[24] F. Liao, H. Wu, R. Wang, T. Zhou, Compression test and analysis of multi-limbs built-up cold-formed steel stub columns, Journal of Constructional Steel Research. 128 (2017) 405-415. https://doi.org/10.1016/j.jcsr.2016.09.005

[25] F.J. Meza, J. Becque, I. Hajirasouliha, Experimental study of the cross-sectional capacity of cold-formed steel built-up columns, Thin-Walled Structures. 155 (2020) 106958. https://doi.org/10.1016/j.tws.2020.106958

[26] F.J. Meza, J. Becque, I. Hajirasouliha, Experimental study of cold-formed steel built-up columns, Thin-Walled Structures. 149 (2020) 106291. https://doi.org/10.1016/j.tws.2019.106291

[27] S. Nie, T. Zhou, M.R. Eatherton, J. Li, Y. Zhang, Compressive behavior of built-up double-box columns consisting of four cold-formed steel channels, Engineering Structures. 222 (2020) 111133. https://doi.org/10.1016/j.engstruct.2020.111133

[28] S.-F. Nie, T.-H. Zhou, Y. Zhang, B. Liu, Compressive behavior of built-up closed box section columns consisting of two cold-formed steel channels, Thin-Walled Structures. 151 (2020) 106762. https://doi.org/10.1016/j.tws.2020.106762

[29] J. Yang, Y. Shi, W. Wang, L. Xu, H. Al-azzani, Experimental and numerical studies on axially restrained cold-formed steel built-up box columns at elevated temperatures, Journal of Constructional Steel Research. 171 (2020) 106143. https://doi.org/10.1016/j.jcsr.2020.106143

[30] J. Yang, W. Wang, Y. Shi, L. Xu, Experimental study on fire resistance of cold-formed steel built-up box columns, Thin-Walled Structures. 147 (2020) 106564. https://doi.org/10.1016/j.tws.2019.106564

[31] K. Roy, J.B. Lim, Numerical investigation into the buckling behaviour of face-to-face built-up cold-formed stainless steel channel sections under axial compression, Structures, Elsevier, 2019, pp. 42-73. https://doi.org/10.1016/j.istruc.2019.02.019

[32] K. Roy, C. Mohammadjani, J.B. Lim, Experimental and numerical investigation into the behaviour of face-to-face built-up cold-formed steel channel sections under compression, Thin-Walled Structures. 134 (2019) 291-309. https://doi.org/10.1016/j.tws.2018.09.045

[33] T.A. Stone, R.A. LaBoube, Behavior of cold-formed steel built-up I-sections, Thin-Walled Structures. 43 (2005) 1805-1817. https://doi.org/10.1016/j.tws.2005.09.001

[34] M. Abu-Hamd, M.M. Abdel-Ghaffar, B.M. El-Samman, Buckling strength of axially loaded cold formed built-up I-sections with and without stiffened web, Ain Shams Engineering Journal. 9 (2018) 3151-3167. https://doi.org/10.1016/j.asej.2017.11.004

[35] D.C. Fratamico, S. Torabian, X. Zhao, K.J. Rasmussen, B.W. Schafer, Experiments on the global buckling and collapse of built-up cold-formed steel columns, Journal of Constructional Steel Research. 144 (2018) 65-80. https://doi.org/10.1016/j.jcsr.2018.01.007

[36] K. Roy, T.C.H. Ting, H.H. Lau, J.B. Lim, Effect of thickness on the behaviour of axially loaded back-to-back cold-formed steel built-up channel sections-Experimental and numerical investigation, Structures, Elsevier, 2018, pp. 327-346. https://doi.org/10.1016/j.istruc.2018.09.009

[37] T.C.H. Ting, K. Roy, H.H. Lau, J.B. Lim, Effect of screw spacing on behavior of axially loaded back-to-back cold-formed steel built-up channel sections, Advances in Structural Engineering. 21 (2018) 474-487. https://doi.org/10.1177/1369433217719986

[38] B. Chen, K. Roy, A. Uzzaman, G. Raftery, J.B.P. Lim, Axial strength of back-to-back cold-formed steel channels with edge-stiffened holes, un-stiffened holes and plain webs, Journal of Constructional Steel Research. 174 (2020) 106313. https://doi.org/10.1016/j.jcsr.2020.106313

[39] S. Kechidi, D.C. Fratamico, B.W. Schafer, J. Miguel Castro, N. Bourahla, Simulation of screw connected built-up cold-formed steel back-to-back lipped channels under axial compression, Engineering Structures. 206 (2020) 110109. https://doi.org/10.1016/j.engstruct.2019.110109

[40] C.H.T. Ting, H.H. Lau, Compression test on cold-formed steel built-up back-to-back channels stub columns, Advanced Materials Research, Trans Tech Publ, 2011, pp. 2900-2903. https://doi.org/10.4028/www.scientific.net/AMR.201-203.2900

[41] T. Ting, H.H. Lau, A Numerical Investigation on Cold-Formed Steel Bulit-up Back-to-Back Channel Stub Columns, Advances in Steel and Aluminum Structures. (2011) 443-449. https://doi.org/10.3850/978-981-08-9247-0_rp063-icsas11

[42] K. Roy, T.C.H. Ting, H.H. Lau, J.B. Lim, Nonlinear behaviour of back-to-back gapped built-up cold-formed steel channel sections under compression, Journal of Constructional Steel Research. 147 (2018) 257-276. https://doi.org/10.1016/j.jcsr.2018.04.007

[43] M. Anbarasu, M. Adil Dar, Axial capacity of CFS built-up columns comprising of lipped channels with spacers: Nonlinear response and design, Engineering Structures. 213 (2020) 110559. https://doi.org/10.1016/j.engstruct.2020.110559

Recent Advancements in Geotechnical Engineering - NCRAG'21   Materials Research Forum LLC
Materials Research Proceedings **19** (2021) 9-17   https://doi.org/10.21741/9781644901618-2

[44] M. Muthuraman, R. Anuradha, P.O. Awoyera, R. Gobinath, Numerical simulation and specification provisions for buckling characteristics of a built-up steel column section subjected to axial loading, Engineering Structures. 207 (2020) 110256. https://doi.org/10.1016/j.engstruct.2020.110256

[45] S. Vijayanand, M. Anbarasu, Behavior of CFS built-up battened columns: Parametric study and design recommendations, Structural Engineering and Mechanics. 74 (2020) 381-394.

[46] S. Vijayanand, M. Vignesh, Numerical study on strength and behaviour of cold formed steel built-up battened columns, International Journal of Intellectual Advancements and Research in Engineering Computations. 7 (2019) 1634-1640.

[47] J. Dobrić, Z. Marković, D. Buđevac, M. Spremić, N. Fric, Resistance of cold-formed built-up stainless steel columns–part I: experiment, Journal of Constructional Steel Research. 145 (2018) 552-572. https://doi.org/10.1016/j.jcsr.2018.02.026

[48] M. Dabaon, E. Ellobody, K. Ramzy, Nonlinear behaviour of built-up cold-formed steel section battened columns, Journal of Constructional Steel Research. 110 (2015) 16-28. https://doi.org/10.1016/j.jcsr.2015.03.007

[49] M. Dabaon, E. Ellobody, K. Ramzy, Experimental investigation of built-up cold-formed steel section battened columns, Thin-Walled Structures. 92 (2015) 137-145. https://doi.org/10.1016/j.tws.2015.03.001

[50] J.-H. Zhang, B. Young, Numerical investigation and design of cold-formed steel built-up open section columns with longitudinal stiffeners, Thin-Walled Structures. 89 (2015) 178-191. https://doi.org/10.1016/j.tws.2014.12.011

[51] L. Laím, H.D. Craveiro, R. Simões, A. Escudeiro, A. Mota, Experimental analysis of cold-formed steel columns with intermediate and edge stiffeners in fire, Thin-Walled Structures. 146 (2020) 106481. https://doi.org/10.1016/j.tws.2019.106481

[52] M.S. Deepak, G. Beulah Gnana Ananthi, K. Mahendran, Behaviour of thin-walled intermediate stiffened back-to-back columns under axial compression, Materials Today: Proceedings. (2020). https://doi.org/10.1016/j.matpr.2020.07.575

[53] I. Georgieva, L. Schueremans, L. Pyl, Composed columns from cold-formed steel Z-profiles: Experiments and code-based predictions of the overall compression capacity, Engineering Structures. 37 (2012) 125-134. https://doi.org/10.1016/j.engstruct.2011.12.017

[54] X. Liu, T. Zhou, Research on axial compression behavior of cold-formed triple-lambs built-up open T-section columns, Journal of Constructional Steel Research. 134 (2017) 102-113. https://doi.org/10.1016/j.jcsr.2017.03.015

[55] M. Anbarasu, M. Venkatesan, Behaviour of cold-formed steel built-up I-section columns composed of four U-profiles, Advances in Structural Engineering. 22 (2019) 613-625. https://doi.org/10.1177/1369433218795568

Recent Advancements in Geotechnical Engineering - NCRAG'21
Materials Research Proceedings **19** (2021) 18-27

Materials Research Forum LLC
https://doi.org/10.21741/9781644901618-3

A Review on Application of Formaldehyde in Cement-Based Materials

SKM. Pothinathan[1,a*], M. Muthukannan[2,b], Narayanan Selvapalam[3,c], S. Christopher Gnanaraj[4,d]

[1]Department of Civil Engineering, Kalasalingam Academy of Research and Education, Krishnankoil-626126, Tamilnadu, India

[2]Department of Civil Engineering, Kalasalingam Academy of Research and Education, Krishnankoil-626126, Tamilnadu, India

[3]Department of Chemistry, Kalasalingam Academy of Research and Education, Krishnankoil-626126, Tamilnadu, India

[4]Department of Civil Engineering, Kalasalingam Academy of Research and Education, Krishnankoil-626126, Tamilnadu, India

[a]s.k.m.pothinathan@klu.ac.in, [b]m.muthukannan@klu.ac.in, [c]n.selvapalam@klu.ac.in, [d]s.christophergnanaraj@klu.ac.in

Keywords: Formaldehyde, Construction Material, Construction Industry, Admixture, Cement

Abstract. Formaldehyde is environment contamination, which causes irritation in the eyes, nose, and throat with concentration above 1.0ppm. But still, it is used as a construction material as an admixture and furthermore to make paints, adhesives, pressed wood, and flooring materials, etc. This paper reviews the impact of formaldehyde in the cement on flow, strength, and durability properties. In this most of the researchers studied the water reducing nature of formaldehyde-based cementitious materials (FBCM) because of its repulsive property, that can ensure improved workability and provides good mechanical strength. Finally, the challenges in the application of formaldehyde in cement-based materials are discussed to conclude some future scope in the field of the construction industry to use formaldehyde in cement.

Introduction

Formaldehyde is a by-product of naturally occurring organic material by the reaction with methane, oxygen, and other hydrocarbons in the presence of sunlight. Formaldehyde is a colorless component, and it is also adopting in several different forms like monomeric formaldehyde, trioxane, paraformaldehyde, and methanediol. Butlerov (1859), a Russian chemist, first reported the formaldehyde in the name of methylene dioxide in 1859. Hofmann announced the amalgamation techniques for formaldehyde in the laboratory by oxidation of methanol. Still, the Hofmann methods are in practice for making formaldehyde. Formaldehyde is not only used in construction industries and also for many industrial applications like to produce fabrics in the textile industry and to make brake shoes in the automobile industry. It is also used in making paints, foams, cosmetics, glues, adhesives, plywood, fiberboards, and to kill bacteria and fungi.

On the other hand, formaldehyde is an environmental pollutant, causes pungent-smell, eye and throat irritation, skin rash, and severe allergic reactions. IARC, 2004 stated the hazard value of formaldehyde depends on the concentration between 0.1 to 0.5 mg/m3 slight aggravation; at level 0.5 to 1 mg/m3 will irritate eyes, nose, and throat above 1 mg/m3 produce outrageous distress. So, the World Health Organization has suggested the concentration of formaldehyde indoor should be

Recent Advancements in Geotechnical Engineering - NCRAG'21   Materials Research Forum LLC
Materials Research Proceedings 19 (2021) 18-27   https://doi.org/10.21741/9781644901618-3

below 0.1mg/m3. Liang et al. (2013) presumed that the indoor formaldehyde concentration of decay is faster up-to 4 hours, and it is controlled by natural ventilation. Chi et al (2016) investigated indoor air contamination and stated that the formaldehyde concentration is sensitive to humidity and temperature, and it is easily predictable. Kim and Joong (2005) contemplated the effect of polyvinyl acetate (PVA) addition in melamine and concluded that the addition of PVA of 30% reduces the formaldehyde concentration. Bourdin et al. (2014) studied the formaldehyde emission from the building materials in the newly build classroom (134.1m3) with one whiteboard, two interactive boards, five chairs, eleven doors, a varnished desk, and painted walls. He concludes that the indoor air quality was not exceeding 8.6µg/m3, which is acceptable as per IARC,2004. Böhm et al. (2012) monitored the emission of formaldehyde from solid wood, blockboard, plywood, flooring, and furnishing materials. The higher concentration of investigated materials ranges from 0.006mg/m3 to 0.048mg/m3, which is very less while comparing the acceptable limits. Pierce et al. (2016) contemplated the assessment of indoor air formaldehyde concentration from laminate flooring in different duration for 63days, and the highest mean concentration range was 0.059mg/m3, which is under threshold value. Therefore, the works of literature providing explicit knowledge about the concentration of formaldehyde is negligible. Due to any external factor, if the concentration is increased, it can be reduced by merely providing natural ventilation or by chemical action.

As a cement-based material, formaldehyde is widely used as admixtures in the construction industry to provide desired property to the concrete like increased workability, increased mechanical strength, reducing the water content, and making self-healing concrete. Many types of formaldehyde-based admixtures are available namely sulfonated melamine-formaldehyde, sulfonated naphthalene-formaldehyde, urea-formaldehyde resin, Aminosulfonatephenol-formaldehyde, Sulfanilate-phenol-formaldehyde, Sulfonated acetone-formaldehyde, Sodium sulfonilatephenol-formaldehyde, etc., The main purpose of the paper is to reviews research result on cement-based formaldehyde composites and discuss the rheological, mechanical and durability properties and conclude some future scope in the field of construction technology for the effective use of formaldehyde in cement.

Types of formaldehyde in rheological application

Sulfonated melamine-formaldehyde (SMF)
A study was conducted by Lahallh et al. (1988) about the SMF as a superplasticizer (SPs) in the concrete. He synthesized SMF in four different processes hydroxymethylation, sulfonation, low pH condensation, and high pH rearrangement with five different doses ranging from 1 percentage to 5 percentage. He found that the increase in superplasticizer leads to a decrease in yield stress and viscosity. He noted the slump of concrete was dropped after 1.75 hours to the original slump. He concluded that the 3% addition of admixture giving better flow properties if used within 45min while comparing with commercial concrete. At the same time, no improvement was noted in the rheological property while increasing the dosage percentage. Collepardi (1998) compared the property of acrylic polymers (AP), SMF, and SNF as water-reducing agents in concrete. AP achieved flowing concrete with a low water-cement ratio than SMF and SNF. SMF and SNF also showed good result in slump loss but in the longer duration the advantage of using water reducers are negotiable, that means no effect in flow property.

Yilmaz et al. (1995) analyzed the influence of SMF in the hydration of cement. The retardation and acceleration of the cement are noted in different temperatures. SMF retards the setting time in low temperature (180C) and accelerates at high temperature (>400C). Rols S et al. (1999) presented the influence of SMF and viscosity modifiers (VM) in self-compacting concrete. He discussed that the flow property of SMF admixed concrete was achieved but the self-compacting was not achieved without VM. VM helps to reduce the segregation and bleeding of concrete. Arosio et al. (2007) investigated the influence of SMF in building blocks using cement and clay paste. The patent also there in the manufacturing of SMF in 1994 by the inventor Spiratos (1994) and another patent to use the SMF as an additive by Absi-Halabi (1987).

Hekal and Kishar (1999) studied the SNF effect of ettringite formation. The percentage of SNF in the cement affects the size of the ettringite which results in the delayed setting during the early stage up to 24 hours. Mezhov et al. (2020) used three different commercial Polynaphtalene Sulfonate (PNS) with varying molecular weight as SP for his study. The SPs were dissolved in water and added to the cement paste. From the result, he concludes that the dosage and molecular weight of PNS plays important role in rheological property. Higher molecular weight PNS need a higher dosage to trigger the polymerization and the low molecular weight PNS highly retard the hydration process. Typical rheological behavior was observed at the dosage level of 0.2 percentage.

Aminosulfonate phenol-formaldehyde (APF)
The rheological property of super-plasticized cementitious material using aminosulfonate–phenol–formaldehyde was studied by Pei et al. (2008) In this study, two APF named p-aminobenzenesulfonate (AS) and N-dimethylaminobenzenesulfonate (SDMAS) were used. The flow property of the AS and SDMAS are equal during the initial stage and comparatively high with the control specimen. But the SDMAS performed well than AS. NH_2 group in the AS produced better hydrogen bonding and result in low flow property comparing to SDMAS. Zhao et al. (2012) synthesized sulfonated aminophenol using formaldehyde, phenol, acid, and sodium sulfanilate. The surface tension of the cement particles decreases with APF water reducers concentration increases. Zhao et al. (2015) used aminosulfonate -phenol-formaldehyde (APF) and aminosulfonate-bisphenol A- formaldehyde (ABPF) as SPs in his study. 0.3 percentage of incorporation of APF and ABPF in concrete result in 20 percent of water reduction. Further increasing the dosage of APF and ABPF, APF shows better water reduction than the ABPF. ABPF exhibits improved performance in slump loss because of high molecular ratio than APF.

Sulfanilate-phenol-formaldehyde (SPF)
Pei et al. (2000) used ulfanilate-phenol-formaldehyde as a superplasticizer in concrete and compared it with SNF and SMF conventional superplasticizers. SPF reduced water up to 18% without affecting the workability. Due to strong absorption in cement paste SPF provides high rheological property comparing others. El-Didamony et al. (2012) contemplated the effect of sodium sulfanilate phenol formaldehyde in sulfate resisting cement. The result shows that the addition of SPF decreased water consistency. Slump increases with an increase in SPF due to the negative charge of sulfanilate groups in the SPF repulse and achieved good fluidity.

Sulfonated acetone-formaldehyde (SAF)
Pei et al. [2004] studied the effect of SAF as a superplasticizer in concrete. He concludes that the SAF having excellent property to control the slump loss and it is most suitable for using the pumping concrete. Mahmoud et al. (2010) studied the effect of using SAF as water reducers in concrete. The SAF in concrete reduces the water-cement ratio up to 19%, air content decreased 1.9%, and retardation increases in the increase in SPs content. Lou et al. (2012) used SAF as a superplasticizer with different molecular weights (MW) to study the absorption and dispersion properties. Results show the increase in MW decrease in water-cement ratio for the same workability. Due to the electrostatic repulsion of higher MW dispersibility of the cement paste

Recent Advancements in Geotechnical Engineering - NCRAG'21   Materials Research Forum LLC
Materials Research Proceedings **19** (2021) 18-27   https://doi.org/10.21741/9781644901618-3

increases. In the Zhang et al. (2015) study, SAF and black liquor were used to prepare copolymer and used as high range water reducers in concrete. He concludes that the pure SAF admixed cement paste increase fluidity and the presence of black liquor promotes the flow property up to 20% weight percentage. The temperature during the copolymerization also affects the fluidity property. The fluidity of the copolymer gave a better result than the pure SAF of temperature up to 100^0C. But the high temperature of copolymer leads to crosslinking to the molecules and reducing the fluidity.

Zhao et al. (2020) investigated water soluble SAF as a superplasticizer with two different synthesis methods. The first method was produced by the chemical reaction between sodium pyrosulfite, acetone, and formaldehyde. The second method was prepared from anhydrous sodium sulfite, acetone, and formaldehyde. In the first method, the SAF contains a higher molecular weight comparing to the second method. The first method SAF and second method SAF introduced to the concrete mix about 0.32 percentage and 0.48 percentage and the water content was reduced up to 19 percentage and 18 present age. SAF also increased the fluidity, air content, and setting time of concrete. Yang Xu et al. (2020) conducted a comparison study between amphoteric polycarboxylate (APC) and SAF in elevated temperatures above 60^0C. The author concludes that the APC performed well in rheological property that the SAF due to the repulsion effect. SAF has a longer absorption amount of cement practical than the APC which promotes the hydration process.

Types of formaldehyde in strengthening application.

Sulfonated melamine-formaldehyde (SMF)
In the Lahallh et al. (1988) experiment shows the 3% addition of SMF shows improved compressive strength by 50 percentage, tensile strength enhanced by 26 percentage, flexural strength increased by eight percentage, and elastic modulus enhanced by 12%. Based on the test result he concluded that the formaldehyde ratio does not affect the strength. Yunchao et al. (1995) compared High-sulfonated melamine-formaldehyde (HSMF) and SMF as water reducing agent in his study. HSMF is more effective superplasticizer (SPs) than SMF and no increase in the compressive strength was noticed in both HSMF and SMF.
Ramachandran V et al. (1995) studied the hydration of cement using SMF as SPs in different cement Type I to V as per ASTM. Compression strength result shows that the higher strength achieved in early stage of concreting and the difference gradually decreased after 3days test. Type I cement performed well in addition to SMF, but Type V shows lower hydration and less strength development with SMF. For better results in Type V cement, it was suggested to keep the SMF level below 0.3 percentage. In Rols et al. (1999) study the self-leveling nature of concrete using SMF as SPs with the viscosity modifier starch and precipitated silica. A compression test was conducted in 1, 7,28, and 90days. The SMF admixed concrete gave elevated strength during the initial stage and achieved equal strength after 28days testing. This strength rise is because of the reaction with tricalcium silica at an initial age.

Sulfonated naphthalene-formaldehyde (SNF)
Theobald and Johann Plank (2020) used β-Naphthalene sulfonate formaldehyde as a seeding material with normal and finer Portland cement. He noticed an increase in the compressive strength in early-stage from 6 hours to 24 hours and at 28 days no significant change in strength for finer cement. This is because of the high reactive property of the finer cement. At the same time, the normal courser Portland cement has a less reactive nature and shows strength development after 10 hours.

Urea-formaldehyde resin (UF)
Yue et al. (2000) observed the effect of UF treated cotton fiber in cement-based composite material. The UF treated plant fiber adhere with cement particle and produced dense concrete which results in high strength and water resistance. According to result of Faramarzi et al. (2016), UF as grouting material increased the compressive strength by 125 percent of the concrete specimen. UF grout filling the pores and voids of the specimen. Increasing the UF content results in increasing the strength of the injected specimen. Han et al. (2020) investigated the strength property of epoxy/urea-formaldehyde microcapsules into the cement mortar. Urea-formaldehyde is used as a shell and epoxy as a core for the microcapsule. 0 to 15 percentage microcapsules are added related to cement content. The compression strength result shows that increasing the microcapsule content decreasing the strength and fluidity property. This means the microcapsules affects the internal structure of the specimen.

Aminosulfonate-phenol-formaldehyde (APF)
Pei (2008) used AS and SDMAS based aminosulfonate–phenol–formaldehyde as a superplasticizer. The AS specimen having low w/c ratio than the SDMAS, which possesses higher strength property of AS at the 7days test. But in the 28 days test on compressive and bending strength, SDMAS are $1.54N/mm^2$ and $0.64N/mm^2$ higher than AS due to the inhibiting the hydration process. Zhao et al. (2015) compared the impact of APF and ABPF as water reducers in concrete. Both SPs enhanced the air content of the specimen. Increasing the SPs result in higher air content. Therefore, it should be limited for better strength. Due to less water-cement ratio, both SPs result in high compression and flexural strength. But APF performed a little higher in mechanical strength than the ABPF.

Sulfanilate-phenol-formaldehyde (SPF)
In the Pei et al. (2000) study the SPF performed well in rheology and strength property comparing with sulfonated naphthalene formaldehyde and sulfonated melamine formaldehyde. 7 days and 28days test was conducted for the compressive strength test. In both times SPF gave higher results than the others due to higher water reduction. El-Didamony et al. (2012) investigate the strength property of cement paste with SPF in sulphate resisting cement with silica fume. The addition of the SPF was delayed by 0 to 15 min in 5min interval and the reaction of the delayed time was also noted. The compressive strength test was conducted in 1,3,7.28 and 90 days hydration. Due to the water reducing effect with delayed addition, the compression strength increases up to 10min delayed time. Because of the retarder effect of the polymer after 10min the strength property decreased. Pang et al. (2012) synthesized modified SPF and studied the water reducing effect in concrete. Modified SPF has incredible repulsion force to cement particles, particularly with a low water-cement ratio. 0.6 percentage addition of modified SPF resulting in 18% water reduction and reduce the bleeding of mortar. This water reduction leads to higher mechanical strength.

Sulfonated acetone-formaldehyde (SAF)
Pei et al. (2004) used SAF to enhance the strength property of the concrete. And noted that the plasticizing effect of SAF admixed concrete improved the compressive strength in 3, 7, 28 days test. Zhang et al. (2015) investigated the strength behavior of superplasticizer admixed cement paste using the copolymers SAF and black liquor. He conducted 1,3,7 and 28 days of compression strength tests with varying dosages of copolymers. Due to the retarding effect the 1-day strength property of admixed paste is inferior to the control specimen. The result shows the gradual increase in compression strength by means of the age of the paste from 3days onwards. The usage

of copolymer reduces the pore volume up to 6% which results in increasing the strength and promoting the long-term strength.

Zhao et al. (2020) studied two different synthesis method shows improved strength characteristics than the normal concrete because of less water percentage. Comparatively, the first method shows higher mechanical properties for the reason of higher water reducing rate. This improved strength result was achieved in all mechanical properties test like compression, tension, and ultra-sonic pulse velocity test. The curing period has a positive impact on the mechanical strength with means at 28 days test the result shows a rapid increase in strength in all test. In the Xu et al. (2020) study the APC and SAF as used as superplasticizers and compared the effects in mechanical property. The test was conducted on 1, 3, and 7days and the test results show no noticeable strength rise up to 3 days in both control and admixed specimen. But with the APC admixed specimens have low porosity and show improved microstructure which leads to higher mechanical strength than the SAF after 3days. Mahmoud et al. (2010) performed the strength test using SAF in concrete. Using 2 percentage SAF the specimen yields higher compressive strength. This strength rise is directly related to water reduction and air content in the concrete.

Performance of formaldehyde in durability condition

Sulfonated melamine-formaldehyde (SMF)
The effect of SMF on the creep of concrete is studied by Lahallh et al. (1988) for a year as per ASTM C512. He observed that the deformation of concrete was controlled by 30 percentage while treated by three percentage of superplasticizer in concrete, and the creep modulus of treated concrete was almost twice the value of untreated concrete with a superplasticizer.

Sulfonated acetone-formaldehyde (SAF)
To perform a durability study Mahmoud et al. (2010) used sulphate and acid attack test. SAF admixed concrete specimens are immersed for about 6 months in the sulfuric acid for acid attack test and magnesium sulphate for sulphate resisting test. The use of SAF decreases water absorption and pores. That results increased durability property in an antagonistic environment.

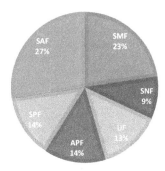

Fig.1. Different types of formaldehyde-based admixtures used in this paper

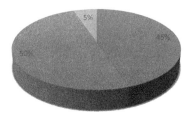

■ Rheology   ■ Strength   ■ Durability

Fig.2. Properties reviewed in this paper

Research Summary

Cement is a widely used building material, which is not suitable for all the environmental conditions. To implicate special property to the normal cement/mortar/concrete, admixtures are used. In this paper formaldehyde-based cementitious (FBCM) construction materials and their effects were studied. There are approximately 37 papers were studied. The majority of the researchers focused on using formaldehyde as high range water reducers and some used it in self-healing and self-compacting/leveling. In this paper rheological, mechanical properties, and durability properties were noted and the effect of different types of SPs was also summarized. Fig.1. shows the percentage of different types of formaldehyde-based cementitious used among 37 reviewed papers. 23% of sulfonated melamine-formaldehyde (SMF), 9% of sulfonated naphthalene-formaldehyde (SNF), `13% of urea-formaldehyde resin (UF), 14% of Aminosulfonate-phenol-formaldehyde (APF), 14% of Sulfanilate-phenol-formaldehyde (SPF), and 27% of Sulfonated acetone-formaldehyde (SAF). It seems that more work is done using SAF and SMF. Fig.2. shows the properties reviewed using the above said formaldehyde-based cementitious materials. 45 percentage rheology property, 50 percentage strength property, and only 5 percentage of durability properties have been studies. In this most of the researchers studied the water reducing nature of FBCM because of its repulsive property and some FBCM particularly urea-formaldehyde resin used to make self-healing concrete and UF are mixed with concrete as microcapsule form. From this research overview, it clearly shows that formaldehyde is an inevitable construction material. It improves the cementitious property and shows great advantages in practical application. The pollution and hazard of the formaldehyde can be minimized by following the standard guidelines like IARC, 2004 hazard value.

Conclusion

This session discussed the future scope and research ideas in the field of using formaldehyde-based cementitious material (FBCM). Comparing the commercially available cement FBCM provides excellent fresh and hardened properties particularly using FBCM as superplasticizer it gives outstanding rheological with minimum water-cement ratio and its leads to higher mechanical strength. It found that most of the researchers concentrated on rheological and strength properties. But FBCM also uses for bonding old and new concrete, grouting, self-healing, making insulating foam boards, tiles, and manufacturing brick, etc., It also observed that less work was conducted on durability and temperature effects and need to be studied in a detailed manner. Formaldehyde based polymer materials also there to enhance the property of concrete.

References

[1]　Arosio F, Castoldi L, Ferlazzo N, & Forzatti P (2007) Influence of solfonated melamine formaldehyde condensate on the quality of building blocks production by extrusion of cement–clay pastes. Applied Clay Science, 35(1-2):85–93. https://doi.org/10.1016/j.clay.2006.06.004

[2]　Böhm M, Salem MZM, Srba J (2012) Formaldehyde emission monitoring from a variety of solid wood, plywood, blockboard and flooring products manufactured for building and furnishing materials. Journal of Hazardous Materials 221:68– 79. https://doi.org/10.1016/j.conbuildmat.2020.120240

[3]　Bourdin D, Mocho P, Desauziers V, Plaisance H (2014) Formaldehyde emission behavior of building materials: On-site measurements and modeling approach to predict indoor air pollution. Journal of Hazardous Materials 280:164–173. https://doi.org/10.1016/j.jhazmat.2014.07.065

[4]　Butlerow A (1859) Ueber einige Derivate des Jodmethylens [On some derivatives of methylene iodide]. Annalen der Chemie und Pharmacie. 111:242–252. https://doi.org/10.1002/jlac.18591110219

[5]　Chi C, Chen W, Guo M, Weng M, Yan G, Shen X. (2016). Law and features of TVOC and Formaldehyde pollution in urban indoor air. Atmospheric Environment. 132:85-90. https://doi.org/10.1016/j.atmosenv.2016.02.043

[6]　Collepardi M (1998) Admixtures used to enhance placing characteristics of concrete. Cement and Concrete Composites 20(2-3):103–112. https://doi.org/10.1016/S0958-9465(98)00071-7

[7]　Didamony E, Heikal M, Aleem SAE (2012) Influence of delayed addition time of sodium sulfanilate phenol formaldehyde condensate on the hydration characteristics of sulfate resisting cement pastes containing silica fume. Construction and Building Materials 37:269–276. https://doi.org/10.1016/j.conbuildmat.2012.07.023

[8]　Faramarzi L, Rasti A, Abtahi SM (2016) An experimental study of the effect of cement and chemical grouting on the improvement of the mechanical and hydraulic properties of alluvial formations. Construction and Building Materials 126:32–43. https://doi.org/10.1016/j.conbuildmat.2016.09.006

[9]　Han T, Wang X, Li D, Li D, F Xing, N Han (2020) Influence of strain rate on mechanical characteristic and pore structure of self-healing cementitious composites with epoxy/urea-formaldehyde microcapsules. Construction and Building Materials. https://doi.org/10.1016/j.conbuildmat.2020.121138

[10]　Hekal EE, & Kishar EA (1999) Effect of sodium salt of naphthalene-formaldehyde polycondensate on ettringite formation. Cement and Concrete Research 29(10):1535–1540, DOI: https://doi.org/10.1016/S0008-8846(99)00110-6

[11]　Kim S, Kim HJ (2005) Effect of addition of polyvinyl acetate to melamine-formaldehyde resin on the adhesion and formaldehyde emission in engineered flooring, International Journal of Adhesion & Adhesives 25:456–461. https://doi.org/10.1016/j.ijadhadh.2005.01.001

[12]　Lahallh SM, Halabi MA, Mali A (1988) Effect of polymerization conditions of sulfonated-melamine formaldehyde superplasticizers on concrete. Cement and Concrete Research 18:513-531. https://doi.org/10.1016/0008-8846(88)90044-0

[13]　Lahalih S, Absi-Halabi M (1987) Highly stable sulfonated melamine-formaldehyde condensate solution. Patent no: US4820766A,

[14] Li W, Zhu X, Zhao N, Jiang Z (2016) Preparation and Properties of Melamine Urea-Formaldehyde Microcapsules for Self-Healing of Cementitious Materials. Materials, 9(3). https://doi.org/10.3390/ma9030152

[15] Liang W, Yang X (2013) Indoor formaldehyde in real buildings: Emission source identification, overall emission rate estimation, concentration increase and decay patterns, Building and Environment 69 :114-120. https://doi.org/10.1016/j.buildenv.2013.08.009

[16] Lou H, Ji K, Lin H, Pang Y, Deng Y, Qiu X, Zhang H, Xie Z (2012) Effect of molecular weight of sulphonated acetone-formaldehyde condensate on its adsorption and dispersion properties in cementitious system. Cement and Concrete Research 42:1043–1048. https://doi.org/10.1016/j.cemconres.2011.11.002

[17] Mahmoud AAM, Shehab MSH, El-Dieb AS (2010) Concrete mixtures incorporating synthesized sulfonated acetophenone–formaldehyde resin as superplasticizer. Cement and Concrete Composites, 32(5):392–397. https://doi.org/10.1016/j.cemconcomp.2010.02.005

[18] Mezhov A, Ulka A, Gendel Y, Charles E. Diesendruck, Konstantin Kovler (2020) The working mechanisms of low molecular weight polynaphthalene sulfonate superplasticizers. Construction and Building Materials, 240. https://doi.org/10.1016/j.conbuildmat.2019.117891

[19] Pang Y, Wen WN, Lou HM, Ouyang XP, Qiu XQ (2012) Synthesis of Lignin-Modified Sulfanilate-Phenol-Formaldehyde Condensate and Application as Concrete Superplasticizer. Applied Mechanics and Materials, 174-177:1238–1246. https://doi.org/10.4028/www.scientific.net/AMM.174-177.1238

[20] Pei M, Wang D, Hu X, Xu D (2000) Synthesis of sodium sulfanilate-phenol-formaldehyde condensate and its application as a superplasticizer in concrete. Cement and Concrete Research 30:1841-1845. https://doi.org/10.1016/S0008-8846(00)00389-6

[21] Pei M, Yang Y, Zhang X, Zhang J, Dong J (2004) Synthesis and the effects of water-soluble sulfonated acetone–formaldehyde resin on the properties of concrete. Cement and Concrete Research. 34:1417–1420. https://doi.org/10.1016/j.cemconres.2004.01.012

[22] Pei M, Wang Z, Li W, Zhang J, Pan Q, Qin X (2008) The properties of cementitious materials superplasticized with two superplasticizers based on aminosulfonate–phenol–formaldehyde. Construction and Building Materials 22:2382–2385. https://doi.org/10.1016/j.conbuildmat.2007.09.003

[23] Pierce JS, Abelmann A, Lotter JT, Ruestow PS, Unice KM, Beckett EM, Fritz HA, Bare JL, Finley BL (2016) An assessment of formaldehyde emissions from laminate flooring manufactured in China. Regulatory Toxicology and Pharmacology 81:20-32. https://doi.org/10.1016/j.yrtph.2016.06.022

[24] Ramachandran V S, Lowery MS, & Malhotra VM (1995) Behaviour of ASTM Type V cement hydrated in the presence of sulfonated melamine formaldehyde. Materials and Structures, 28(3):133–138. https://doi.org/10.1007/BF02473220

[25] Rols S, Ambroise J, & Péra J (1999) Effects of different viscosity agents on the properties of self-leveling concrete. Cement and Concrete Research, 29(2):261–266. https://doi.org/10.1016/S0008-8846(98)00095-7

[26] Spiratos MD (1994) Processes for manufacture of sulfonated melamine-formaldehyde resins. Patent no: US5424390A,

[27] Theobald M, Plank J (2020) β-Naphthalene sulfonate formaldehyde-based nanocomposites

as new seeding materials for Portland cement. Construction and Building Materials 264. https://doi.org/10.1016/j.conbuildmat.2020.120240

[28] Xu Y, Hua M, Chen D, Liu Z, Yu Y, H Zhang, J Guo (2020) Performance and working mechanism of amphoteric polycarboxylate-based dispersant and sulfonated acetone formaldehyde polycondensate-based dispersant in oil well cement. Construction and Building Materials 233. https://doi.org/10.1016/j.conbuildmat.2019.117147

[29] Yilmaz VT, & Glasser FP (1989) Influence of sulphonated melamine formaldehyde superplasticizer on cement hydration and microstructure. Advances in Cement Research, V:2(7), P:111–119. https://doi.org/10.1680/adcr.1989.2.7.111

[30] Yilmaz VT, Kindness A, & Glasser FP (1989) Quantitative analysis of sulphonated melamine formaldehyde superplasticizer in cement. Advances in Cement Research, 2(7):107–110. https://doi.org/10.1680/adcr.1989.2.7.107

[31] Yue Y, Li G, Xu X, Zhao Z. (2000). Properties and microstructures of plant-fiber-reinforced cement-based composites. Cement and Concrete Research, 30(12):1983–1986. https://doi.org/10.1016/S0008-8846(00)00376-8

[32] Yunchao H, Fansen Z, Hu Y, Chunying L, Zhaoqiang W, Weining L, & Shukai Y (1995) Synthesis and properties of high-sulfonated melamine–formaldehyde resin. Journal of Applied Polymer Science, 56(12):1523–1526. https://doi.org/10.1002/app.1995.070561201

[33] Zhang T, Gao J, Deng X, Liu Y (2015) Graft copolymerization of black liquor and sulfonated acetone formaldehyde and research on concrete performance. Construction and Building Materials 83:308–313. https://doi.org/10.1016/j.conbuildmat.2015.03.046

[34] Zhao H, Zhou W, & Gao B (2012) Synthesis and dispersion mechanism of AH polymers on cement particles. Advances in Cement Research, 24(1):41–47. https://doi.org/10.1680/adcr.2012.24.1.41

[35] Zhao H, H Zhao, & Deng M (2015) Feasibility Study on Bisphenol A as Phenol Replacement to Produce Aminosulfonate-Phenol-Formaldehyde Superplasticizer for Application in Concrete. Journal of Materials in Civil Engineering, 27(6). https://doi.org/10.1061/(ASCE)MT.1943-5533.0001141

[36] Zhao H, Deng M, Tang M (2020)   The molecular structures and the application properties of sulfonated acetone-formaldehyde superplasticizers at different synthetic methods. Construction and Building Materials 241. https://doi.org/10.1016/j.conbuildmat.2020.118051

[37] Zhu H, Xu S (2019) Synthesis and properties of rigid polyurethane foams synthesized from modified urea-formaldehyde resin. Construction and Building Materials. 202:718–726. https://doi.org/10.1016/j.conbuildmat.2019.01.035

Recent Advancements in Geotechnical Engineering - NCRAG'21　　　　　Materials Research Forum LLC
Materials Research Proceedings 19 (2021) 28-35　　　　　https://doi.org/10.21741/9781644901618-4

A Study on Fresh and Hardened Properties of Concrete with Partial Replacement of Bottom Ash as a Fine Aggregate

I. Ramana[1,a] *, S. Venkatachalam[2,b], K. Vishnuvardhan[2], Dr. M.M. Saravanan[3]

[1]PG Student, Department of Civil Engineering, Kongu Engineering College, Perundurai, Erode, Tamil Nadu, India

[2] Assistant Professor, Department of Civil Engineering, Kongu Engineering College, Perundurai, Erode, Tamil Nadu, India

[3]Associate professor, Department of Civil Engineering, Vivekananda College of Technology for Women, Tiruchengode, TamilNadu, India

[a]ramanashri97@gmail.com, [b]bsvvenkat@gmail.com

Keywords: Concrete, Bottom Ash, Industrial Waste, Fresh Properties, Hardened Properties, Durability

Abstract. To overcome the shortage of natural resources for the production of concrete, many waste materials are used to replace the raw materials of concrete. In this way, bottom ash is one of the major industrial wastes which shall be used as the replacement of materials in concrete production. It shall be used to replace the materials either up to one-third. This review brings out the evaluation of the industrial waste material which can be repeatedly used as a substitution for concrete as fine aggregate. This paper reviewed the use of industrial waste i.e., bottom ash as fine aggregate in the concrete. The parameters discussed were physical, chemical, fresh, and hardened properties of the concrete with partial replacement of bottom ash. By reviewing some of the research papers, concluded that 10-15% replacement of fine aggregates is acceptable for all the properties of concrete. High utilization of natural sources -gives the pathway to produce more industrial wastes which are responsible for the development of new sustainable development.

1. Introduction

The concrete production has a large amount of negative thoughts in the field of environment and globe .Concrete is one of the most used and widely manufactured material in the world. Concrete mainly derieved from fine aggregate, cement and sand [1]. Out of these material cement is the major part of concrete which acts as a unaltered material in the field of construction .Concrete is produced by burning of natural materials like fly ash and slag of industrial by products ,limestone and clay [2].Concrete is one of the major production material in the world due to its cost effectiveness ,long term performance and easy application [3].Concrete is mainly used in the construction of parking garges ,offshore structures railway bridges in large numbers. The reinforcement of concrete structures, in particularly in bridges is one of the key to face difficulties during their service time in front of multinational structural engineers [4] .Such concrete structures as consequence due to ineffective loads and decay corrosion .In addition most of the concrete structures were constructed during the year of 1950s and 1960s which is incompatible with current requirements[5] .In concrete structures the increased in fatigue is normally subjected to millions of repetitive axle load cycles during their passive traffic during their life time that can collapse during low load limits.[6]..The main exposure of the concrete structures is fire poses. The properties of concrete includes durability ,mechanical and physical is the major effect of fire production in concrete. The mechanical characteristics of concrete are most significant during the

Recent Advancements in Geotechnical Engineering - NCRAG'21   Materials Research Forum LLC
Materials Research Proceedings **19** (2021) 28-35   https://doi.org/10.21741/9781644901618-4

fire exposure. The endurance quality of concrete cannot be determined in any situation. The investigation of concrete has been founded that the properties of concrete affect the fire properties of concrete which include additives, industrial wastes, and types of aggregate[7]. The longiviety of concrete is not only for the structures to perform well but also for the mechanical requirements. concrete can be able to avoid more damage to structures and also withstand durability is often gives importance from the engineers. Concrete is a mixture of aggregate, cement and the water. Concrete can be able to withstand equal distribution to reduce the risk of separation of compatibility and the workability as per the building codes and the standards the concrete can be able to withstand heavy loads sufficiently. To attain the strength of concrete curing of 28 days is required. Concrete can be able to produced all degradation process which produced as a result of constituent materials[8].To reduce the disadvantages of concrete nonmetallic reinforcement become feasible which acts substitute for the conventional concrete reinforcement[9].To maintain stable growth and safe functional environment concrete plays an important role in the field of civil engineering.[10].In order to stabilize the stability of concrete to maintain the aim of concrete waste. The main aim of the concrete is to examine the flexural properties of concrete waste[11].

The bottom ash can be obtained from the cold-fired plants that can be used as a by- product. During the ignition process the ash is softened as a result the large particles is produced and the displacement in water vessel beneath the surface of the material these large particle obtained is bottom ash.[12].The generation of industrial waste is produced tons of bottom ash in millions. The control technique for municipal and the industrial solid waste is commonly done by using energy recovery with the incineration process. In swedoon the bottom ash gives rise to the production of just about one million tone wastes burned annually. In Switzerland and Norway the production of bottom ash is just about 18 million ton annually[13]. In similar the bottom ash can be used fpr many construction purpose after treatment. In general the treatment process involves dividing the metal pieces which goes along with the natural weathering(ageing) to produce the bottom ash more secure to filter metal by means of sparkle.[14].Bottom ash gives up the possibility of burning up of heavy metals hence suitable pre-processing before it can be applied landfilled or it can be used as a supporting raw material. Although the direct reuse of bottom ash is not achievable and it is durable and maintain the stable cost and economic benefits from using alternative material for bottom ash. The building construction produces an outstanding results for utilization of exactly treated as bottom ash[15]. Depending upon the preparation of the aggregates can be used in the form of bottom ash in the bottom of bottom of the road and in the production concrete is replaced by the natural aggregates because of pozzolanic characteristics[16]. To find the quality of bottom ash we have to concentrated on two mix design foremost one is W/c ratio and second important is stable slump value. It has been observed the exact compressive strength, drying shrinkage, and wc ratio bottom ash is increased with decreases when it mixed with concrete. In other hand in constant slump there is an equivalent amount of compressive strength mixes with concrete. The drying shrinkage enlarge when the increased natural sand is replaced by bottom ash with 30%[5].The bottom ash concrete reveals good dimensional concrete, better water resistance to sulphuric acid and chloride particles with the comparision of traditional concrete[17].[18] observed when the high strength of concrete with chloride content is replaced by fine bottom ash with fine aggregate finally the outcome shows the chloride diffusion is reduced in the presence of high concrete strength in the bottom).

Recent Advancements in Geotechnical Engineering - NCRAG'21   Materials Research Forum LLC
Materials Research Proceedings **19** (2021) 28-35   https://doi.org/10.21741/9781644901618-4

Figure:1.Bottom Ash

2. Properties of concrete:

In major the properties of concrete can be classified into two major parts they are
Fresh concrete
Hardened concrete

2.1 Properties of fresh concrete
Workability
In fresh concrete the workability is complex property which involve the various needs of strength portability, cooperative, finishability and the placeability. The best method to find suitable workability or consistency of concrete is slump cone test. The appearance of excellent waste of bottom ash in concrete gives rise to grow up the demand of concrete when contrast with standard sand particles. To maintain the standard values of workability in slump cone test the water content was slowely increased when the replacement of sand is increased with waste factory and bottom ash which gives an clear explanation about the demand of water[19].
Density
The thickness of the concrete is reduced with the enlargement of low content due to the presence of bottom ash in the relative density of bottom ash. The analysis shows due to the low content of specific gravity in bottom ash the density of concrete is less. The thickness of the concrete is reduced in hardened state with gradual increase in the bottom ash [20].

2.2 Properties of hardened concrete
The concrete has various properties among them strength are the most important properties. To find strength some of the test are discussed
Compressive strength
Split tensile test
Flexural strength test
Compressive strength test
The compressive strength is decreased when the concrete is mixed with the involvement of bottom ash as the substitution of particular sand. The mixture with restore fine aggregates has little difference when compared to the mix with age of 365 days[21]. The strength variation is observed due to the formation of same properties of bottom ash[22].The development of concrete strength is increased when we added bottom ash. During the 7 days of curing the bottom ash has gained its strength as 5% and 20% which is greater than the control specimen at the level of 10% and 15% correspondingly this is due to the action of pozzolanic reaction of the bottom ash. Due to the

substitution of bottom ash the porosity of concrete is increased. Due to the presence of silica jel in the bottom ash the C-S-H is produced the strength is increased due to the presence of jel[23].

Split Tensile Test
When the sand is replaced with bottom ash in split tensile test has less strength when compared to control concrete specimen in all the ages. Bottom ash produces split tensile strength approximately ranges from 121-126% at 90 days of the normal concrete at 28 days.[24].The substitution of bottom ash in concrete the strength is increased at 7 days and 28 days is the most perfect one.The workability of concrte is reduced when the bottom ash is added as a fine aggregate[25].In 7,and 28 days the split tensile test is increased for 10% to 30% replacement in remaining substitution the split tensile test was decreased[26].In 7 days the split tensile test was increase at the ratio of 0.7%,5.70% and 12.16% for 10,20 and 30% of substitution. For the substitution of 50% there is a dropping of 15.20% at the curing of 7 days. During the replacement of 20 and 30% the strength of the split tensile test in increased in 28 days of curing[27].

Flexural Strength Test
The difference in the strength between bottom ash and normal concrete become less clear after 28 days. The substitution of fine aggregates in the flexural strength the concrete is proceed to extend with all the ages of bottom ash .The adding of 30 % of bottom ash with concrete and sand the strength of the flexural properties is high. It is observed that the flexural strength of concrete is about linearly decreased when the substitution level of bottom ash is increased[20].

3. Physical characteristics of commercial waste as fine aggregate

Physical characteristics of construction waste includes particle size distribution, thickness specific gravity absorption and fine substances helps to realize its ability and the workability when the concrete is replaced by fine aggregate.

Some of the physical charecteristics are:
Specific Gravity
Water Absorption
Bulk Density
Shape and Appearance
Particle Size Distribution

3.1 Specific gravity

Different investigators have been observed that the specific gravity of some of the industrial waste substances are discussed below. The bottom ash has the SG lies between 1.39 and 2.33[35] when compared to the specific gravity is in between 1.93,1.39 and 1.87[36].The specific gravity of unused manufactured sand was investigated to be 2.18.It has been clearly investigates that the specific gravity of waste manufacturing sand ranges from 2.39-2.79.[37]The specific gravity of steel slag is 3.15[38].

3.2 Water absorption:

It is studied that the absorption of water in BA is 5.4% and 6.1 % respectively[42].The water absorption present in the waste manufacturing sand is1.2%.[29]The absorption of water in copper slag is 0.17%[43].The absorption of water in GGBS was found to be 10.0%[15].The presence of water content in steel salg is 0.80%[13]

3.3 Bulk density

The bulk density of bottom ash is 660 kg/ m3[28] when it is differentiated to the loose density of BA is 620 kg/m3[31].The compacted bulk density of manufacturing sand is 1890 Kg/m3[39] while the loose density of the manufacturing sand is 1690 Kg/m3.[37].The density of copper slag varies from 1900 kg/m3 to 2150 kg/m.[40]. The unit weight of copper slag is 2395 Kg/m3 and the packing thickness of copper slag is 1475 kg/m3[41]

3.4 Shape and appearance
Bottom ash have the rough quality and sharp, uneven and porous material it is well placed sand – sized material. The bottom ash has black to grey colour .The liquid content of the bottom ash ranged from 70 to 80 % of the ash in the presence of dry weight[28].Generally manufacturing sub-rakish sand in the form of spherical in shape. Foundry sand are grey or dark while chemical manufacturing sand are grey in colour[29] . IFS slag is dark in Colour, it is granular and vitreous and it carry toxic metal[30].The copper slag is powdered and dark in nature, shiny particles .The particle size distribution is same as normal sand[31].

3.5 Particle size distribution
The distribution of grain size in bottom size is replaced with 55% material then it ranges in between 1.12 and 0.16 [32]. The particle size distribution of copper slag is just about 75% particles ranges in between 0.3 and 1.18 [33].Particle size distribution is similar in foundry sand is ranges from 85-95% of the material lies between 0.6mm to 0.15mm and greater or smaller than 5-20% of manufacturing sand is lesser than 0.75mm[34].

4.Chemical characteristics of bottom ash as a fine aggregate
The chemical characteristics of bottom ash is identified based upon the process of burning and the types of coal used. The BA is generally composed of aluminium ,iron and silica dueto the presence of small amount of Sulphate, magnesium and calcium.[35].

5.Behaviour of bottom ash
Bottom ash is produced by the incineration process of municipal solid waste management it includes combustible ash, unburned carbon and the noncombustible inorganics based on the characteristics of waste and the classification of incinerators. In common the bottom ash is produced with the mixture of boiler ash is treated with slag. After the completion of incineration process the bottom ash is produced through the furnace bottom and it need to be water-cooled before it produced.[44].

6.Conclusion
Utilization of various industrial waste as fine aggregate replacement was discussed. All the concrete characteristics like hard and freshened, physical were explained and compared among them. The large amount of industrial wastes are used as a partial replacement of fine aggregate like bottom ash, steel slag, copper slag, waste foundry and fly ash.

Physical properties like shape and appearance, particle size distribution ,specific gravity, water absorption all the industrial wastes are nearly to the characteristics of sand excluding particle size distribution of manufacturing sand.

References
[1] Al-Jabri K S, Al-Saidy A H and Taha R 2011 Effect of copper slag as a fine aggregate on the properties of cement mortars and concrete *Construction and Building Materials***25** 933-8. https://doi.org/10.1016/j.conbuildmat.2010.06.090

[2] Tayeh B A, Hasaniyah M W, Zeyad A and Yusuf M O 2019 Properties of concrete containing recycled seashells as cement partial replacement: A review *Journal of Cleaner Production***237** 117723. https://doi.org/10.1016/j.jclepro.2019.117723

[3] Jindal B B 2019 Investigations on the properties of geopolymer mortar and concrete with

mineral admixtures: A review *Construction and Building Materials***227** 116644. https://doi.org/10.1016/j.conbuildmat.2019.08.025

[4]   Andrade L, Rocha J and Cheriaf M 2009 Influence of coal bottom ash as fine aggregate on fresh properties of concrete *Construction and Building Materials***23** 609-14. https://doi.org/10.1016/j.conbuildmat.2008.05.003

[5]   Bai Y, Darcy F and Basheer P 2005 Strength and drying shrinkage properties of concrete containing furnace bottom ash as fine aggregate *Construction and Building materials***19** 691-7. https://doi.org/10.1016/j.conbuildmat.2005.02.021

[6]   Al-Saadi N T K, Mohammed A, Al-Mahaidi R and Sanjayan J 2019 A state-of-the-art review: near-surface mounted FRP composites for reinforced concrete structures *Construction and Building Materials***209** 748-69. https://doi.org/10.1016/j.conbuildmat.2019.03.121

[7]   Memon S A, Shah S F A, Khushnood R A and Baloch W L 2019 Durability of sustainable concrete subjected to elevated temperature–A review *Construction and Building Materials***199** 435-55. https://doi.org/10.1016/j.conbuildmat.2018.12.040

[8]   Kanellopoulos A, Petrou M F and Ioannou I 2012 Durability performance of self-compacting concrete *Construction and Building Materials***37** 320-5. https://doi.org/10.1016/j.conbuildmat.2012.07.049

[9]   Abdulla N A 2017 Concrete filled PVC tube: A review *Construction and Building Materials***156** 321-9. https://doi.org/10.1016/j.conbuildmat.2017.08.156

[10]   Popescu C, Sas G, Blanksvärd T and Täljsten B 2015 Concrete walls weakened by openings as compression members: A review *Engineering Structures***89** 172-90. https://doi.org/10.1016/j.engstruct.2015.02.006

[11]   Seara-Paz S, González-Fonteboa B, Martínez-Abella F and Eiras-López J 2018 Flexural performance of reinforced concrete beams made with recycled concrete coarse aggregate *Engineering Structures***156** 32-45. https://doi.org/10.1016/j.engstruct.2017.11.015

[12]   Pormmoon P, Abdulmatin A, Charoenwaiyachet C, Tangchirapat W and Jaturapitakkul C 2020 Effect of cut-size particles on the pozzolanic property of bottom ash *Journal of Materials Research and Technology***10** 240-9. https://doi.org/10.1016/j.jmrt.2020.12.017

[13]   Devi V S and Gnanavel B 2014 Properties of concrete manufactured using steel slag *Procedia Engineering***97** 95-104. https://doi.org/10.1016/j.proeng.2014.12.229

[14]   Tiberg C, Sjöstedt C and Fedje K K 2020 Speciation of Cu and Zn in bottom ash from solid waste incineration studied by XAS, XRD, and geochemical modelling *Waste Management***119** 389-98. https://doi.org/10.1016/j.wasman.2020.10.023

[15]   Etxeberria M, Pacheco C, Meneses J and Berridi I 2010 Properties of concrete using metallurgical industrial by-products as aggregates *Construction and Building Materials***24** 1594-600. https://doi.org/10.1016/j.conbuildmat.2010.02.034

[16]   Romero A R, Salvo M and Bernardo E 2018 Up-cycling of vitrified bottom ash from MSWI into glass-ceramic foams by means of 'inorganic gel casting'and sinter-crystallization *Construction and Building Materials***192** 133-40. https://doi.org/10.1016/j.conbuildmat.2018.10.135

[17]   Singh M and Siddique R 2014 Compressive strength, drying shrinkage and chemical resistance of concrete incorporating coal bottom ash as partial or total replacement of sand *Construction and Building Materials***68** 39-48. https://doi.org/10.1016/j.conbuildmat.2014.06.034

[18]   Kim H, Jang J G, Choi Y and Lee H-K 2014 Improved chloride resistance of high-strength concrete amended with coal bottom ash for internal curing *Construction and Building Materials***71** 334-43. https://doi.org/10.1016/j.conbuildmat.2014.08.069

[19]   Aggarwal Y and Siddique R 2014 Microstructure and properties of concrete using bottom ash and waste foundry sand as partial replacement of fine aggregates *Construction and Building Materials***54** 210-23. https://doi.org/10.1016/j.conbuildmat.2013.12.051

[20]   Nadig V R, Sanjith J, Ranjith A and Kiran B 2015 Bottom Ash as Partial Sand Replacement in Concrete-A Review *IOSR Journal of Mechanical and Civil Engineering (IOSR-JMCE) e-ISSN* 2278-1684

[21]   Siddique R, Aggarwal Y, Aggarwal P, Kadri E-H and Bennacer R 2011 Strength, durability, and micro-structural properties of concrete made with used-foundry sand (UFS) *Construction and Building Materials***25** 1916-25. https://doi.org/10.1016/j.conbuildmat.2010.11.065

[22]   Yüksel İ and Bilir T 2007 Usage of industrial by-products to produce plain concrete elements *Construction and Building Materials***21** 686-94. https://doi.org/10.1016/j.conbuildmat.2006.06.031

[23]   Andrade L B, Rocha J and Cheriaf M 2007 Evaluation of concrete incorporating bottom ash as a natural aggregates replacement *Waste Management***27** 1190-9. https://doi.org/10.1016/j.conbuildmat.2006.06.031

[24]   Aggarwal P, Aggarwal Y and Gupta S 2007 Effect of bottom ash as replacement of fine aggregates in concrete

[25]   Bhuvaneshwari P and Murali R 2013 Strength characteristics of glass fiber on bottom ash based concrete *International Journal of Science, Environment and Technology***2** 90-102

[26]   Kadam M and Patil Y 2013 Effect of coal bottom ash as sand replacement on the properties of concrete with different w/c ratio *International Journal of Advanced Technology in Civil Engineering, ISSN* 2231-5721

[27]   Soman K, Sasi D and Abubaker K 2014 Strength properties of concrete with partial replacement of sand by bottom ash *International Journal of Innovative Research in Advanced Engineering (IJIRAE)* 2349-163

[28]   Dash M K, Patro S K and Rath A K 2016 Sustainable use of industrial-waste as partial replacement of fine aggregate for preparation of concrete–A review *International Journal of Sustainable Built Environment***5** 484-516. https://doi.org/10.1016/j.ijsbe.2016.04.006

[29]   Singh G and Siddique R 2012 Abrasion resistance and strength properties of concrete containing waste foundry sand (WFS) *Construction and building materials***28** 421-6. https://doi.org/10.1016/j.conbuildmat.2011.08.087

[30]   Khatib J, Herki B and Kenai S 2013 Capillarity of concrete incorporating waste foundry sand *Construction and building materials***47** 867-71. https://doi.org/10.1016/j.conbuildmat.2013.05.013

[31]   Ambily P, Umarani C, Ravisankar K, Prem P R, Bharatkumar B and Iyer N R 2015 Studies on ultra high performance concrete incorporating copper slag as fine aggregate *Construction and Building Materials***77** 233-40. https://doi.org/10.1016/j.conbuildmat.2014.12.092

[32]   Bilir T 2012 Effects of non-ground slag and bottom ash as fine aggregate on concrete permeability properties *Construction and Building Materials***26** 730-4. https://doi.org/10.1016/j.conbuildmat.2011.06.080

[33] Kou S-C and Poon C-S 2009 Properties of concrete prepared with crushed fine stone, furnace bottom ash and fine recycled aggregate as fine aggregates *Construction and Building Materials***23** 2877-86. https://doi.org/10.1016/j.conbuildmat.2009.02.009

[34] Kaur G, Siddique R and Rajor A 2012 Properties of concrete containing fungal treated waste foundry sand *Construction and Building Materials***29** 82-7. https://doi.org/10.1016/j.conbuildmat.2011.08.091

[35] Siddique R 2014 Utilization of industrial by-products in concrete *Procedia Engineering***95** 335-47. https://doi.org/10.1016/j.proeng.2014.12.192

[36] Siddique R, Singh G, Belarbi R and Ait-Mokhtar K 2015 Comparative investigation on the influence of spent foundry sand as partial replacement of fine aggregates on the properties of two grades of concrete *Construction and Building Materials***83** 216-22. https://doi.org/10.1016/j.conbuildmat.2015.03.011

[37] Singh G and Siddique R 2012 Effect of waste foundry sand (WFS) as partial replacement of sand on the strength, ultrasonic pulse velocity and permeability of concrete *Construction and building materials***26** 416-22. https://doi.org/10.1016/j.conbuildmat.2011.06.041

[38] Qasrawi H, Shalabi F and Asi I 2009 Use of low CaO unprocessed steel slag in concrete as fine aggregate *Construction and Building Materials***23** 1118-25. https://doi.org/10.1016/j.conbuildmat.2008.06.003

[39] Yüksel İ, Siddique R and Özkan Ö 2011 Influence of high temperature on the properties of concretes made with industrial by-products as fine aggregate replacement *Construction and building materials***25** 967-72. https://doi.org/10.1016/j.conbuildmat.2010.06.085

[40] Wu W, Zhang W and Ma G 2010 Optimum content of copper slag as a fine aggregate in high strength concrete *Materials & Design***31** 2878-83. https://doi.org/10.1016/j.matdes.2009.12.037

[41] Wu W, Zhang W and Ma G 2010 Mechanical properties of copper slag reinforced concrete under dynamic compression *Construction and Building Materials***24** 910-7. https://doi.org/10.1016/j.conbuildmat.2009.12.001

[42] Kim H-K and Lee H-K 2011 Use of power plant bottom ash as fine and coarse aggregates in high-strength concrete *Construction and Building Materials***25** 1115-22. https://doi.org/10.1016/j.conbuildmat.2010.06.065

[43] Velumani M and Nirmalkumar K 2014 Durability and characteristics of copper slag as fine aggregate and fly ash as cement in concrete. In: *Second International Conference on Current Trends In Engineering and Technology-ICCTET 2014*: IEEE) pp 222-7. https://doi.org/10.1109/ICCTET.2014.6966291

[44] Youcai Z 2016 *Pollution control and resource recovery: municipal solid wastes incineration: bottom ash and fly ash*: Butterworth-Heinemann)

Recent Advancements in Geotechnical Engineering - NCRAG'21   Materials Research Forum LLC
Materials Research Proceedings **19** (2021) 36-43   https://doi.org/10.21741/9781644901618-5

Experimental Study of Photocatalytic Effect on Paver Blocks

P. Jeganmurugan[1a], A. Sree Rameswari[2b], N. Anuja[3c] and V. Sherin[4d]

[1] Assistant Professor, Department of Civil Engineering, Karpagam College of Engineering, Coimbatore, Tamil Nadu, India

[2] Assistant Professor, Department of Civil Engineering, PSNA College of Engineering and Technology, Dindigul, Tamil Nadu, India

[3] Assistant Professor, Department of Civil Engineering, Mepco Schlenk Engineering College, Sivakasi, Tamil Nadu, India

[4] Assistant Professor, Department of Civil Engineering, KCG College of Technology, Chennai, Tamil Nadu, India

[a]jeganmurugan1086@gmail.com*, [b]sreerameswari@gmail.com, [c]anu_priya1031@yahoo.com, [d]vsherin2911@gmail.com

Keywords: Paver Block, Titanium Dioxide, UV Radiation, Photocatalytic Effect

Abstract. The increasing population and massive use of vehicles caused the atmospheric air to be more polluted and its effect on human beings is increasing all over the world and hence the introduction of pollution controlling paver blocks can helps in absorbing the vehicles pollution. From this paver block the venture is being made to reduce the pollution using titanium oxide and other chemicals by photocatalytic method. The titanium dioxide absorbs pollutions by the reaction with UV radiation titanium dioxide power is applied in three different methods on the paver blocks in order to find the most effective pollution absorbing capacity of the paver blocks.

Introduction

In today's world the three major things we are focusing is industrialization, globalization and modernization. Due to above three the 21st century is moving towards devastation. The green lawn areas are reducing consecutively and its being one of the causes of global warming. But it is not too dangerous. However in future this problems may create big impact, therefore proper initiation need to be taken from today. The most common problems in all metropolitan cities are increasing population, industrial pollution, traffic jams, road accidents etc., This are some of the highlighted issues which are creating pollutions on urban cities. The major cause for air pollution is created by vehicles. To avoid this problem the road system need to contribute in the way of absorbing pollutant gases emits by the vehicle directly to the atmosphere.

To achieve this idea in successful manner by, adding chemicals to the paver blocks in order to absorb pollutant gases and reducing air pollution in atmosphere. In this project, we are using titanium dioxide (TiO_2), as a photo catalyst. Titanium is a naturally occurring oxide compounds, it can decompose pollutant gases present in atmosphere with the presence of ultra violet radiation. Adding TiO_2 to the pavement by various methods, we can obtain reduction in the level of emission of pollutant gases in atmosphere. When TiO_2 is added to paver blocks, the air will get purified on sunny days due to photocatalytic process. By this innovative idea, the project members aim to identify the effective method of adding TiO_2 to the paver blocks to produce an eco-friendly road environment.

Materials used

Cement (OPC 53 grade)
Ultratech cement of 53 grades (Ordinary Portland cement) was used in this project. The OPC 53 grade cement was tested by IS code of 12269-1987 & 4031-1988. The properties of OPC 53 grade cement were mentioned in Table 1.

Figure 1 Cement

Table 1 Properties of (OPC 53 Grade) Cement

S.No	Property	Result
1.	Fineness of cement	96%
2.	Relative density	3.16
3.	Standard Consistency	30%
4.	Initial setting time	33 min

Fine Aggregate
River sand (Figure 2) had been used as fine aggregate for this project. The River sand was sieved through 4.75mm size of sieve to remove the particles of size greater than 4.75mm. The aggregates were tested by IS code of 383- 1970 and the properties were mentioned in Table 2.

Figure 2 Fine Aggregate

Table 2 Properties of Fine aggregate (River Sand)

S.No	Property	Result
1.	Fineness modulus (IS 2386 – 1963) Part III	2.34
2.	Relative density	2.6

Recent Advancements in Geotechnical Engineering - NCRAG'21   Materials Research Forum LLC
Materials Research Proceedings **19** (2021) 36-43   https://doi.org/10.21741/9781644901618-5

Coarse Aggregate

Aggregate (Figure 3) of size 10mm is desirable for the paver block. Well graded rounded or cubical shape aggregates are generally used. In this project work aggregates of maximum size 10mm has been used in order to increase the strength of the block. The properties of coarse aggregate were tested and mentioned in Table 3.

Figure 3 Coarse Aggregate

Table 3 Properties of Coarse aggregate

S.No	Property	Result
1.	Fineness modulus (IS 2386 – 1963) Part III	6.65
2.	Relative density	2.86
3.	Size	10mm

Water

Portable water having pH value of greater than 6 were used for this project as per the requirement of IS 456-2000 for mixing of concrete and curing process.

Titanium dioxide

Titanium dioxide or titanium is a naturally occurring oxide compound and it is generally used in toothpaste, paint, sunscreen, cosmetics, plastics, and other products. TiO_2 is white in colour it doesn't produce any harmful effects and an inexpensive fine powder material. TiO_2 powder (Figure 4) is used as pigments in ancient times. TiO_2 is an important alloying agent with many metals and that alloy metals used to make aircrafts, spacecraft and missiles. It can be used as absorbent (absorbing UV light rays) in sunscreen without being consumed in the reaction. Titanium dioxide is inorganic substance, non-flammable, thermally stable, less soluble, and not produced hazardous effects. TiO_2, available naturally in certain types of rocks and mineral sands. It is a most common element in upper surface of earth.

Figure 4 Titanium dioxide Powder

Table 4 Properties of Titanium dioxide (TiO₂)

S.No	Property	Result
1.	Colour	White
2.	Odour	Nil
3.	Specific Gravity	4.32
4.	Density	3.82 g/cc

Mix Proportion

The mix design is formed by using IS code of 10262-2009 and M_{30} mix proportion value of 1:1.94:1.82 has been obtained. The quantity of materials required per m^3 of concrete were found and mentioned in Table 4.

Table 5 Mix Proportion of Paver Block

S.No	Material	Quantity (kg/m³)
1.	Cement (OPC 53grade)	450
2.	Fine aggregate (River sand)	874.5
3.	Coarse aggregate (10mm)	820.33
4.	Water (pH > 6)	220.48
5.	Water cement ratio	0.45

Methods of Application of TiO₂ on the Paver Blocks

To absorb the pollutions like CO_2 and NO_2 we applied the titanium dioxide powder in three methods over the paver blocks. Those methods are

- TiO_2 surface coating.
- TiO_2 mixed with concrete.
- TiO_2 curing process.

The paver block which is subjected to the application of TiO_2 have the capability of reactingwith ultra violet radiations and hence has the capacity of absorbing the pollutions (Table 5).

Table 6 Percentage of TiO₂

Method of application	Amount of TiO₂ added into cement	Amount of cement
TiO₂ surface coating	20% (The percentage of TiO₂ is fixed 20% by trial and error method)	80%
TiO₂ mixed with concrete.	20% (The percentage of TiO₂ is fixed 20% by trial and error method)	80%
TiO₂ curing process	TiO₂ powder (is insoluble in water) is mixed with water, approximately 20g for 1 litre of water.	

Experimental program
Dimensions of the Paver Block
Length   : 225mm
Breadth   : 150 mm
Area of specimen   : 33750 mm^2
The paver block has four projections at corners we measured the area of the block by cutting two projections at one side of the block and filled inside the gaps on other side.

Figure 5 Paver blocks without and with TiO₂

Compressive Strength of Concrete Paver Block
Compressive strength is the capability of a material to withstand compressive forces acting on that. Tensile strength is also the ability of a material to withstand forces trying to elongate   (Table 6).

Pollution Absorption Test
With the use of TiO₂ treated paver blocks corresponding pollution absorbing capacity will be found. The paver blocks absorb pollutions only if the surface is exposed to Ultraviolet radiations which were naturally obtained by the sunlight means of photocatalytic activity (Table 7).

Recent Advancements in Geotechnical Engineering - NCRAG'21   Materials Research Forum LLC
Materials Research Proceedings **19** (2021) 36-43   https://doi.org/10.21741/9781644901618-5

Experimental Setup
Air Tight Glass Chamber

The photo catalytic process of TiO_2 is achieved under the condition of Ultraviolet radiation. Hence the transparent air tight glass chamber of size 22.86cm x 15.24cm x 15.24cm is made in order to effectively absorb the vehicles pollutions.

The glass chamber is able to contian the TiO_2 applied concrete paver block which helps in lowering the pollutions which was emitted by the vehicles.

Figure 6 Air Tight Glass Chamber

Gas Analyser

Normal pollution analyser is used to test the pollution absorbing capacities of three types of TiO_2 treated paver blocks. The analyser is capable of analysing the carbon monoxide, carbon dioxide, oxygen and hydro carbon by which the initial and final level of pollution content inside the air tight glass chamber was found.

Initially the pollution gas reading is obtained from the exhaust of the petrol engine powered vehicle, then that exhaust gas is allowed to fill the air tight glass chamber. After 30 minutes of exposure to Ultraviolet radiation final readings are noted down and found the reduction level of pollution gas.

Test Results
Compressive Strength Test Results of Paver Block

Table 6 shows the compressive strength test results of Paver Block at 7 days and 28 days.

Table 7 Compressive Strength Test Results of Paver Blocks

Sample	Compressive strength of paver block at 7 days		Compressive strength of paver block at 28 days	
	Load in kN	Compressive strength in N/mm²	Load in kN	Compressive strength in N/mm²
Sample 1	790	23.40	1080	32
Sample 2	780	23.11	1050	31.11
Sample 3	760	22.51	990	29.33
	Average	**23 N/mm²**	**Average**	**30.81N/mm²**

Pollution Absorption Test

Table 8 Pollution Absorption Test

Types of gas	Initial level of pollution	Final level of pollution (ppm)		
		TiO₂ surface coating	TiO₂ mixed with concrete	TiO₂ curing process
Oxygen (%)	21.95	21.75	**21.84**	21.30
Hydro carbon (%)	633	105	**98**	234
Carbon dioxide (%)	3.36	1.90	**1.84**	2.40
Carbon monoxide (ppm)	2.063	1.99	**2.03**	2.53

Results and Discussion

The compressive strength of M_{30} grade of concrete paver block at 7 days and 28 days was 23 N/mm² and 30.81 N/mm² respectively. The average percentage value of hydro carbon absorbed by TiO_2 surface coating method was 83.41% and TiO_2 mixed with concrete was 84.51%. 43.45% of carbon dioxide was absorbed by TiO_2 surface coating method and 45.08% of carbon dioxide was absorbed by TiO_2 mixed with concrete method. Both TiO_2 surface coating and TiO_2 mixed with concrete method has the slightly decreased variation in the oxygen level.

Conclusion

1. From the compression test results at 7 days and 28 days maximum strength was attained for mix proportion of M_{30} grade of concrete paver block.
2. As expected the TiO_2 treated paver block effectively absorbed the pollutions emitted by the vehicle.

3. Out of these three methods of TiO_2 applied paver blocks, the TiO_2 mixed with concrete performs more effective in absorbing the vehicles pollution.
4. Comparatively TiO_2 mixed with concrete involves in the less alteration of oxygen and the percentage of hydro carbon level was highly absorbed by this method.
5. The percentage of carbon dioxide was absorbed efficiently by TiO_2 mixed with concrete method.
6. Hence the Titanium dioxide mixed with concrete method was highly recommended and effective for the absorption atmospheric vehicle pollutions.

References

[1] Aniket Pisal, Akshay Jambhale, Sanket Gurav, Anandrao Jagtap, Rahul Mardhekar (2017), Eco Sensitivity Of Paving Block By Using Titanium Di-Oxide.

[2] Poonam Sharma, Ramesh Kumar Batra (2015), Cement concrete paver blocks for rural roads.

[3] Elia Boonen* and Anne Beeldens (2014), Recent Photocatalytic Applications for Air Purification in Belgium. https://doi.org/10.3390/coatings4030553

[4] Marwa M. Hassan, Heather Dylla, Louay N. Mohammad, and Tyson Rupnow (2012), Methods for the Application of Titanium Dioxide Coatings to ConcretePavement.

[5] Gian luca Guerrini, Anne Beeldens (2012), Environmental benefits of innovative photocatalytic cementitious road materials.

[6] Shihui Shen, Maria Burton, Bertram Jobson, and Liv Haselbach (2011), Pervious Concrete with Titanium Dioxide as a Photocatalyst Compound for a 1 Greener Urban Road Environment. https://doi.org/10.1016/j.conbuildmat.2012.04.097

[7] Lu Yang, Amer Hakki (2008), photocatalysis efficiency in concrete technology:The effect of photocatalysis placement.

[8] Anne Beeldens (2006), Environmental friendly concrete pavement blocks: air purification in the centre of Antwerp

[9] http://pubchem.ncbi.nlm.gov/compound/titanium_dioxide (Properties of titanium dioxide)

[10] http://pubchem.ncbi.nlm.gov/compound/zinc_oxide (Properties of zinc oxide)respectively

Recent Advancements in Geotechnical Engineering - NCRAG'21   Materials Research Forum LLC
Materials Research Proceedings **19** (2021) 44-50   https://doi.org/10.21741/9781644901618-6

Stabilization of Black Cotton Soil with Groundnut Shell Ash

R. Premkumar[1,a*], B. Subha[1], S. Pattu Sandhiya[1], K. Shankar Narayanan[2]

[1]School of Environmental and Construction Technology, Department of Civil Engineering,
Kalasalingam Academy of Research and Education, Krishnankoil, Tamil Nadu, India

[2]F Geotechnical Engineer, Ayothi Consultancy, Rajapalayam, Tamil Nadu, India

[a]prem.ce@gmail.com, * corresponding author

Keywords: California Bearing Ratio (CBR), Unconfined Compressive Strength (UCS), Stabilization, Groundnut Shell Ash (GSA), Black Cotton Soil

Abstract. The analysis of GSA for the stabilization of soil samples is the subject of this research paper. In recent years, soil stabilization techniques have been effective in improving the shear strength parameters of poor soils. GSA is a naturally occurring substance that causes human health and environmental issues. Physical properties of soil were calculated, including Atterberg's limits, compaction characteristics, and strength characteristics of virgin soil samples. GSA was applied to the soil in various percentages (2 to 10 percent). The soil sample's intensity increased up to 6% before decreasing. It is clear that 6% of GSA to the soil is an optimum percentage and it leads to an increase in shear strength and bearing capacity in expansive soil.

Introduction

In this high-level period of science and innovation, man has made fast walks in all fields since the old ages. Directly from the dim ages till the current data age, man has developed significantly and has attempted to come around a wide range of issues experienced. From a designing perspective, particularly from a geotechnical viewpoint, land use for improvement work has brought to the front, the issue of intense land lack [1]. This has prompted the recovery of unusable land for advancement exercises. Ground improvement innovation has been the main thrust that has achieved this insurgency in the recovery of unusable land, which has lead to abrupt spray informative exercises. Likewise, this innovation, however gainful severally, had natural effects. With quick urbanization and industrialization, this innovation turned into the main thrust for all land recovery work. With the rising utilization of a portion of these procedures, for example, concrete grouting, lime segments, and soon, the effect on the climate came to be gradually perceived [2]. Regular materials and their utilization in ground improvement is one such territory of potential and guarantee.

Black cotton soil is clay soil with a lot of space. Clay poses a significant challenge to building construction due to its low shear strength and strong bulge (swelling) characteristics [3]. To regulate this action, the worthy cohesive soil reacts with chemical compounds or any other suitable material that can change its engineering actions. The study's goal was to increase soil strength while lowering construction costs by using locally available materials in the most efficient way possible.GSA has self-hardening and bonding characteristics, so it will help the soil particles to bond with each other. Then it became dense automatically density of the soil gets increased. Researchers Robert, et.al. In this paper, they are using fly ash, rice husk ash for stabilizing soil effectively [4]. It is much more effective but economically it cost more. It is economically not suitable. In the current world, the research work is done in geotechnical Engineering and materials used in construction. Misra, et. are using fly ash, bagash, blast furnace slag, etc. because it is economical and environmentally friendly[5-6]. It gives good strength. Replacement did for fully (or) partially.

Materials

Figure 1 depicts the soil sample used in the ongoing investigation. Necessary tests were used to determine the strength characteristics of soil specimens. A soil sample was taken in Rajapalayam, Virudhunagar District. The samples were taken at a depth of 2 meters and are disturbed. Before the experiments, it was air-dried and pulverized.

Figure 1.Preparation of Specimen

Groundnut shell ash

Groundnut shells were spread on the ground and air-dried for 2 days to encourage simple processing. After air-drying the groundnut shell was physically broken and processed into ordinary temperature (37°c) debris structures shown in figure 2. The properties of groundnut shell ash are Groundnut shell ash is unscented and Groundnut shell ash contains CaO, Al_2O_3, SiO_2, Fe_2O_3, MnO, and MgO.

Figure 2.Groundnut Shell Ash

Experimental Investigation

The various tests were carried out on virgin soil specimens following IS Standard (IS: 2720). Primarily, the black cotton soil that had been prepared was examined. The soil was then combined with groundnut shell ash to measure its compaction characteristics, which included determining the optimum moisture content and maximum dry density of the specimen using a standard proctor test, as well as the specimen's strength characteristics using CBR and UCC tests.

Results and Discussion

Table 1.Virgin soil specimen engineering properties

S.No	Specification	Results
1	Free swell (%)	65
2	Liquid limit (%)	58.4
3	Plastic Limit (%)	20.34
4	Plasticity index (%)	38.04
5	Shrinkage Limit (%)	6
6	Specific gravity (%)	2.75
7	Maximum dry density (g/cc)	1.64
8	Optimum moisture content (%)	15
9	CBR value (%)	5.71
10	UCC value (kN/m2)	125
	Grain size distribution	
11	Sand (%)	27.3
	Silt + Clay (%)	72.7
12	Soil classification	CH

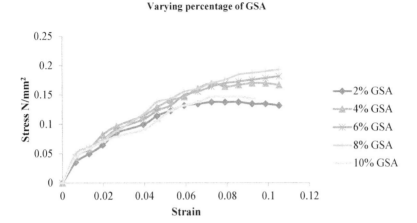

Figure 3.Stress-Strain curve for soil with GSA

The virgin soil specimen's properties were tabulated in Table 1. The free swell percentage was 65% which is higher than 50% so it is identified to be rapidly expansive depends on IS-2720(part XL)-1997. The specimen's shrinkage limit is 6%, which is lower than 11 percent, and it has a large swelling capacity, according to IS: 2720(part6). The BC soil's normal basic gravity is (2.65-2.90). The BC used in the experiment had a test outcome of 2.75 percent. For the plain soil sample, the maximum dry density was 1.64g/cc and the optimum moisture content was 15%. The virgin soil sample has a CBR value of 5.71 percent (According to IS-2720 part 16, the fair CBR value of the mid soil is 4-6). The virgin soil specimen's unconfined compressive intensity is $0.125N/mm^2$. The UCC values are in the middle of $(0.100\text{-}0.200N/mm^2)$ which denotes the soil's stiff consistency. According to the test result liquid limit of the specimen is 58.4% and plasticity index= (LL-PL) = 38.04. It is beyond A-Line in the plasticity chart. From the results, the soil specimen is separated as highly compressible clay (CH).

Table 2.UCC values of GSA with soil specimen

Differing percentage of Groundnut Shell Ash%	q_u N/mm^2
0	0.125
2	0.127
4	0.154
6	0.161
8	0.173
10	0.135

The difference in strain vs. stress of the different percentages of Groundnut Shell Ash with soil specimen is shown in Figure 3. Virgin soil specimen has a UCC value of 0.125N/mm2. After

Materials Research Forum LLC
https://doi.org/10.21741/9781644901618-6

combining 8% off GSA, it increased to 0.173N/mm2. Due to the mixing of GSA and the soil particle, the intensity of the soil initially increases as the percentage of GSA increases. Later on, as the volume of GSA increases, the intensity decreases. With an increase in ash content, the ash did not properly mix with the soil, resulting in poor ash dispersion in the soil matrix and decreased load transfer efficiency. The optimal GSA percentage has been determined to be 8%. The UCC value decreases when 10% GSA is combined. As a result, an increase in GSA content reduces the soil's intensity. It is due to the fact that stray-oriented ash recharges the soil particles on its own.

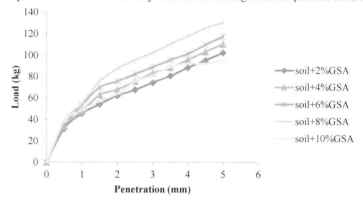

Figure 4: Load-penetration curve for soil with GSA

Table 2 shows the effect of UCC strength on soil with GSA. It shows that the strength of the soil is rapidly increasing after a combination of the GSA in percentage, which is due to the soil and GSA interchange. When the quantity of GSA is getting increased, it leads to ash interchange which reduces the strength of the soil. Also, 8% of GSA, the strength of the soil increases from $0.125N/mm^2$ to $0.173N/mm^2$, which is identified to be 54.67% from the virgin soil specimen. Besides 10% GSA with soil specimen, the strength is higher than virgin soil specimen but lower than 8% GSA. This concludes 8% off GSA to be the optimum percentage.

Table 3.CBR test results of soil sample with the differing percentage of GSA

Differing percentage of GSA	CBR(%)
0	5.71
2	6.75
4	7.27
6	7.70
8	8.31
10	7.27

Figure 4 depicts the load penetration of soil with higher GSA percentages. With a high GSA, the CBR value is high. Figure 5 shows the optimum GSA value for obtaining the full CBR value at 2.5 mm penetration. The combination of GSA and clayey soil results in an improvement in CBR

Recent Advancements in Geotechnical Engineering - NCRAG'21   Materials Research Forum LLC
Materials Research Proceedings **19** (2021) 44-50   https://doi.org/10.21741/9781644901618-6

value. It is more capable of changing the soil stress along with the ash due to better associate enhancement with mid soil particles and the ash permit. Despite this, the rise in an ash-ash associate may be to blame for the decrease in CBR values above the optimum ash content. After increasing the percentage of GSA above 8%, the load penetration curve of the soil specimen decreases.

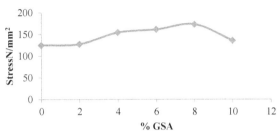

Figure 5:UCC % comparison

Table 3 shows the CBR value of the soil with different percentages of GSA. The CBR value for a virgin soil specimen was 5.71 percent, but after combining 8% GSA, it increased to 8.31 percent. The addition of GSA to the soil has resulted in a rise in CBR values. Thus the increase in value might be due to better interchange adhesion in the middle of the soil particles and the ash matrix interface.

Conclusion
It can be inferred from the experiments performed on soil specimens with Groundnut Shell Ash that GSA can be used as a natural reinforcing agent for the stabilization of soft clayey soils. The benefits of using GSA include its high durability to biodegradability, low cost, and strength properties. It's also good for keeping slopes stable. GSA may be used as a reinforcing material to help stabilize ductile pavements and reduce the thickness of the sub-grade. The following is the test result of our experiment. The soil specimen has a liquid cap of 58.4 percent. Highly compressible clay is the classification of the soil sample (CH). The maximum dry density and optimum moisture content of virgin soil samples are 15% and 1.64 g/cc, respectively. The untreated soil sample's unconfined compressive strength (UCS) is 0.125 N/mm^2. The UCC intensity increases to 0.173N/mm^2 when GSA is combined, but decreases as the percentage of GSA increases.

- A virgin soil specimen has a California Bearing Ratio (CBR) of 5.71. The CBR value increased to 8.31 percent when 8 percent GSA was added.
- The addition of GSA raised the soil specimen's intensity to 56.6 percent.
- The strength characteristics UCS of a virgin soil sample were 0.125N/mm^2, but after adding 8% GSA, the UCS value rose to 0.173N/mm^2.
- By combining 8% GSA with the soil specimen, the optimum strength of the soil was achieved.

- To avoid environmental issues such as open-air dumping, this can be used as a stabilization material in soil stabilization methods.
- Ash can alter the behavior of vast soil and correct it in a variety of geotechnical applications.

References

[1] Srinadh D, Praneeth P, Reddy D, Chamberlin K, Kumar NS. Stabilization of Black Cotton Soil using Lime and G.G.B.S (Ground Granulated Blast Furnace Slag) as an Admixtures. International Journal of Innovative Technology and Exploring Engineering (IJITEE). 2019; 9(2):2133–2136. https://doi.org/10.35940/ijitee.B7577.129219

[2] Atahu MK, Saathoff F, Gebissa A. Mechanical behaviors of expansive soil treated with coffee husk ash. Journal of Rock Mechanics and Geotechnical Engineering. 2018. Available from: https://doi.org/10.1016/j.jrmge.2018.11.004.

[3] Noorzad R, Motevalian S. Improvement of Clayey Soil with Lime and Industrial Sludge. Geotechnical and Geological Engineering. 2018;36(5):2957–2966. Available from: https://dx.doi.org/10.1007/s10706-018-0515-x.

[4] Dr.Robert, M.Brooks, A Soil stabilization with fly ash and rice husk ash (2009), International journal research and reviews in applied science, 2009;1(3):209–217

[5] Misra, A.Stabilization Characteristics of Clays Using Class C Fly Ash,Transportation Research Record, 2000, Transportation Research Board, National Research Council, Washington, D.C, 1611, 46-54. https://doi.org/10.3141/1611-06

[6] Sivapulliah P.V., Subba Rao K.S., and Gurumurthy, J.V., Stabilization of rice husk ash as a cushion below foundations on expansive soils, Ground Improvement, 2004, Vol. 8, No. 4, pp 137-149. https://doi.org/10.1680/grim.2004.8.4.137

[7] IS: 2720 (Part 5) - 1985 Indian Standard Code of practice for Determination of Liquid Limit.

[8] IS: 2720 (Part 6) - 1972 Indian Standard Code of practice for Determination of Plastic Limit.

[9] IS: 2720 (Part 8) - 1983 Indian Standard Code of practice for Determination of Modified Proctor Compaction parameters.

[10] IS: 2720 (Part 16) - 1979 Indian Standard Code of practice for Determination of California Bearing Ratio (CBR).

[11] IS: 2720 (Part 10) - 1991 Indian Standard Code of practice for Determination of Unconfined Compressive Strength of Soils (UCS).

Recent Advancements in Geotechnical Engineering - NCRAG'21
Materials Research Proceedings **19** (2021) 51-59

Materials Research Forum LLC
https://doi.org/10.21741/9781644901618-7

Effect of Sulfonated-Melamine Formaldehyde as Superplasticizer in Cementitious Systems

SKM. Pothinathan[1,a*], J. Millar[2,b], S. Christopher Gnanaraj[3,c]

[1] Department of Civil Engineering, Kalasalingam Academy of Research and Education, Krishnankoil-626126, Tamilnadu, India

[2] Student, Mater of Technology, Department of Civil Engineering, Kalasalingam Academy of Research and Education, Krishnankoil – 626126, Tamilnadu, India

[3] Department of Civil Engineering, Kalasalingam Academy of Research and Education, Krishnankoil-626126, Tamilnadu, India

[a*]s.k.m.pothinathan@klu.ac.in, [b]davidmillar5554@gmail.com, [c]s.christophergnanaraj@klu.ac.in

Keywords: Sulfonated-Melamine Formaldehyde, Concrete, Superplasticizer, Fresh Concrete Properties, Mechanical Strength

Abstract. This paper studied the effect of Sulfonated-Melamine Formaldehyde (SMF) on the water cement ratio, setting time, compressive strength at various ages and an acid resistance test was conducted using sulfuric acid. Sulfonated-Melamine Formaldehyde is classified as superplasticizer. SMF was mixed with concrete at 1%-5% in volume fraction. But not much investigation was made. In this study it was found that the Sulfonated-Melamine Formaldehyde incorporated concrete mixture performing well in strength property and have more resistance to aggressive environment when compared to conventional concrete.

Introduction

In concrete ingredient, water cement ratio plays a vital role in enhancing properties like workability, strength, and durability. Higher water cement ratio gives good workability but leads to segregation of concrete ingredients and not consumed water during hydration process results in pores and cracks that affects the concrete strength and durability. Lower water concrete proportion prompts to higher strength and durability but make the mixture difficult to achieve uniform mix and may not flow well to compact and place the concrete. These problems can be resolve with water reducing admixtures. The water reducing admixtures are available in synthetic, organic, and water-soluble products. This water reducers are further classified into four groups Polynaphthalene sulfonates (PNS), Polymelamine sulfonates (PMS), Vinyl copolymers (VC) and Polycarboxylic ethers (PCE) [1]. In this the effect of PNS, PMS, VC is based on electrostatic repulsion and PCE is on steric hindrance effect [2].

Ibragimov [3] studied the early strength, and durability properties of concrete using four different superplasticizers namely naphthalenesulfonate and organic accelerator, polyoxyethylene derivatives of polymethacrylic acid, polyether carboxylates, and polyoxyethylene derivatives. He concluded that the naphthalenesulfonate and organic accelerator performed well in all aspect comparing other superplasticizers. Naphthalenesulfonate and organic accelerator gave improved strength in compression by 14-21 percentage, flexural strength by 54 percentage. The water absorption and shrinkage reduced by 45–54 percentage and 53 percentage. Nakajima [8] studied the mechanism of calcium sulphate in cement with Polynaphthalene sulfonates. The results indicate the concentration of calcium sulphates result in flow loss of cement paste. He concluded that the increased polynaphthalene sulfonates content results in decreased calcium sulphates absorption. This causes the less flow loss.

Cheah [4] examined the polycarboxylate-based superplasticizer in the properties of high-performance concrete. He used methoxy polyethylene glycols and isoprenyl polyethylene glycols as admixture. He also studied performance of blending both polycarboxylate. The result shows that the blended superplasticizer provides reduction in mechanical strength because of both foil and fibril like C-S-H gel co-formation the pores increases. He concludes that by comparing all admixed concrete methoxy polyethylene glycols shows slightly improved early compressive strength. Nowak-Michta [5] studied the impact in strength performance of air-entraining and superplasticizing admixed concrete. He used polycarboxylate-based superplasticizer for liquefaction. He concluded that the air entraining agent alone reduced the compressive strength. But the addition of air entraining admixture along with superplasticizer content by 1 to 13 percentage increases the strength performance of concrete.

Gupta [6] used superplasticizer in two types of concrete mix. One is 100 percent GGBS and other one is 50 percent GGBS and 50 percent fly ash admixed geopolymer concrete. He utilized various percentage of Glenium Sky 8630 a polycarboxylic based superplasticizer in his work. He noticed improvement in strength in all dosage of superplasticizer from 1 percentage to 3 percentage. The maximum strength development was noted with 3 percentage polycarboxylic based superplasticizer dosage in both types of mixtures. The superplasticizing effect was studied by Pei et al [12, 20] using sodium sulfanilate-phenol-formaldehyde (SSPF) and soluble acetone–formaldehyde, Mahmoud et al [16] used sulfonated acetophenone–formaldehyde resin and Chen et al [19] used sulphonated phenolic resin. All authors infer improved performance in their SPs.

From the above literatures it clearly signifies that the addition of superplasticizers in all mixtures like OPC, PPC, GGBS with calcium sulphate, fluoride and fly ash decreases the water binder ratio and increase the strength and durability. But there is very less investigation was conducted using Sulfonated-Melamine Formaldehyde as superplasticizer. A study was conducted by Lahallh [9] about the Sulfonated Melamine-Formaldehyde (SMF) as superplasticizer in the concrete on 1988 and concluded that the lab produced SMF performed well in all aspect than the industrial purchased Sulfonated Melamine-Formaldehyde. Arosio [10] used Sulfonated Melamine-Formaldehyde to produce building blocks. Other than these two studies no noticeable investigation was conducted using Sulfonated Melamine-Formaldehyde in cementitious system. The main purpose of the paper is to study the effect of Sulfonated Melamine-Formaldehyde as superplasticizer in concrete.

Experimental study
Concrete Materials
Ordinary Portland cement with 43 grades satisfying IS 8112 requirements was used in this study. The chemical composition and properties of OPC is shown in Table 1. The specific gravity of cement is 3.2g/cm3and Zone I natural river sand were used throughout the study for mortar mix as per IS 383. The specific gravity of fine aggregate is 2.57 and the fineness modulus of 3.353. Crushed stone from quarry as coarse aggregate having a specific gravity of 2.72 and maximum size of 20mm used with specific grading as coarse aggregate.

Materials Research Forum LLC
https://doi.org/10.21741/9781644901618-7

Table 1. Chemical substance and properties of Ordinator Portland cement

Chemical Composition (%)						Density	Specific area
SiO$_2$	CaO	Al$_2$O$_3$	Fe$_2$O$_3$	MgO	Loss on ignition		
19.76	64.53	5.89	3.40	1.45	1.14	3.3g/cm^3	3400cm^2/g

Sulfonated Melamine-Formaldehyde
Industrial available Sulfonated Melamine-Formaldehyde was obtained in liquid form with 20% solid content. It a colorless liquid having specific gravity of 1.1 and viscosity of 5 mPa.s. The pH value of Sulfonated Melamine-Formaldehyde liquid is 8.

Mixing, casting, and curing
The concrete blend composition was according to IS 10262. The cement content was 310kg/m^3. The water content of the conventional concrete and SMF admixed concrete was adjusted to obtain the slump value 80mm [11]. In a rotating drum the concrete ingredients are added. Water and Sulfonated Melamine-Formaldehyde mixed and added to the concrete mixture. After the uniform mixing the concrete mix was cased and kept in room temperature for 24 hours. All specimens are demolded and cured in water until test date.

Fig. 1.*Curing of Specimen*

Testing
Setting time test was conducted confirming to IS 4031 using Vicat's needle apparatus. The time elapsed to fail to pierce the specimen 5.0mm measure from the bottom was noted.

Compressive strength of concrete cubes of size 15 x 15 x 15 cm were used according to IS516 and tension strength was conducted in cylindrical specimen with 300mm long and 150mm diameter according to IS5816. Flexural strength test was conducted by using 15 x 15 x 70 cm prism according to IS 516. The age of compression test were 3 days, 7 days, 14days and 28 days. The ages of split tensile and flexural test were 4 weeks. Average of three specimen was used in each strength test.

Acid resistance test was conducted in cube specimen. After 28days of water curing the specimens were taken out and kept dry in room temperature for 24hrs. Then the specimens were submerged in water with 5% sulfuric acid by weight for 90days. After that the specimens were washed and dried for 24hrs before testing.

Recent Advancements in Geotechnical Engineering - NCRAG'21
Materials Research Proceedings 19 (2021) 51-59

Materials Research Forum LLC
https://doi.org/10.21741/9781644901618-7

Test results and discussion:

Effect on fresh concrete

The effect of Sulfonated Melamine-Formaldehyde as superplasticizers with different dosage level in concrete mixture on water content to attain 80mm slump value was examined. Fig.2. shows the unit water reduction due to the effect of Sulfonated Melamine-Formaldehyde. Sulfonated Melamine-Formaldehyde act as superplasticizer and considerably reduce the water content proportionally. The resin content increases the water content decease simultaneously. 5 percentage increase in SMF content reduced water up-to 30 percentage. The resin neutralizing the surface resistance of the cement grains and reducing the viscosity. This results the rapid scattering of cement particles and workability of the mixture was increasing with decreased water content.

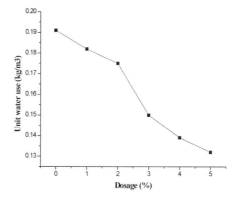

***Fig. 2.** Unit water reduction on concrete mixture*

Fig.3. displays the impact on Sulfonated Melamine-Formaldehyde in initial setting time on concrete mixture comparing to conventional concrete. The test was conducted in Vicat's needle apparatus and the penetration resistance by the needle versus time was noted for different SMF dosage levels. The SMF dispersed the cement particle to increase the flowability and affects the hydration processes of cement. Because of this the initial setting time of cement delayed. This retardation effect is increasing by increasing Sulfonated Melamine-Formaldehyde

Recent Advancements in Geotechnical Engineering - NCRAG'21   Materials Research Forum LLC
Materials Research Proceedings **19** (2021) 51-59   https://doi.org/10.21741/9781644901618-7

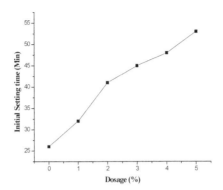

Fig. 3. Initial setting time of concrete mixture

Effect on harden concrete property

Fig. 4. Cube testing

Fig 5. Shows the compression strength of concrete with different dosages (1% - 5%) of Sulfonated-Melamine Formaldehyde at different ages (3days, 7days, 14days and 28days). The SMF incorporated concrete mixture provided higher compression strength than the conventional concrete at all dosages and all tested ages. 5 percentage admixed concrete mixture signifies rise in compression strength when compared with smaller dosages. This strength rise is because of the reduction in water content of fresh concrete mixture. It is a chain reaction that the reduction in water content leads to reduction pores content. So higher dense concrete can be produced with higher workability using high range water reducers. SMF also did the same to the concrete mixture by elevating the compressive strength. But dosage of 3 percentage of Sulfonated-Melamine Formaldehyde represent optimum strength rise. There is strength rise after 3 percentage dosage, but the result indicates no drastic change. As the economic concern, it is advisable to use 3 percentage admixture in the concrete mixture.

Materials Research Forum LLC
https://doi.org/10.21741/9781644901618-7

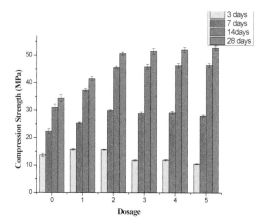

Fig. 5. Compression strength of concrete mixture

Fig 6. Shows the split tensile strength of conventional and SMF admixed concrete after 28days of aging. Tensile strength was improved by increasing the SMF dosage level. It is ostensible that the tensile strength of admixed concrete is higher than the conventional concrete. Due to the water reduction this strength hike is achievable. As discussed in the compression property the 3-percentage dosage of SMF is optimum in tensile strength also.

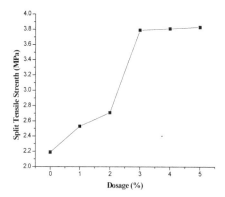

Fig. 6. Split Tensile Strength of Concrete Mixture

The flexural strength of treated and untreated concrete specimens after 28days aging is shown in Fig.7. Regarding the conventional concrete the addition of SMF significantly increases the flexural strength of concrete at age of 28days by 6% with dosage of 5%. This strength rise is achieved by the dense structure of the concrete.

Recent Advancements in Geotechnical Engineering - NCRAG'21   Materials Research Forum LLC
Materials Research Proceedings **19** (2021) 51-59   https://doi.org/10.21741/9781644901618-7

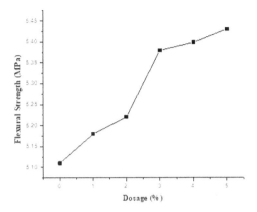

Fig. 7. Flexural strength of concrete mixture

Fig.8. shows the compressive strength result of cementitious system when subjected to acid attack using sulfuric acid with different SMF dosage levels after 90days of immersion in the acid solution. SMF admixed concrete performed well and given higher strength when compared to the conventional concrete. This elevated strength is because of the dense concrete with less water content and less pores. The reduction in pores result in reduction of aggressive solution absorption. So, the acid solution did not have significant damage to the cementitious system. It concludes that the use of SMF improved the resistance against acid environment.

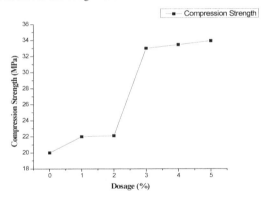

Fig. 8. Acid resistance test

Conclusion

Industrial available Sulfonated Melamine-Formaldehyde with 20% solid content used as superplasticizer for the cementitious system. The effects of fresh and harden concrete property with different dosage and ages are investigated.

- The result infers that the utilization of Sulfonated Melamine-Formaldehyde improves the mechanical strength in compression, tension, and flexural strength test. It also reduces the water content up to 30 percentage when 5 percent increase in SMF.
- The SMF dispersed the cement particle to increase the flowability and affects the hydration processes of cement. Due to this there is a retardation effect in initial setting time test.
- SMF also performed well in acid resistance test. Because the decreased water content and permeable pores improved the durability.
- Higher results were achieved in 5 percentage admix. But dosage of 3 percentage of Sulfonated-Melamine Formaldehyde represent optimum strength rise.
- There is strength rise after 3 percentage dosage, but the result indicates no drastic change. As the economic concern, it is advisable to use 3 percentage admixture in the concrete mixture.
- It concluded that the Sulfonated Melamine-Formaldehyde has the potential to be used as superplasticizer in cementitious system.

References

[1]   MouhcineBen Aicha. (2020). The superplasticizer effect on the rheological and mechanical properties of self-compacting concrete. New Materials in Civil Engineering, Pages 315-331. https://doi.org/10.1016/B978-0-12-818961-0.00008-9

[2]   Dhanya Sathyan, , Kalpathy Balakrishnan Anand. (2019). Influence of superplasticizer family on the durability characteristics of fly ash incorporated cement concrete. Construction and Building Materials, 204, 864-874. https://doi.org/10.1016/j.conbuildmat.2019.01.171

[3]   Ibragimov, R., & Fediuk, R. (2019). Improving the early strength of concrete: Effect of mechanochemical activation of the cementitious suspension and using of various superplasticizers. Construction and Building Materials, 226, 839–848. https://doi.org/10.1016/j.conbuildmat.2019.07.313

[4]   Chee Ban Cheah, Wee Kang Chow, Chuan Wei Oo, Khang Heng Leow (2020). The influence of type and combination of polycarboxylate ether superplasticizer on the mechanical properties and microstructure of slag-silica fume ternary blended self-consolidating concrete. Journal of Building Engineering 31, 101412. https://doi.org/10.1016/j.jobe.2020.101412

[5]   Nowak-Michta, A. (2019). Impact analysis of air-entraining and superplasticizing admixtures on concrete compressive strength. Procedia Structural Integrity, 23, 77–82. https://doi.org/10.1016/j.prostr.2020.01.066

[6]   Gupta, N., Gupta, A., Saxena, K. K., Shukla, A., & Goyal, S. K. (2020). Mechanical and durability properties of geopolymer concrete composite at varying superplasticizer dosage. Materials Today: Proceedings. https://doi.org/10.1016/j.matpr.2020.05.646

[7]   Matsuzawa, K., Atarashi, D., Miyauchi, M., & Sakai, E. (2017). Interactions between fluoride ions and cement paste containing superplasticizer. Cement and Concrete Research, 91, 33–38. https://doi.org/10.1016/j.cemconres.2016.10.006

[8]   Nakajima, Y., & Yamada, K. (2004). The effect of the kind of calcium sulfate in cements on the dispersing ability of poly β-naphthalene sulfonate condensate superplasticizer. Cement and Concrete Research, 34(5), 839–844. https://doi.org/10.1016/j.cemconres.2003.09.022

[9]   Shawqul M.Lahallh, M.Absl-Halabi, Ali M.Ali. (1988) Effect of polymerization conditions of sulfonated-melamine formaldehyde superplasticizers on concrete. Cement and Concrete Research Volume 18, Issue 4, Pages 513-531. https://doi.org/10.1016/0008-8846(88)90044-0

[10] Arosio, F., Castoldi, L., Ferlazzo, N., & Forzatti, P. (2007). Influence of solfonated melamine formaldehyde condensate on the quality of building blocks production by extrusion of cement–clay pastes. Applied Clay Science, 35(1-2), 85–93. https://doi.org/10.1016/j.clay.2006.06.004

[11] Ruslan Ibragimov, Roman Fediuk.(2019). Improving the early strength of concrete: Effect of mechanochemical activation of the cementitious suspension and using of various superplasticizers. Construction and Building Materials, 22 839-848. https://doi.org/10.1016/j.conbuildmat.2019.07.313

[12] Abdullah M.Zeyad, AliAlmalki. (2020). Influence of mixing time and superplasticizer dosage on self-consolidating concrete properties. Journal of Materials Research and Technology, V9, 6101-6115. https://doi.org/10.1016/j.jmrt.2020.04.013

[13] Meishan Pei, Zhenfei Wang, Wenwei Li, Jin Zhang, Qiwei Pan, Xiaojuan Qin (2008). The properties of cementitious materials superplasticized with two superplasticizers based on aminosulfonate–phenol–formaldehyde. Construction and Building Materials 22 2382–2385. https://doi.org/10.1016/j.conbuildmat.2007.09.003

[14] Meishan Pei, Dujin Wang, Xianbo Hu, Duanfu Xu. (2000). Synthesis of sodium sulfanilate-phenol-formaldehyde condensate and its application as a superplasticizer in concrete. Cement and Concrete Research 30 1841 – 1845. https://doi.org/10.1016/S0008-8846(00)00389-6

[15] Alexander N. Chernysheva, Mats Jonssonb, Kerstin Forsberg (2018). Characterization and degradation of a polyaryl ether based superplasticizer for use in concrete barriers in deep geological repositories. Applied Geochemistry95 172-181. https://doi.org/10.1016/j.apgeochem.2018.05.014

[16] A.A.M. Mahmoud, , M.S.H. Shehab, , A.S. El-Dieb. (2010). Concrete mixtures incorporating synthesized sulfonated acetophenone–formaldehyde resin as superplasticizer. Cement & Concrete Composites 32 392–397. https://doi.org/10.1016/j.cemconcomp.2010.02.005

[17] C Rogin Roberta, Dhanya Sathyana, K B Anand. (2018). Effect of superplasticizers on the rheological properties of fly ash incorporated cement paste. Materials Today: Proceedings 5 23955–23963. https://doi.org/10.1016/j.matpr.2018.10.188

[18] Rixom R, Mailvaganam N. (1999) Chemical admixtures for concrete. 3rd ed. London: E & FN Spon. https://doi.org/10.4324/9780203017241

[19] Chen SD, Hwang CH, Hsu KC. (1999) The effects of sulphonated phenolic resins on the properties of concrete. Cement Concrete Research 29(2) 255–259. https://doi.org/10.1016/S0008-8846(98)00098-2

[20] Pei M, Yang Y, Zhang X, Zhang J, Dong J. (2004) Synthesis and the effects of water-soluble acetone–formaldehyde resin on the properties of concrete. Cement Concrete Research ;34(8):1417–1420. https://doi.org/10.1016/j.cemconres.2004.01.012

[21] Pei M, Wang D, Hu X, Xu D. (2000). Synthesis of sodium sulfanilate–phenol–formaldehyde condensate and its application as a superplasticizer in concrete. Cement Concrete Research 30(11) 1841–1845. https://doi.org/10.1016/S0008-8846(00)00389-6

[22] IS383 - Indian Standard Specification for Coarse and Fine Aggregates from Natural Sources for Concrete

[23] IS 10262 - Indian Standard Concrete Mix Proportioning – Guidelines

[24] IS 516 - Indian Standard Methods of Tests for Strength of Concrete

[25] IS 5816 - Indian Standard Splitting tensile strength of concrete

Recent Advancements in Geotechnical Engineering - NCRAG'21
Materials Research Proceedings **19** (2021) 60-65

Materials Research Forum LLC
https://doi.org/10.21741/9781644901618-8

Experimental Investigation of Top Mix Permeable Concrete on Pedestrian Pathway

M.P. Indhu[1,a*], S. Krishnamoorthi[2,b], S. Manivel[1,c]

[1]PG Student, Department of Civil Engineering, Kongu Engineering College, Perundurai, Erode, Tamil Nadu, India

[2]Professor, Department of Civil Engineering, Kongu Engineering College, Perundurai, Erode, Tamil Nadu, India

[*a]indhuperiasamy98@gmail.com, [b]skmoor@kongu.ac.in, [c]manivel2702@gmail.com

Keywords: Hot Island, Permeable, Air Proof Concrete, Pavement, Porosity, Skid Resistance

Abstract. Our towns are increasingly protected by buildings and water paved pavements. Moreover, the city's climate is far from normal. Rainwater is not filtered underground due to the absence of the permeability of the common concrete pavement to water and air permeability. In addition, the exchange of heat and humidity with air is difficult for the soil, and it's not possible to change the temperature and relative humidity of the Earth's surface in urban areas. At the same time, the safety from both car and foot passenger traffic is limited by a plash on the road on a rainy day. Since the 1980s, work on permeable asphalt pavements has started in developed countries like the US and Japan. For roadway applications, permeable concrete is also widely used as a surface course in Europe and Japan Improving skid resistance and reducing noise from traffic. Only about 20 – 30 MPa can the material reach's compressive intensity. Due to their low strength, such materials cannot be used as pavement. Only frames, walking routes, parking garages, and park trails can be used with permeable concrete. Utilizing specified analyses, small materials, admixtures, organic intensifiers and changing the ratio, strength and abrasion resistance of the concrete mix, the porous concrete may be greatly enhanced.

Introduction

Concrete mixture, often referred to as cement mortar and rigid pavements, is a special type of concrete with a highly porous that allows precipitation water to pass through it directly, thereby minimizing the leakage from the properties and allowing water to infiltrate [1]. Using broad aggregates with next to no concrete mixes, permeable concrete is created. Then the pavement layer covers the analyses and helps the concrete slab to move water around [2]. In parking areas, places with rural roads, pedestrian walkways permeable concrete is used. It is important for conventional design and one of the techniques of low impact construction. Porous reinforced concrete is a specific and successful way of addressing key environmental problems and fostering efficient, economic development [3]. Concrete mixture is efficient in water harvesting, decreasing groundwater and storing and allowing storm water to evaporate into the soil [4]. One of it's management techniques (BMPs) recommended by the Environmental Protection Agency is currently the need for a pervious concrete (EPA). By removing the need for detention ponds, and other storm water management devices a productive land usage is created [5]. In being, on a first-cost basis, permeable concrete has the potential to reduce total project costs. Properly regulated amounts of water/cement materials are used to produce a paste that forms a dense coating around fine aggregates. Using enough paste to coat and bind the aggregate particles together requires a great conductivity, porous medium framework that drains easily [6]. Usually, the compressive strength reaches between 15 percent and 25 percent voids, and flow of water rates through concrete mixture are typically about 480 in/hrs. Compared to traditional cementitious materials, both the small mortar content and mechanical strength also decrease intensity, but enough strength is readily obtained for many uses [7].

Although a disturbing amount of uses can be used for concrete mix, its major use is in asphalt. This motivated on the material asphalt mixes, which have also been related to as concrete mixtures, concrete pavers, concrete without fines, concrete with gap grades, and concrete with improved permeability.

Flexible pavement vs permeable pavement

Flexible pavement
- ✓ Subgrade deformation is moved to top layer.
- ✓ The design concept is based on the load distribution features of entire thickness.
- ✓ Flexural strength is low.
- ✓ Repair cost is high.
- ✓ High maintenance cost.
- ✓ Substructure cannot be mounted on the pavement directly, but a sub-base is necessary.
- ✓ As the asphalt has the capacity to contract and expand freely, no thermal stress is caused. This is why extension joints are required.
- ✓ The intensity of the path depends heavily on the intensity of the subsurface.

Permeable pavement
- ✓ Design is based on flexural strength or slab action.
- ✓ Flexural strength is high.
- ✓ Low repair cost.
- ✓ Low maintenance cost.

Applications of permeable concrete
- ➢ Low-volume pavements
- ➢ Residential roads and driveway
- ➢ Sidewalks
- ➢ Slope stabilization
- ➢ Well linings
- ➢ Pavement edge drains
- ➢ Parking areas

Permeable layer

The strong amount of water through a conductive pavement surface facilitates the absorption and percolation of rainfall into the land, decreasing the leakage of groundwater, recharging groundwater, encouraging sustainable development, providing an environmentally conscious building solution, and ensuring developers align with Environmental protection agency rainwater requirements [8].

By regulating rainwater on-site and resolving storm water runoff problems, this specific capacity of permeable concrete provides environmental benefits, public authorities, and property managers. In large cities, or where land is very costly, it can be of particular concern. A porous reinforced concrete and its subsurface will provide adequate groundwater storage to remove the need for culverts, seawalls, and other pollution precipitation management techniques, depending on the specific requirements and the ecosystem [9]. It has some other important uses due to high permeability: it is heat shielding (in building walls, for example) and has excellent thermal conductivity (for sound barrier walls). While asphalt are the dominant U.S. usage for concrete mixture, it has been used in the Europe for several years as a structural material [10]. Applications involve two-story walls, high-rise load-bearing walls (up to 10 stories), and tall building infill plates, sea groin area, paths, and parking lots [11]. Many of these methods take advantage of the strengths of the properties of permeable concrete. However, it is important to prepare a combination of design and construction specifics to achieve these results.

Results and discussion

Compressive strength test

The cube specimen is 150mm x 150mm x 150mm in dimension. If the aggregate's largest nominal size does not exceed 20mm.

By using the relationship, compressive strength was measured.

Compressive strength = (P/A) MPa

Where,

P - Ultimate load in Newton

A - Area of cube in mm^2

Compressive strength of permeable concrete without silica fume

Table 1. *Result of permeable concrete without silica fume*

Specimen	Days of curing	Load in (KN)	Load in (N/mm^2)
Specimen – 1	3	160	7.12
Specimen – 2	7	290	12.89
Specimen – 3	14	410	18.22

Compressive strength of permeable concrete with silica fume (10%)

Table 2. *Result of permeable concrete with silica fume (10%)*

Specimen	Days of curing	Load in (KN)	Load in (N/mm^2)
Specimen – 1	3	180	8
Specimen – 2	7	320	14.23
Specimen – 3	14	440	19.51

Compressive strength of permeable concrete with silica fume (15%)

Table 3. *Result of permeable concrete with silica fume (15%)*

Specimen	Days of curing	Load in (KN)	Load in (N/mm^2)
Specimen – 1	3	195	8.6
Specimen – 2	7	335	14.88
Specimen – 3	14	450	20

Compressive strength of permeable concrete with silica fume (20%)

Table 4. *Result of permeable concrete with silica fume (20%)*

Specimen	Days of curing	Load in (KN)	Load in (N/mm^2)
Specimen – 1	3	185	8.2
Specimen – 2	7	330	14.66
Specimen – 3	14	420	18.67

Infiltration test

$$I = {KM}/{D^2(T)}$$

Where,

M= Water Mass
D= Ring Diameter
T= Time to Infiltrate
K= 126,870 in (constant)

Table 5. *Tabulation for infiltration test*

Description	Trial – 1	Trial – 2
Water mass in (lit)	1.5	3.0
Diameter of ring in (cm)	30	30
Time of infiltration in (sec)	19.65	42.55

Calculation
Trail -1

$$I = \frac{126870 * 1.5}{30^2 * 19.65}$$
$$= 10.761 \text{ mm/sec}$$

Trail -2

$$I = \frac{126870 * 3}{30^2 * 42.55}$$
$$= 9.940 \text{ mm/sec}$$

Permeability test
The cylinder sample is 150 mm long and 95 mm in diameter. If the largest aggregate nominal size does not exceed 12.5 mm.

$$K = \frac{2.303\, aL}{A\, t} \times \log \frac{h1}{h2}$$

Where,

A = the sample cross section area (cm)
a = the cross section of the standpipe of diameter (cm)
L = the height of the permeable concrete sample (cm)
t = time interval (sec)
h1= upper water level (cm)
h2= Lower water level (cm)

Table 6. Tabulation for permeability test

Height (cm)	Time (sec)	Co – efficient of permeability K (cm/sec)
30	0	-
25	10.90	0.251
20	23.70	0.257
15	39.80	0.261
10	59.60	0.276
5	1.45	0.309

Calculation

$$A = a = \frac{\pi}{4} \, x \, 9.5^2 = 70.88 \text{ cm}^2$$
$$L = 15 \text{ cm}$$

$$K_1 = \frac{2.303 \times 70.88 \times 15}{70.88 \times 10.9} \log \frac{30}{25}$$
$$= 0.251 \text{ cm /sec}$$
$$K_2 = 0.257 \text{ cm /sec}$$
$$K_3 = 0.261 \text{ cm /sec}$$
$$K_4 = 0.276 \text{ cm /sec}$$
$$K_5 = 0.309 \text{ cm /sec}$$

$$K = \frac{(K1 + K2 + K3 + K4 + K5)}{5}$$
$$= 0.271 \text{ cm/sec}$$

Results
1. Permeable concrete made from coarse aggregate size 12.5mm has compressive strength of without silica fume is 18.22 N/mm^2 & with silica fume 15% of 20 N/ mm^2.
2. The aggregate/cement ratio of 2.78:1 produced permeable concrete of higher co-efficient of permeability of 0.271 cm/sec for aggregate size 12.5mm respectively.

Conclusions
1. The smaller the scale of the coarse aggregate, the greater the strength properties and the higher the degree of conductivity.
2. The mixtures with aggregate/cement ratio 2.78:1 as M$_{20}$ grade of nominal mix is considered to be useful for laying pavement which requires high permeability.
3. Finally, sufficient research should be done on permeable concrete pavements made with these material compositions to address increased deformation and bending stress caused by high vehicular loads and heavy traffic.
4. Future, studies have to be done for increasing strength using PP fibers.

Recent Advancements in Geotechnical Engineering - NCRAG'21   Materials Research Forum LLC
Materials Research Proceedings **19** (2021) 60-65   https://doi.org/10.21741/9781644901618-8

Reference

[1]   Agar-Ozbek A S, Weerheijm J, Schlangen E and Van Breugel K 2013 Investigating porous concrete with improved strength: Testing at different scales *Construction and Building Materials* **41** 480-90. https://doi.org/10.1016/j.conbuildmat.2012.12.040

[2]   Binitha K, Priyadharshini M and Ragul M 2017 Experimental Investigation of Pervious Concrete for Rigid Pavement *IJETER.* **5** 16-9

[3]   Chandrappa A K and Biligiri K P 2016 Pervious concrete as a sustainable pavement material–Research findings and future prospects: A state-of-the-art review *Construction and building materials* **111** 262-74. https://doi.org/10.1016/j.conbuildmat.2016.02.054

[4]   Chen Y, Wang K, Wang X and Zhou W 2013 Strength, fracture and fatigue of pervious concrete *Construction and Building Materials* **42** 97-104. https://doi.org/10.1016/j.conbuildmat.2013.01.006

[5]   Chindaprasirt P, Hatanaka S, Mishima N, Yuasa Y and Chareerat T 2009 Effects of binder strength and aggregate size on the compressive strength and void ratio of porous concrete *International journal of minerals, metallurgy and materials* **16** 714-9

[6]   Ćosić K, Korat L, Ducman V and Netinger I 2015 Influence of aggregate type and size on properties of pervious concrete *Construction and Building Materials* **78** 69-76. https://doi.org/10.1016/j.conbuildmat.2014.12.073

[7]   Kholshevnikov V, Shields T, Boyce K and Samoshin D 2008 Recent developments in pedestrian flow theory and research in Russia *Fire Safety Journal* **43** 108-18. https://doi.org/10.1016/j.firesaf.2007.05.005

[8]   Kia A, Wong H S and Cheeseman C R 2017 Clogging in permeable concrete: A review *Journal of Environmental Management* **193** 221-33. https://doi.org/10.1016/j.jenvman.2017.02.018

[9]   Lian C and Zhuge Y 2010 Optimum mix design of enhanced permeable concrete–an experimental investigation *Construction and Building Materials* **24** 2664-71. https://doi.org/10.1016/j.conbuildmat.2010.04.057

[10] Lian C, Zhuge Y and Beecham S 2011 The relationship between porosity and strength for porous concrete *Construction and Building Materials* **25** 4294-8. https://doi.org/10.1016/j.conbuildmat.2011.05.005

[11] Moretti L, Di Mascio P and Fusco C 2019 Porous concrete for pedestrian pavements *Water* **11** 2105. https://doi.org/10.3390/w11102105

Recent Advancements in Geotechnical Engineering - NCRAG'21   Materials Research Forum LLC
Materials Research Proceedings **19** (2021) 66-76   https://doi.org/10.21741/9781644901618-9

An Experimental Investigation on Concrete Filled Steel Tube Columns Under Axial Compression

P. Ravichandran[1, a*], M. Shadheer Ahamed[2, b], D. Ambika[3, c]

[1]Assistant Professor, Department of Civil Engineering, Kongu Engineering College, Perundurai, Erode, Tamilnadu, India

[2]PG Scholar, Department of Civil Engineering, Kongu Engineering College, Perundurai, Erode, Tamilnadu, India

[3]Associate Professor, Department of Civil Engineering, Kongu Engineering College, Perundurai, Erode, Tamilnadu, India

[a*]ravicivil@kongu.ac.in, [b]ahamedshadheer@gmail.com, [c]ambika@kongu.ac.in

Keywords: Concrete Filled Steel Tube, Self-Compacting, Self-Curing, Axial Compression, Square Column, Concrete Confinement

Abstract. This paper presents an experimental investigation on the behaviour of concrete filled steel tube columns under axial compression. The steel columns were filled with self-compacting and self-curing concrete instead of normal conventional concrete. A test program consisting of square column, circular column and rectangular column was firstly conducted. The behaviour of three concrete filled steel tubular sections (CFSTs) under axial load is presented. The effect of steel tube dimensions, shapes and confinement of concrete are also examined. Measured column strengths are compared with the values predicted by Euro code 4 and American codes. Euro code 4, gives good estimation of self-compaction concrete. However, lower values as measured during the experiments were predicted by the American Concrete Institute (ACI) equation. Also, the effect of thickness of steel tubes, concrete cube strength and steel percentage is also studied. In addition to CFST column the steel tube also acts as confinement for concrete.

Introduction

For earthquake resistance structures, concrete filled steel tube (CFST) columns can provide good structural properties. The steel member has more advantages such as high strength, high ductility and large absorption capacity. In this steel tubes using in civil and offshore construction like bridges, offshore platforms, high rise buildings, and airport structures [1]. The concrete members have some advantages such as high compressive strength and fire resistance. In this column combine both steel and concrete and the steel tubes are stiffened by the concrete core. It is applicable value for repairing damaged or enhancing the capacity subjected to increase the load [2]. These are well-known tensile stress and has influenced by their constituent material properties, such as compressive strength, the steel ratio and the yield strength of the steel moreover, in this column due to provide the supporting effect by the core concrete, the inward buckling of steel tube can be prevented, resulting in the higher buckling resistance [3]. The self-compacting concrete possesses high deformability, high workability. It does not need vibration (or) tamping after pouring [4]. This reduced the noise level while manufacturing plants and reduction in labor cost. Therefore, there is an excellent potential for using CFST with SCC in structure. Hence, the Self-curing possesses more durability when comparison of conventional water cured concrete. It reduces permeability, protects reinforcement steel.

Recent Advancements in Geotechnical Engineering - NCRAG'21   Materials Research Forum LLC
Materials Research Proceedings **19** (2021) 66-76   https://doi.org/10.21741/9781644901618-9

Self-Compacting Concrete (SCC)

The social problem concerning the durability of concrete structures that evolved in Japan around 1983 was the motive for the development of SCC. It is used in new buildings due to its compact size, flexibility, ease of manufacture and good mixing consistency [3]. As a result, there is a single solution for achieving durable concrete structures, independent of the quality of the construction work, which could be compacted into each corner of the shell, by its own weight by itself [5].

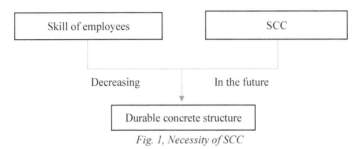

Fig. 1, Necessity of SCC

- *Passing capacity:* The capacity is to flow without segregation such as spaces between steel reinforcement bars. The mix is testing by the slump flow, V funnel and increased by having a suitable w/p ratio. Super plasticizers help to develop the feasibility.
- *Filling Ability:* This fresh concrete property is entirely relevant to the flexibility of. By addition of super plasticizers and by optimizing the packing of fine particles by adding fillers is carried out.
- *Resistance to Segregation:* Under high flow conditions, the mixture must preserve its equilibrium, i.e., it should not be separated and should remain homogeneous in composition during transport and homogeneity. A proportion of coarse aggregate is replaced by fine aggregate as the standard concrete mix shows signs of segregation. The consistency is preserved in this analysis by the use of cementation fines, fly ash instead of coarse aggregate.

Self-Curing

The proper curing of the concrete framework enables hydration of cement and it also gain strength to the concrete the curing is the process of applying water to the concrete externally after the concrete was being put, blended and finished. It provides the most productive cement hydration with additional concrete moisture and to minimize self-desiccation. In construction industry requires more amount of water while in the curing process. The days later that all the construction industry has to switch into an alternative curing system, not only to save water for the environment, because of in some case pf indoor and outdoor construction activities areas where there is scarcity of water. The hydration of cement and self-evaporation is not required as an internal curing [6]. The advantages of self-curing are such as self-curing are increased hydration process and developed the strength to concrete., reduced permeability and self-curing increased durability.

Mechanism of Internal Curing

The evaporation of water reduces from the concrete surface by using poly-ethylene glycol (PEG) and also helps to increase the effectiveness of the protection of the concrete environment. Due to a difference in chemical potential between the vapour and the liquid states, constant evaporation of moisture takes place from the exposed surface [7]. Hydrogen bonds with particles are mainly formed by the composites applied to the mix which reduce the chemical ability of the particles by decreasing the moisture and reducing the evaporation from the surface of the concrete.

Experimental of Fresh Concrete

Materials used and properties
In this study were OPC 53 grade, river sand, coarse aggregate with maximum size 12.5mm high range water reducing admixture type master Glenium sky 8233 and Polyethylene Glycol (PEG). OPC 53 grade was used in this cement have been tested. River sand with fraction passing through 4.75 sieve [8]. The improvement properties tested for fine aggregate. Crushed granite coarse aggregate of passing through 12.5mm and retained on 10mm. the important properties tested for coarse aggregate were given below [9].

Table 1, Properties of Sand

Properties	Values
Specific gravity	2.67
Fitness modulus	2.87
Size	Passing through 4.75mm sieve

Mix Composition
The output standards for concrete are obtained by the composition of the blend in both fresh and brittle environments. The specifications of EN 206 are satisfied in the hardened state.

Table 2, Mix Composition

Material	Proportion by Weight	Weight in Kg/M3
Cement	1.35	400 kg/m3
Fine aggregate	2.63	780
Coarse aggregate	2.53	750
W/c ratio	0.54	160
Master glenium sky 8233	1.2%	1.2%
Polyethylene glycol	1%	1%

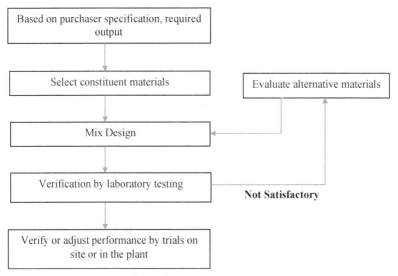

Fig. 2, *Mix Design Procedure*

Experimental Procedure

In general, the specification, preparation of mould, the method of casting and curing are briefly described. The number of column specimens are casted and moulded specification are square with the size of 87.7mm diameter with 600mmlongand 4mm thickness, circular with the size of 87.5mm diameter, 600mm long and 4mm thickness, rectangular section with the size of 87.5mm length and 50mm breadth, with 600mm long and 2mm thickness. The composite structures and steel reinforced concrete can improve the workability [3]. For the advanced research, twelve specimens were examined. It is divided into three different groups, each group consists of four specimens, three are filled with self-compacting concrete and the continuation of one column was tested for reference processes as hollow sections (designated as HS) [10]. In one CFT column as a benchmark [11]. Both the specimens were made of, circular, rectangular and square filled in self-compacting and self-curing aggregate concrete. The durability of the columns improved and compared with conventional concrete [11]. For the steel conduct, calculated ultimate load values and flexural stress values were 260 and 320 MPa. Elasticity modulus Es observed to be 20 x 105 MPa. In the modern research investigation, the parameters of the research samples were particle form, sample height, concrete strength and column D/t ratio. Each of the parameters chosen within the realistic limits of the context. The steel with local buckling is to stop hollow column section, ACI (1995) allows the steel sections of length (B/t) ratio to be not greater than the maximum $\sqrt{}$ (3Es /fy). And tested in circular column L/D = 7 with B/t = 17.5, and for square column L/D = 7 with B/T = 21.8 and rectangular column L/D = 12 with B/t = 25. B/T has been identified to be less than the mentioned limit ($\sqrt{}$ (3Es /fy) = 48.04). The strain and axial shortening of separate interval has been maintained [3] Tests of slenderness ratio and were designed the parameters [12].

Materials Research Forum LLC
https://doi.org/10.21741/9781644901618-9

Table 3, Column Detail

Type	Diameter	Length	Thickness
Square	87	600	4
Circular	87	600	5
Rectangle	87	600	2

Table 4, Testing methods of SCC

Method	Acceptance Criteria		Properties
	Minimum	Maximum	
Slump flow test (mm)	650	800	Filling abilities
V-funnel test (sec)	6	12	Filling abilities
L-box test (h_2/h_1)	0.8	1.0	Passing abilities
T_{50} slump flow	2	5	Passing abilities

Curing of Specimen

Self-curing is a process to supply concrete with extra moisture for more efficient cement hydration and decreased self-desiccation. After 28 days of curing, the specimen is taken out. then the specimen is tested.

Fig. 3, Self-Curing of Concrete

Experimental Results and Discussions

Failure Modes

The failure mode on circular column of 600mm short column as subjected to bending to the supports by each column. Failure mode and specimens are not affected by cement ratio and leads to destruction [2]. Local buckling near the supports, as shown by circles in each section, is the failure mode on a square column of 600 mm short column. It indicates the failure mode on the 600

Recent Advancements in Geotechnical Engineering - NCRAG'21   Materials Research Forum LLC
Materials Research Proceedings **19** (2021) 66-76   https://doi.org/10.21741/9781644901618-9

mm short column rectangular column is by local buckling near to the supports, as shown by circles with substantial lateral deflection in each column and total buckling closer to the mid-height of the column. Elongation at peak is also known as fracture strain. The elongation at break can be determined by tensile testing is given in below.

Fig. 4, *Failure mode of Cicular Specimen (600 mm Short Columns)*

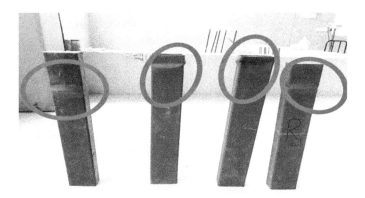

Fig. 5, *Failure mode of Rectangular Specimen (600 Mm Short Columns)*

Fig. 6, *Failure mode of Rectangular Specimen (600mm Short Column)*

Table 5, *Specimen properties*

Specimen	D (mm)	T (mm)	D/t	Length L(mm)	L/D	Steel strength fy (mpa)	Load at peak (KN)	Elongation at peak (mm)	Compression strength (N/mm²)
C1-HS	87.5	5	17.5	600	6.8	260	624.590	19.840	1022.71
C2-scc₁	87.5	5	17.5	600	6.8	260	911.870	15.100	95.95
C3-scc₂	87.5	5	17.5	600	6.8	260	949.030	12.580	99.86
C4-scc₃	87.5	5	17.5	600	6.8	260	906.980	12.680	95.43
S1-HS	87.5	4	21.8	600	6.8	260	295.220	0.630	1035.86
S2-scc₁	87.5	4	21.8	600	6.8	260	707.160	8.960	1964.33
S3-scc₂	87.5	4	21.8	600	6.8	260	707.160	8.960	1964.33
S4-scc₃	87.5	4	21.8	600	6.8	260	745.920	4.340	2072
R1-HS	90	2	45	600	6.6	260	118.240	7.430	117.2
R2-scc₁	90	2	45	600	6.6	260	190.750	0.00	706.48
R3-scc₂	90	2	45	600	6.6	260	321.210	2.300	1189.66
R4-scc₃	90	2	45	600	6.6	260	491.170	12.740	89.76

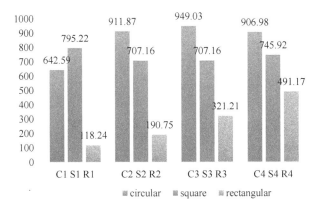

Fig. 7, *Comparison of Load Carrying Capacity of all columns*

Test Results

Fig. 8,9,10 shows it filled with self-compacting concrete, the axial load of circular, square and rectangular columns. And it occurs the axial deflection produced by the transvers load. The axial compression in a bending moment and deflection of beam is more serious type of axial load is given below. Fig. 11,12,13 shows that hollow as well as packed with self-compacting concrete of lateral displacement, the load bearing capacity of square columns of all sizes. In all columns shows that in rectangular, the load carrying of all sizes, both solid and reinforced with self-compacting concrete. This test occurs high load and stresses and it was investigated [13]. From the fig. 7, shows that comparison of all columns is in load bearing capacity. The graph shows that the hollow square column performs better and rectangular columns as well. It can be observed that the self-compacting of circular columns performs better than the self-compacting concrete of square and rectangular columns.

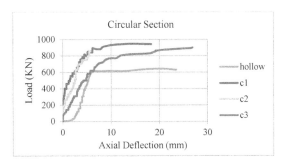

Fig. 8, *Comparison of Axial load*

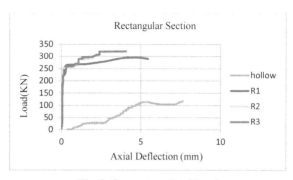

Fig. 9, Comparison Axial Load.

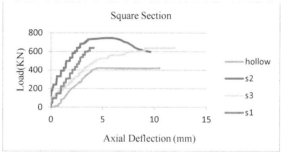

Fig. 10, Comparison Axial load.

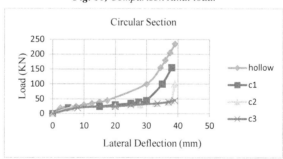

Fig. 11, Load at Lateral displacement.

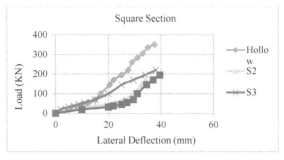

Fig. 12, Load at Lateral displacement.

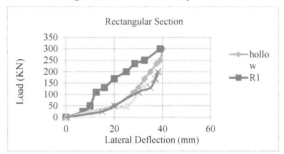

Fig. 13, Load at Lateral displacement.

Conclusion
Twelve columns were tested under axial compression. Four specimens were hollow structure columns and remaining eight are self-compacting concrete. Columns were ranged in shape, including circular, square and rectangular sections, lateral load deflection, failure mode. Concrete column strength has been tested against the efficiency of current concrete models and a model is proposed to fit various types of concrete, column forms and slenderness ratio.
- The failure modes the radial expansion, columns with a lower slenderness ratio are failed. Local buckling caused rectangular columns to collapse more frequently. Shear is failed by higher strength concrete than lower strength concrete.
- Column stiffness and concrete toughness also had an impact on the force reaction. Higher-strength concrete columns showed higher peak load characteristics. In general, an improvement in axial strength and an increase in column slenderness, with the exception of a few columns, has been observed.
- Biaxial stress factors were mainly based on cross-sectional, as the lateral stress factor for circular was higher for square and rectangular columns. In circular CFST subjected greater transverse stress development, providing a more confining effect. Thus, size reduction is necessary for square columns.
- The use of SCC greatly shortened the time between the steel tubes for in-filling the concrete. With an increase in the CFST column diameter, the load carrying capability of concrete filled steel tube columns has been raised. It was found that the load bearing capacity of the CFST

columns was exactly the same when the thickness of the outer steel tube was increased from 4 mm to 5 mm.

Reference

[1] Ahmad S, Kumar A and Kumar K 2020 Axial performance of GGBFS concrete filledsteel tubes. In: Structures: Elsevier) pp 539-50. https://doi.org/10.1016/j.istruc.2019.12.005

[2] Ding F-x, Lu D-r, Bai Y, Gong Y-z, Yu Z-w, Ni M and Li W 2018 Behaviour of CFRP-confined concrete-filled circular steel tube stub columns under axial loading Thin-Walled Structures 125 107-18. https://doi.org/10.1016/j.tws.2018.01.015

[3] Yu F, Chen L, Bu S, Huang W and Fang Y 2020 Experimental and theoretical investigations of recycled self-compacting concrete filled steel tubular columns subjected to axial compression Construction and Building Materials 248 118689. https://doi.org/10.1016/j.conbuildmat.2020.118689

[4] Prabhavathy S and Surendar D 2012 Comparative Study of Concrete Filled Tubes with Hollow Double Skinned Composite Columns In-Filled With Self Compacting Concrete. In: Proceedings of International Conference on Advances in Architecture and Civil Engineering (AARCV 2012), pp 195-9

[5] Concrete S-C 2005 The European guidelines for self-compacting concrete BIBM, et al 22

[6] Mandiwal P and Jamle S 2019 Tensile Strength & Durability Study on Self-Curing Concrete as a Partial Replacement of Cement by PEG-400 International Journal for Research in Engineering Application & Management (ISSN: 2454-9150) 4 244-8

[7] Poovizhiselvi M and Karthik D 2017 Experimental Investigation of Self Curing Concrete International Research Journal of Engineering and Technology (IRJET) Volume 4

[8] Karimi A and Nematzadeh M 2020 Axial compressive performance of steel tube columns filled with steel fiber-reinforced high strength concrete containing tire aggregate after exposure to high temperatures Engineering Structures 219 110608. https://doi.org/10.1016/j.engstruct.2020.110608

[9] Onuaguluchi O and Banthia N 2016 Plant-based natural fibre reinforced cement composites: A review Cement and Concrete Composites 68 96-108. https://doi.org/10.1016/j.cemconcomp.2016.02.014

[10] Hossain K M and Chu K 2019 Confinement of six different concretes in CFST columns having different shapes and slenderness International Journal of Advanced Structural Engineering 11 255-70. https://doi.org/10.1007/s40091-019-0228-2

[11] Wei Y, Zhang Y, Chai J, Wu G and Dong Z 2020 Experimental investigation of rectangular concrete-filled fiber reinforced polymer (FRP)-steel composite tube columns for various corner radii Composite Structures 244 112311. https://doi.org/10.1016/j.compstruct.2020.112311

[12] Pacheco-Torgal F and Jalali S 2011 Cementitious building materials reinforced with vegetable fibres: A review Construction and Building Materials 25 575-81. https://doi.org/10.1016/j.conbuildmat.2010.07.024

[13] Gunawardena Y and Aslani F 2019 Behaviour and design of concrete-filled spiral-welded stainless-steel tube short columns under concentric and eccentric axial compression loading Journal of Constructional Steel Research 158 522-46. https://doi.org/10.1016/j.jcsr.2019.04.013

Recent Advancements in Geotechnical Engineering - NCRAG'21
Materials Research Proceedings 19 (2021) 77-85

Materials Research Forum LLC
https://doi.org/10.21741/9781644901618-10

An Assessment of Flexural Improvement of Light Weight Concrete via Hybrid Fibres along with Sisal Fibres in Addition to Banana Fibres

S. Southamirajan[1,a*], K. Anbarasi[2,b], S. Elango[3,c] Dhivyaprakash[4,d], B. Bharath4[,e]

[1]Assistant Professor, Department of Civil Engineering in Kongunadu College of Engineering and Technology, Trichy, Tamilnadu, India

[2]Assistant Professor, Department of Civil Engineering in Kongunadu College of Engineering and Technology, Trichy, Tamilnadu, India

[3]Assistant Professor, Department of Civil Engineering in K.S.R.College of Engineering, Namakkal, Tamilnadu, India

[4]Bachelor's degree in Department of civil engineering in kongunadu college of Engineering and technology, Trichy,Tamilnadu, India

*[a]southamirajan@gmail.com, [b]kbanbuarun@gmail.com, [c]s.elango@ksrce.ac.in, [d]dhivyaprakashappu@gmail.com, [e]bharath27091999@gmail.com

Keywords: Lightweight Concrete, Sisal Fibre, Banana Fibre, Hybrid Fibre

Abstract: Innate fibres, these days have become the topic of argument in the research field between different scientists to inculcate it in the formation of lightweight concrete mixture. This is due to a variety of rewards connected with natural fibres like recyclable, economical, availability in large quantity and its bio-degradability. Plenty of projects have been carried out in the production of natural fibre reinforced lightweight concrete. In this project, we would like to take the naturally existing fibre named sisal fibre and banana fibre as partial replacement material. The adding of natural fibre to the lightweight concrete will enhance the diverse strength parameters like flexural strength, compressive strength, and increase the ductile behaviour. In the current work, it is intended to explore the mechanical properties of lightweight concrete with substitution of sisal fibre and banana fibre for cement in different percentages. The compressive strength, flexural strength, deflection of the beam is calculated with the reflection of M30 concrete specimens. Totally 45 number of 500 x 100 x 100mm flexural member, 45 numbers of cubes and 45 numbers of cylinders are cast and tested. It is suggested that up to 1.5% substitution of sisal fibres and banana fibre with cement provide at M30 grade of concrete giveing the most beneficial increases of strength values. The assessment outcome indicated that the sisal fibres and banana fibre were efficient in improving the performance of lightweight concrete

Introduction

A random try have been made in the earlier period to reduce the self weight of concrete to increase the effectiveness of concrete as a structural material [2]. Lightweight concrete (LWC) is a fascinating field of explore and has been extensively used in buildings since many decades. It has much reward such as better thermal insulation, sound assimilation, fire and frost control and increased seismic performance. The light-weight concrete is a concrete which has a density of 300 to 1850 kg/m^3 [4] .There are many benefits of having low density. It helps in reduction of deceased load, increases the augmentation of building. The self weight of a building on the foundation is a significant aspect, in case of loose soil and it can be rectified by using the light weight concrete as one of the way [5]. Air-conditioning is required in the structure where it is obtained by the using

Recent Advancements in Geotechnical Engineering - NCRAG'21   Materials Research Forum LLC
Materials Research Proceedings 19 (2021) 77-85   https://doi.org/10.21741/9781644901618-10

light weight concrete with low thermal conductivity will be appropriate [6]. The light weight concrete can be obtained by using industrial wastes such as clinker, fly ash, steel slag and bamboo etc. and by the addition of air in concrete.

Natural fibre has extraordinary application in the ground of civil Engineering [8]. Natural fibres are a good reinforcing substance. Sisal fibre shows prospective strengthening effect in light weight concrete on relation of its with low cost, ease of use, low density, non hazardous one, sustainable and high specific strength and modulus [9]. The configuration and properties of sisal fibre have been scrutinized by several researchers. Sisal fibre in reinforced concrete along with light weight concrete effect over other conventional material seems largely from their higher specific strength, stiffness and fatigue uniqueness which enable structural performance to be more adaptable.

Materials Used

Cement
Cement, a well accepted obligatory material, it is forever advantageous to use the finest cement in constructions. Consequently, the selection of cement may be varying on the type of construction. Ordinary Portland cement is available in three different grades of 33, 43, and 53. In this assignment, 53 grade ordinary Portland cement is used for the scrutinizing.

Table 1 Properties of cement

Properties	Value
Fineness Modulus	3.5
Specific gravity	2.9
Consistency	30.2%
Initial Setting Time	30 Minutes
Final Setting Time	1 Hour

Manufacturing Sand (M Sand)
M Sand is worn like a fine aggregate in this project. The sand used in this project where nearby procured. M sand is acknowledged as manufactured sand. It is a crushed aggregate product from hard granite stone which has irregular edges, washed and graded with consistency to be used as a replacement of river sand. The practice of M Sand can overcome the defects taking place in concrete such as honeycombing, segregation, voids, capillarity etc. Usage of M-Sand can radically decrease the cost, it does not hold impurities and wastage.

Table 2 Properties of fine aggregates

Properties	Value
Specific Gravity	2.55
Fineness Modulus	2.65%
Water Absorption	1.50%
Size	Passing through 4.75mm sieve

Coarse Aggregate
The coarse aggregate obtained from the crushing plant is used in the present study. The physical parameters of coarse aggregate like specific gravity, water absorption and fineness modulus are tested in accordance with IS: 2386. The coarse aggregate used in this examination is of the dimension 20mm. It gives sufficient strength to the concrete. The aggregate takes up 70-80 per cent of the volume of the concrete. The meticulous selection of aggregate in any mix of concrete is chosen for their durability, strength, workability, and capability to obtain good results.

Table 3 Properties of coarse aggregates

Properties	Value
Fineness Modulus	8.12
Specific gravity	2.9
Water absorption	2.8
Size	20 mm

Coarse aggregate bamboo

The bamboo is less in weight, elastic, hard, high durable with great tensile characteristic, and economical material than the other building materials. Bamboo can be used in a variety of building mechanism. Bamboo structures are good in flexibility, earthquake resistant nature with high torsion resistance, light weight and economical. Practice of bamboo may be lead for green buildings and sustainable growth, Bamboo can be used as bamboo flooring, decking, decorative paneling, and siding and as coarse aggregate for light weight concrete. Due to its natural characteristics of bamboo houses hold the both earthquake and cyclone resistant effects. In this project the bamboo are wrecked into a parts of required sizes associated to coarse aggregate and sieved through 4.75mm sieve to eliminate the smaller particles.

Table 4 Properties of coarse aggregate bamboo

Properties	Value
Fineness Modulus	8.95
Specific gravity	0.6
Water absorption	21%
Size	20mm

Figure 1 Bamboo

Sisal Fibre

Sisal fibre is one of the most important accepted natural fibres and is enormously easily cultivated with a lesser amount of water requirement. It has a small crop growing period and grows in nature in the cultivable and non-cultivable lands, the material is selected based on the improvement of different strength properties of the structure to gain sustainability and higher performance. Short distinct vegetable fibre (sisal) is examined for its appropriateness for merging in cement concrete. Sisal fibre requires only a little amount of process In the current investigation, sisal fibre is constantly used in all mix with different ratios.

Table 5 Physical Properties of Sisal Fibre

Properties	Value
Average length(mm)	300
Average Diameter(mm)	0.12
Average Tensile Strength(N/mm^2)	1090
Elongation	18.2
Water Absorption (%)	76.7%

Figure 2 Sisal Fibres

Banana Fibre

The banana is a fibrous fraction casing the stem. It constitutes 25–45% of the total size of the fruit. Banana husk fibres are primarily constituted of hemicelluloses and not of cellulose. Banana fibres hold 13 to 24.6% of lignin, 35 to 64.8% of hemicelluloses, 4.4% of ash content and leftover 8 to 25% of water content. The fibres bordering the internal layer are unevenly lignified group of cells with banana fibres and the portions of the core coating surround soft fibres. Banana fibre is extremely hemi cellulosic and superior to that of any other fibres. The Properties of Banana fiber are given in table 2.6. Banana fibres are durable, tough, resistant, resilient and long-lasting. Banana fibre is a replacement in the mix with a percentage to the weight of cement

Figure 3 Banana Fibres

Materials Research Forum LLC
https://doi.org/10.21741/9781644901618-10

Table 6 Physical Properties of Banana Fibre

Properties	Value
Width(micron meter)	250
Density(Kg/m^3)	1150
Initial Modulus(Gpa)	5
Tensile strength(Mpa)	115
Elonagtion(%)	35

Water
Amalgamation and curing is done by clean water, which was gratis from any other impurities like oils, acids, alkalis, sugar, salts, and organic ingredients that may be injurious to concrete or steel. The pH for clean water is supposed to not be less than 6 for concreting.

Preparation and testing of specimen:
General
The investigational work was planned to examine the mechanical properties like flexural behavior of concrete with 15% of replacement of coarse aggregate by bamboo and 1%, 1.5%, 2% and 2.5% of sisal fibres and banana fibre as hybrid fibre reinforced concrete with the weight of cement and for M30 grade of concrete all along with 0.1% of replacement of water with super plasticizer due to adding up of sisal fibres and banana fibre in concrete. The compressive strength of the cube, split tensile strength of cylinder and flexural behavior of the beam is analysis for 7, 14, 28 days.

For the test models, 53 grades Ordinary Portland Cement, M sand, coarse aggregate, bamboo, super plasticizer, sisal fibres and banana fibre are being analyses.

The greatest size of the coarse aggregate was restricted to 20mm. the concrete mix proportions of M30 grade with the water-cement ratio of 0.50 were utilized. The concrete mix was proposed to attain the flexural strength of 30MPa after 28 days curing period. The concrete beams (500mm × 100mm × 100mm) for regular as well as other mixes were cast. Each layer was compacted with 25 blows using a 16mm diameter rod.

Figure 4 Test samples

Recent Advancements in Geotechnical Engineering - NCRAG'21   Materials Research Forum LLC
Materials Research Proceedings **19** (2021) 77-85   https://doi.org/10.21741/9781644901618-10

Table 7. Sample Specimen Details

S.No	Specimens	Details
1	Sample 1	1% sisal and banana fibre for weight of cement and 15% bamboo for weight coarse aggregate
2	Sample 2	1.5% sisal and banana fibre for weight of cement and 15% bamboo for weight coarse aggregate
3	Sample 3	2% sisal and banana fibre for weight of cement and 15% bamboo for weight coarse aggregate
4	Conventional concrete	M_{30} grade of light weight concrete

Compressive strength test

The sample cubes of size 150mm x 150mm x 150mm is cured for respective days as 7,14 and 28 days, the specimen is tested in compression testing machine with sample set as per date.

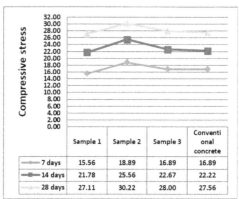

	Sample 1	Sample 2	Sample 3	Conventional concrete
7 days	15.56	18.89	16.89	16.89
14 days	21.78	25.56	22.67	22.22
28 days	27.11	30.22	28.00	27.56

Figure 5 Graph Showing the Results of Compressive Strength of HFRC.

Tensile Strength test

The sample cylinder specimens shall be 150 mm in diameter and 300 mm long is cured for respective days as 7, 14 and 28 days, the specimen is tested in compression testing machine with a sample set as per date.

Materials Research Forum LLC
https://doi.org/10.21741/9781644901618-10

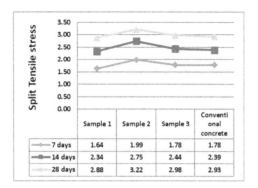

Figure 6 Graph Showing the Results of tensile strength test of HFRC.

Flexural strength Test
The concrete beam is placed in the testing machine in such a method the load shall be applied on the surface of the beam. The load shall be applied from the initial stage and then rises at a steady rate until the first crack of the specimen to the increasing load maximum up to the breakdown of the specimen. The highest load applied to the sample shall be noted and the exterior surface cracks are recorded at a different level. The samples are analyzed to find out the mechanical properties.

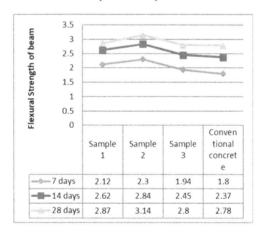

Figure 7 Graph Showing the Results of Flexural strength of HFRC.

Result and Discussion
The experimental results of adding Sisal fibre, banana fibre and Bamboo as a replacement of cement and coarse aggregates in concrete are represented in the work. The comparison of mechanical properties of the hybrid fibre reinforced concrete and conventional concrete is discussed. The hardened concrete properties are analyzed and compared for all the sample sets.

Recent Advancements in Geotechnical Engineering - NCRAG'21   Materials Research Forum LLC
Materials Research Proceedings **19** (2021) 77-85   https://doi.org/10.21741/9781644901618-10

We found that the use of Sisal fibre and banana fibre increases the flexural strength of the concrete. Thus, the building work with Bamboo concrete is environmentally safe and also economical. Sisal fibre and banana fibre can be used as a partial alternate for cement which will reduce the cost of cement in concrete and also diminish the expenditure of construction. Therefore, it is safe to swap the cement in practically with 1.5% Sisal fibre and banana fibre to obtain good strength parameters. It also enhances the workability of fresh concrete. It is proved that the flexural strength is enlarged up to the optimal level of replacement of Sisal fibre, banana fibre and Bamboo. The optimum percentage of replacement Sisal fibre and banana fibre by cement is 1.5% and Bamboo by coarse aggregate at 15%. Adjustment of water level in mix design is balanced by adding a super plasticizer by 0.1% of water, thus results in good workability of concrete. Reduction in cement content did not cause any violent result in strength parameters. 7 days, 14days & 28 days compressive strength, split tensile strength and flexural strength is extra than the conventional light concrete. The hybrid fibre reinforced concrete with Sisal fibre, banana fibre and bamboo is shows good result in strength characteristics.

Figure 8 Experimental setup

Conclusion

It is proved that the flexural strength is enlarged up to the optimal level of replacement of Sisal fibre, banana fibre and Bamboo as 27%. The optimum percentage of replacement Sisal fibre and banana fibre by cement is 1.5% and Bamboo by coarse aggregate at 15%.

References

[1] Srinivasa Rao Naraganti, Rama Mohan Rao Pannem, Impact resistance of hybrid fibre reinforced concrete containing sisal fibres, Ain Shams Engineering Journal(ASEJ) 10 (2019) 297-305. https://doi.org/10.1016/j.asej.2018.12.004

[2]Venkateshwaran.S, Kalaiyarrasi. A. R, Sisal Fiber Reinforced Concrete, Journal of Emerging Technologies and Innovative Research (JETIR) 5 (2018) 65-69.

[3]Radha K T Sumithra, ABS Dadapheer, Experimental Investigation on The Properties of Sisal Fibre Reinforced Concrete, International Research Journal of Engineering and Technology (IRJET) 04 (2017) 2774-2777.

[4]Chao-Lung Hwang, Vu-An Tran, Jhih-Wei Hong and You-Chuan Hsieh, Effects of short coconut fiber on the mechanical properties, plastic cracking behavior, and impact resistance of cementitious composites, Construction and Building Materials (CBM) 127 (2016) 984–992. https://doi.org/10.1016/j.conbuildmat.2016.09.118

[5]Karunya Latha V, B. Beeraiah, Natural Sisal Fibre Reinforced Concrete with Experimental Studies, International Research Journal of Engineering and Technology (IRJET), 06 (2019) 1419 -1423

[6]Raghuveer H. Desai, L. Krishnamurthy, T. N. Shridhar, Effectiveness of Banana(Betel) Fiber as a Reinforcing Material in Eco-friendly Composites: A Review, Indian Journal of Advances in Chemical Science (IJACS) (2016) 27 – 33.

[7]Syed Viqar Malik, Anil Achyut Kunte(2020),Structural Behavior Due to Hybridization of Sisal and Nylon Fibers in Concrete, International Journal of Recent Technology and Engineering (IJRTE) 8 (2020) 1875 – 1879. https://doi.org/10.35940/ijrte.F7122.038620

[8]Anayatullah Bhat, Zishan Raza Khan, Behaviour of Autoclaved Aerated Concrete Blocks using Alkali-Resistant Glass Fibre as Additive, International Journal of Recent Technology and Engineering (IJRTE) 8 (2020) 3508 -3513. https://doi.org/10.35940/ijrte.F8478.038620

[9]Kanchidurai S., Nanthini T. and Jai Shankar P, Experimental Studies On Sisal Fibre Reinforced Concrete With Groundnut Shell Ash, ARPN Journal of Engineering and Applied Sciences(ARPN) 12 (2017) 5914 - 5920

[10] MałgorzataPająk, TomaszPonikiewski, Experimental Investigation on Hybrid Steel Fibers Reinforced Self-compacting Concrete under Flexure, Procedia Engineering(PE), 2017, Pages 218-225. https://doi.org/10.1016/j.proeng.2017.06.207

[11] K.F.Li, C.Q.Yang, Effects of hybrid fibers on workability, mechanical, and time-dependent properties of high strength fiber-reinforced self-consolidating concrete, Construction and Building Materials(CBM), 277 (2021), 1 -12. https://doi.org/10.1016/j.conbuildmat.2021.122325

[12] Saravanakumar P, Sivakamidevi M, An experimental study on hybrid fiber reinforced concrete beams subjected to torsion, Materials today Proceeding(MTP) 2021. https://doi.org/10.1016/j.matpr.2020.12.1003

[13] TaoWu, LixinSun, Uniaxial performance of circular hybrid fibre-reinforced lightweight aggregate concrete columns, Engineering Structures(ES), 238 (2021), 112263. https://doi.org/10.1016/j.engstruct.2021.112263

[14] Tuan KietTran, Ngoc ThanhTran, Enhancing impact resistance of hybrid ultra-high-performance fiber-reinforced concretes through strategic use of polyamide fibers, Construction and Building Materials(CBM), 271(2021), 121562. https://doi.org/10.1016/j.conbuildmat.2020.121562

[15] Dia EddinNassani, Experimental and analytical study of the mechanical and flexural behavior of hybrid fiber concretes, Structures, 28 (2020), 1746-1755. https://doi.org/10.1016/j.istruc.2020.10.014

[16] Poongodi K, AlmasKhan et.al(2021),Strength properties of hybrid fibre reinforced quaternary blended high performance concrete, Materials today Proceeding(MSP), 39 (2021) 627-632. https://doi.org/10.1016/j.matpr.2020.09.007

Recent Advancements in Geotechnical Engineering - NCRAG'21   Materials Research Forum LLC
Materials Research Proceedings 19 (2021) 86-91   https://doi.org/10.21741/9781644901618-11

Experimental Investigation of Concrete using Sugarcane Baggase Ash as a Partial Replacement for Cement

Dinesh Kumar Palanisamy[1,a*], Yogeshwaran Nagarajan[2,b],
Snekalaxmi Chandrasekar[2,c], Ram Nithin Mani[2,d]

[1]Assistant Professor, Kongu Engineering College, Perundurai, India

[2]UG Students, Kongu Engineering College, Perundurai, India

[a] pdkcivil@gmail.com, [b] yogeshnks291@gmail.com, [c] snekacinivasan173@gmail.com,
[d] ramnithinkpm@gmail.com

Keywords: SCBA Concrete, Silica Fume, Compressive Strength, Flexural Strength, Tensile Strength Sorptivity Rest

Abstract. Cement being a major contributor to carbon emission needs a revolution in its production or modification to the existing cement. One such way to reduce cement usage is to replace the cementitious compound with a suitable material that does not alter the original purpose of cement in concrete. The sugarcane bagasse ashes (SCBA), which are ashes from biomass burning, are found to act as supplementary cementitious material. Moreover, studies were conducted to relate the strength and durability of concrete by the percentage of replacement of sugarcane bagasse ash to cement. The studies revealed that the SCBA imparts more strength to cement at 10% replacement when compared to 20% replacement. However, this study is intended to use 20% of SCBA replacement in cement by adding silica fume. Concrete being mainly reinforced with steel has the problem of corrosion. To overcome the problem of corrosion as well as to reduce the use of cement and to attain the compressive strength of 10% replacement of SCBA. This experiment is intended to analyze the behavior of concrete up to 20% replacement of SCBA with silica fume at different concentrations such as 0%,5%,10%,15%.

Introduction

Utilization of industrial and agricultural waste as source of raw material for the construction of not only encourages sustainable and pollution free environment but also provides the economic situation. One of such fibrous waste product from the sugarcane refining industry is sugarcane bagasse ash. When compared to other types of agro wastes it serves as a best cementitious additive material. The usage of 15 % of SCBA for replacement of cement does not affect the compressive & tensile strength of concrete [1]. Result is such that by replacing 15 % of bagasse ash, high strength concrete can be produced. [2].Silica fume a byproduct of smelting process in the silicon and ferrosilicon industry helps in improving the strength and performance of concrete. It also helps in preventing the reinforcement Steel from corrosion. Adding 15% silica fume increases compressive strength & split tensile strength [3].Adding silica fume in 10% - 20% of cement increases ITZ (interfacial transition zone) around aggregate [4].in this paper we are going to use bagasse ash   as a replacement of cement with 20% by altering the amount of silica fume such as 0% ,5% ,10% and 15%.

Material and method

In the study raw materials used are cement fine aggregate natural coarse aggregate sugarcane bagasse and silica fume. Binding material like PPC 53 grade cement of compressive strength 54 N/mm² in 28 days meeting the standard of 12269 2013.Sugarcane bagasse ash is purchase from sivagiri and silica fumes is purchased from kangeyam was used as an admixture in cement. Fine aggregate such as river sand from zone 2 grading as per 383 1970 is used.

Table 1: Properties of cement, SCBA, silica fume

PARAMETERS	CEMENT	SCBA	SILICA FUME
Specific gravity	3.12	1.94	2.23
Consistency	30%	30%	-
Initial setting (mins)	80	140	-
Fineness modulus	5	-	-
Specific surface (cm2/g)	-	4710	15000-30000

Table 2: Properties of sand

PARTICULARS	VALUE
Loose air dried bulk density	-
Moisture content	4.25%
Specific gravity	2.61
water absorption (24HRS)	1.12%
Crushing	-
Impact	-
Fineness modulus	2.52
Bulking	28%
Sieve analysis	Zone II

Table 3: Mix proportion

MIXES	% OF SILICA FUMES	w/b	SCBA %	Mix ratio by weight Cement:sand:coarse aggregate
M1	0%conventional concrete	0.45	20%	1:1.5:3
M2	5%	0.45	20%	1:1.5:3
M3	10%	0.45	20%	1:1.5:3
M4	15%	0.45	20%	1:1.5:3

SCBA CONCRETE. SCBA being a good supplementary cementitious material, it is replaced at the rate of 20%.To support high strength of concrete silica fume was added different proportions such as 0%, 5% ,10% ,15% of cement. This concrete is used in load bearing structure.

Experimental methods
Compression test
Compression test are used to find the material properties under load .The compression testing machine gives maximum stress that the specimen can withstand. Here the size of the specimens are

Recent Advancements in Geotechnical Engineering - NCRAG'21   Materials Research Forum LLC
Materials Research Proceedings 19 (2021) 86-91   https://doi.org/10.21741/9781644901618-11

of size 150 mm3 SCBA concrete as per is 516:1959. Load at the failure point divided by area provides the compressive strength of concrete.

Fig. 1 compression test

Flexural strength
Flexural strength is one of the measures of tensile strength of concrete. It is a measure of an unreinforced concrete beam or slab to resist failure in bending. It is measured by loading 100mm cross 100 mm beam with a spanning length of three times the depth. The load is applied and increased gradually until the specimen is fails.

Fig. 2 flexural test

Split tensile test
Split tensile test is the indirect method of testing the tensile strength of concrete which is done by applying load vertically across the diameter of cylinder. The test provides the safety and integrity of the specimen. The dimensions of the specimen are 150mm diameter and 300mm long.

Recent Advancements in Geotechnical Engineering - NCRAG'21   Materials Research Forum LLC
Materials Research Proceedings **19** (2021) 86-91   https://doi.org/10.21741/9781644901618-11

Figure. 3 splitting test

Sorptivity
In order to find sorptivity coefficient water absorption test is carried out. The specimens are preconditioned in the oven at 105 degree Celsius for 24 hours and then cooled down for 24 hours. All the sides of the specimen is covered by an electrician tape to avoid evaporation effect and the opposite sides remains open. Prior to immersion in water the initial weights were recorded. With one side immersed in the water, absorption of water at regular intervals was noted. The sorptivity coefficient is calculated by $S=(Q/A)\,t^{1/2}$.

Results and discussion
Compression strength
The compression strength results for all the mixtures at 7 days and 28 days are given in figure 4. Result proves that the compressive strength of 20% SCBA concrete with 10% silica fume is higher when compared to other mixes. It also indicates the increase of strength of mixtures at later days is due to its pozzolanic properties.

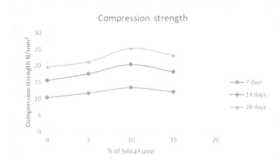

Fig. 4 compressive test of sugarcane bagasse ash concrete

Flexural strength
The flexural strength results for all the mixes at 28 days are given in figure 5. The result shows that 20% SCBA concrete with 10% of silica fume is higher when compared to other mixes.

Recent Advancements in Geotechnical Engineering - NCRAG'21   Materials Research Forum LLC
Materials Research Proceedings **19** (2021) 86-91   https://doi.org/10.21741/9781644901618-11

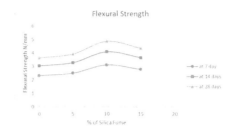

Fig. 5 flexural strength of sugarcane bagasse ash concrete

Tensile strength
The tensile strength result for all the mixes at 28 days are given in figure 6. The strength of mix with 0% silica fume is the highest whereas the mix with 15% is the lowest. The result shows that, when percentage of silica fume increases the tensile strength decreases.

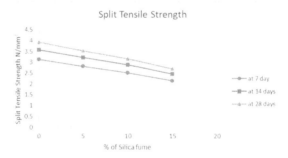

Fig. 6 tensile strength of sugarcane bagasse ash concrete

Sorptivity
The sorptivity results for all the mixtures are given in figure 7. The results show that sorptivity increases as a percentage of silica fume increases. Silica fume being high pozzolanic material it absorbs more water and it is reflected as high sorptivity in results.

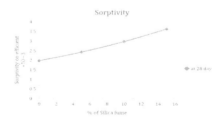

Fig. 7 sorptivity test of sugarcane bagasse ash concrete

Conclusion

This experimental investigation indicates that the adding silica fume in concrete increases Mechanical properties.

1) While adding 10% of silica fume and 20% SCBA, concrete increases both compressive and flexural strength.
2) Split tensile strength is inversely proportional to percentage of silica fume.
3) Sorptivity is directly proportional to silica fume percentage.

From the above conclusion we can see that adding 10% of silica fume is optimum, which have a direct bearing on durability of concrete

References

[1] Sugar cane bagasse ash as a partial substitute of Portland cement: Effect on T mechanical properties and emission of carbon dioxide.Romildo A. Berenguera, Ana Paula B. Caprarob, Marcelo H. Farias de Medeirosb, Arnaldo M.P. Carneiroa, Romilde A. De Oliveirac.UFPE - Programa de Pós-GraduaçãoemEngenharia Civil, Av. Prof. MoraesRego, 1235, CidadeUniversitária, Recife, PE, CEP: 50670-901, Brazil.2020
https://doi.org/10.1016/j.jece.2020.103655

[2] Durability characteristics of Ultra High Strength Concrete with treated sugarcane bagasse ash. A. Rajasekar , K. Arunachalam , M. Kottaisamy , V. Saraswathy. Department of Chemistry, Thiagarajar College of Engineering, Madurai 625015, Tamil Nadu, India.2018
https://doi.org/10.1016/j.conbuildmat.2018.03.140

[3] Evaluation of high-performance concrete with recycled aggregates: Use of densified silica fume as cement replacement.D. Pedro , J. de Brito , L. Evangelista.CERIS-ICIST, IST – University of Lisbon, Av. RoviscoPais, 1049-001 Lisbon, Portugal.2017
http://dx.doi.org/10.1016/j.conbuildmat.2017.05.007

[4] Impact of silica fume, fly ash, and metakaolin on the thickness and strength of the ITZ in concrete.V. Nežerka, P. Bílý, V. Hrbek, J. Fládr.Faculty of Civil Engineering, Czech Technical University in Prague, Thákurova 7, 166 29, Praha 6, Czech Republic.2019
https://doi.org/10.1016/j.cemconcomp.2019.05.012

Recent Advancements in Geotechnical Engineering - NCRAG'21   Materials Research Forum LLC
Materials Research Proceedings **19** (2021) 92-99   https://doi.org/10.21741/9781644901618-12

Assessment on the Behaviour of Cold-Formed Steel Built-up Beams

S. Vijayanand[1, a*], E. Gowshika[2,b], P.K. Greevan[2,c] and P. Gunaseelan[2,d]

[1*] Assistant Professor, Department of Civil Engineering, Kongu Engineering College, Perundurai, Erode, Tamil Nadu, India

[2]UG Students, Department of Civil Engineering, Kongu Engineering College, Perundurai, Erode, Tamil Nadu, India

[a*]atmvijay.anand@gmail.com, [b]gowshika03@gmail.com, [c]greevan1999@gmail.com, [d]gunaseelanp07@gmail.com

Keywords: Cold-Formed Steel, Built-Up Flexural Beams, Buckling, Eurocode and North American Specifications

Abstract. Cold-formed steel, thin-walled steel product finds a wide application in construction worldwide. It has many advantages such as flexibility, convenient handling and fabrication and so on. The CFS is commonly used in structures like bridges, railway coaches etc., as it is economical when compared with hot-rolled steel. It can be used as single or built-up flexural members. Generally, the open section beams are susceptible to failure by lateral- torsional buckling due to the position of its centre of shear and centroid of the cross-section. To overcome this issue, open doubly-symmetric built-up sections or built-up closed sections have been used by many researchers. The parametric studies were conducted by many researchers to find the accuracy of the design strength predictions of the built-up beams. In parametric study, Eurocode specifications, the direct strength method and effective width method based on the North American specifications were used. The study reveals that there are no proper design guidelines available in the current Eurocode and North American specifications. Therefore, the paper provides an outline of research works done on various CFS sections by the researchers and their proposed design recommendations to the codal specifications were also reviewed.

Introduction

Usage of CFS load bearing members has become more fashionable over the last few decades. CFS members are structural items that are prepared by shaping flat sheets of steel at room temperature in various forms that can be used to meet structural requirements and practical requirements [1].On comparing hot rolled sections, using CFS section is one of the efficient ways to save construction material [2].In construction, CFS beams are generally utilized as main eg. Structural elements, floor joist and as subsidiary eg. girders, rafter [3].CFS has various advantages namely lightweight, flexibility, convenient handling, transportation, stacking, high specific strength and high stiffness to weight ratio, mass production, ease of prefabrication, uniform quality etc. The uncertainties in CFS beams include distortional buckling, local buckling, lateral-torsional buckling. CFS sections include single section such as C, I, R, Z, sigma, lipped channel, etc., and built up such as built-up open and built-up closed. Thus, the works of investigators on these sections are consolidated and presented in this paper.

Recent Advancements in Geotechnical Engineering - NCRAG'21   Materials Research Forum LLC
Materials Research Proceedings **19** (2021) 92-99   https://doi.org/10.21741/9781644901618-12

Open built-up beams
Typical built-up open sections are shown in fig.1.

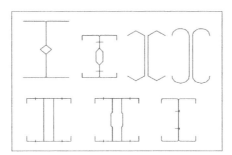

Figure 1. Built-up open sections

Open sections from I sections [1, 4-7], lipped channels [8-12], C sections [2, 13-16] are presented. Research works of an open section from I section were assembled by screws [4, 6, 7] and bolts [5]. Dar et al [1] investigated CFS beams with double trapezoidal corrugated webs and concluded that the strengthening schemes do not require new structural members and it is economic, time-saving, enhance load carrying capacity and reduce deflections. Laim et al [4], Meza et al [5], Anbarasu et al [6] and Yao et al [7] investigated built up I sections and inferred that good agreement between numerical and experimental results were achieved.

Wang and Young [8] investigated lipped channels with perforated web connected back to back using screws and on comparing with North American specification [17], DSM formulae are capable for calculating design strength. Wang and Young [9] investigation showed that design equations were progressive for lipped channels connecting back to back for design strength prediction. Dar et al [10] on doing a study using lipped channel assembled back to back with angle stiffeners found that design strength computed as per North American specification[17]and European Code are conservative. Manikandan and Thulasi [11]on investigating lipped channel stiffened at intermediate web revealed that the provision of intermediate web and edge stiffeners will improve the behaviour and increase the strength of the section. Muftah et al [12] investigated bolted built-up samples of two types as extended stiffener and outstand stiffener. Bolted built-up section with extended stiffener expressed a good outcome of flexural strength. Often, the flexural power of both beams depends on the space or position of the bolt only.

Ghannam [2] done on C section connected back to back in which DS(Direct strength) and EW(Effective width)gave a conservative result for bending moment capacity also more experimental works are required to compensate for the lack of data in this field study. Serror et al [13] experimented with C sections connected back to back and Hassan et al [16] done numerical prediction on C section, curve section and broken section connected back to back found that the C section is in need of stiffeners to enhance ductility. Wang and Young [14] investigated C sections connected back to back using screws with intermediate stiffeners and found that the numerical and experimental investigation are good in terms of ultimate moments, failure modes and the moment-curvature behaviour. Wang and Young [15] took two different configurations of two identical channel sections stiffened at intermediate back to back and face to face using self-tapping screws. Modified DSM equations are recommended.

Recent Advancements in Geotechnical Engineering - NCRAG'21   Materials Research Forum LLC
Materials Research Proceedings **19** (2021) 92-99   https://doi.org/10.21741/9781644901618-12

Closed Built-up Beams
Typical built-up closed sections are shown in fig.2

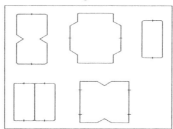

Figure 2. Built-up closed sections

R beams [4], plain channels [8], lipped channels [9], C sections [2, 14, 15], I sections [7] and sigma sections [18] were connected by screws [2, 4, 7-9, 14, 15] and spot welding [18] to form a closed section and investigations were carried out. Laim et al [4] investigated R built-up close section and 2R connected together by U profile's web and concluded that the 2R beam showed the best specific strength. Wang and Young [8] investigated plain channels with web perforations connected face to face. It was clear that DSM formulae in North American specification [17] are capable for the prediction of design strength. Wang and Young [14] investigated C section assembled face to face with intermediate stiffeners and inferred that numerical and experimental investigation are in good agreement. Wang and Young [15] investigated three configurations (two different closed sections with connection at flanges, closed section with connection at webs), in which two different closed sections with connection at flanges are unconservative, hence modified DSM (Direct strength method) equations are recommended. Wang and Young [9] investigation showed that design strength prediction. Ghannam [2] investigated a C section connected face to face in which DS and EW gave a conservative result for bending moment capacity also more experimental works are needed to fill the shortage of data in this field research. Selvaraj and Madhavan [18] tested built-up closed sigma sections with intermediate stiffeners interconnected by spot welding concluded that Modified design procedures and design equations are recommended. Yao et al [7] investigated I section connected face to face and concluded that good agreement among numerical and experimental results was achieved.

Single Sections
Typical single sections are shown in fig.3

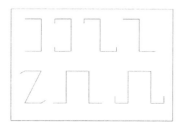

Figure3. Single sections

Research works on Z sections [3, 19-22], C sections [3, 4, 20, 21, 23-27], I sections [28, 29], plain channel [30], lipped channel [30, 31] and super sigma section [31] were carried out. Put et al [19] and Put et al [23] investigated Z and C respectively and found that on comparing AS 4100 and AS 4600, AS 4600 design method produce high predictions. Yu and Schafer [20], on investigating Z and C sections found that AISI, S136 and the new NAS (North American Specification) design method provide adequate predictions. Chu et al [24] inferred that for C sections, modified DSM equations are recommended for a beam with boundary conditions other than simply supported. Schafer and Yu [3] tested Z and C beams and concluded that Eurocode is unconservative and recommended DSM equation. Yu and Schafer [21] investigation on Z and C section inferred that DSM is a reliable tool by using a suitable elastic buckling moment. Paczos and Wasilewicz [28] and Laim et al [4] investigation on I and C section respectively inferred that the analytical and numerical results are in good agreement. Nethercot and Haidarali [22] investigation on Z beams provides effective means of investigating various forms of buckling. Cheng et al [25] tested the C section and came up with the fact that the difference in temperature within the section has a major effect on the beam slenderness calculation.

Hadjipantelis et al [26] tested C section at prestressing and imposed loading stages. Hadjipantelis et al [27] worked on C sections in which a practical worked example is used to illustrate the implementation of the design recommendations. Abou-Rayan et al [29] found that for section Design code of European code (EN 1995) is conservative in terms of bending moment capacity. Gatheeshgar et al [31] tested out lipped channel (LCB), optimized LCB, super-sigma and folded-flange in which super-sigma was discovered to be an efficient section under shear, bending and web crippling.

Nie et al [32] investigated corroded CFS beams and inferred that Elastic modulus, yield strength and ultimate strength of the corroded specimens decreased greatly. Samuel et al [33] tested CFS beam with diagonal rebars in the web and concluded that use of beams with diagonal rebars can provide an alternate economic solution to construction industries. Sangeetha et al [34] investigated CFS hollow beams with web opening and came up with a fact that the stiffness of a rectangular hollow beam was higher than the square hollow beams.

Single Section with Stiffeners
Typical single sections with stiffeners are shown in fig.4

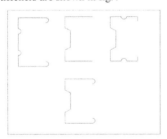

Figure 4. Single section with stiffeners

Single sections with stiffeners were investigated in [35-38]. Wang and Zhang [35] compared DSM equations with numerical results of C sections with inclined, upright and edge stiffeners. In lateral-torsional buckling, none of the specimens was failed and also each specimen possessed high bending strength. Haidarali and Nethercot [36] investigated Z sections stiffened at edge and intermediate. The numerical investigation showed that distortional buckling occurred only at the edge stiffeners and concluded that only the design guidelines for lip/flange distortional buckling need to be considered in case of both intermediate and edge stiffeners in the Eurocode calculations. Pham and Hancock [37] on investigating C and Supacee sections with web stiffeners came up with an alternative proposal that instead of using yield moment (My), using plastic moment (Mp) provides good agreement with the results. Wang and Young [38] tested C sections with web stiffeners and found that DSM predictions are conservative, hence modified DSM equation was recommended.

Single Sections with Perforations
Typical Single section with Perforation is shown in fig.5

Figure 5 *single section with Perforation*

Investigation on C sections with web perforations was carried out in [39, 40] concluded that the critical moment PCFS beam decreases with the increase of hole size. Yuan et al [39] analytical analysis using EN1993-1-3. Nan-ting Yu et al [40] inferred that the effect of the stress gradient on distortional buckling gradually decreases as the length of the beam increases

Conclusion
A clear summary of the research works in the CFS sections was given. All the sections investigated were different from each other in geometry. Usage of stiffeners seems to be more effective as it increases the stiffness of the beam for both single and built-up sections. The analysis also showed that the load bearing capacity of the beams was affected by a number of factors. Thus it is important to consider these factors viz., length of the beam, spacing between perforations etc while designing the beam sections. Many investigators came up with new provisions as the current codes are not good at predicting the strength of built-up beams. Although there were many research pieces, not many creative single sections were assembled to build a section that was built-up. There is also a broad opportunity to explore many creative built-up sections that may be economical. This paper will enable future researchers to know more about the various CFS sections investigated.

References

[1] M.A. Dar, N.Subramanian, A.Dar, M.Majid, M. Haseeb and M.Tahoor, Structural efficiency of various strengthening schemes for cold-formed steel beams: Effect of global imperfections, Steel and Composite Structures. 30 (2019) 393-403.

[2] M.Ghannam, Bending moment capacity of cold-formed steel built-up beams, International Journal of Steel Structures. 19 (2019) 660-71.. https://doi.org/10.1007/s13296-018-0155-2

[3] C.Yu and B.W.Schafer, Distortional buckling tests on cold-formed steel beams, Journal of Structural Engineering. 132 (2006) 515-28..
https://doi.org/10.1061/(ASCE)0733-9445(2006)132:4(515)

[4] L.Laim, J.P.C.Rodrigues and L.S.da Silva, Experimental and numerical analysis on the structural behaviour of cold-formed steel beams, Thin-Walled Structures. 72 (2013) 1-13.. https://doi.org/10.1016/j.tws.2013.06.008

[5] F.J.Meza, J.Becque and I.Hajirasouliha, Experimental study of cold-formed steel built-up beams, Journal of Structural Engineering. 146 (2020) 04020126.. https://doi.org/10.1061/(ASCE)ST.1943-541X.0002677

[6] M.Anbarasu , A.Dar, A.I.Rather and M.A.Dar, Effect of external strengthening on the flexural capacity of cold-formed steel beams, Materials Today: Proceedings. 39 (2020) 1270-1274.. https://doi.org/10.1016/j.matpr.2020.04.171

[7] X.Yao, X. Zhou, Y. Shi, Y. Guan and Y. Zou , Simplified calculation method for flexural moment capacity of cold-formed steel built-up section beams, Advances in Structural Engineering. 23 (2020) 3153-67.. https://doi.org/10.1177/1369433220931208

[8] L.Wang and B.Young, Beam tests of cold-formed steel built-up sections with web perforations, Journal of Constructional Steel Research. 115 (2015) 18-33.. https://doi.org/10.1016/j.jcsr.2015.08.001

[9] L.Wang and B.Young, Behaviour and design of cold-formed steel built-up section beams with different screw arrangements, Thin-Walled Structures. 131(2018) 16-32.. https://doi.org/10.1016/j.tws.2018.06.022

[10] M.A. Dar, N.Subramanian, A.Dar, M.Anbarasu, J.B.Lim and M.Atif, Behaviour of partly stiffened cold-formed steel built-up beams: Experimental investigation and numerical validation, Advances in Structural Engineering. 22 (2019) 172-86.. https://doi.org/10.1177/1369433218782767

[11] P.Manikandan and M.Thulasi, Investigation on cold-formed steel lipped channel built-up I beam with intermediate web stiffener, International Journal of Advanced Structural Engineering. 11 (2019) 97-107.. https://doi.org/10.1007/s40091-019-0220-x

[12] F.Muftah, M.S.H.M.Sani and M.M.M.Kamal, Flexural strength behaviour of bolted built-up cold-formed steel beam with outstand and extended stiffener, International Journal of Steel Structures. 19 (2019) 719-32.. https://doi.org/10.1007/s13296-018-0157-0

[13] M.H.Serror, E.M.Hassan and S.A.Mourad, Experimental study on the rotation capacity of cold-formed steel beams, Journal of Constructional Steel Research. 121 (2016) 216-28.. https://doi.org/10.1016/j.jcsr.2016.02.005

[14] L.Wang and B.Woung, Behavior of cold-formed steel built-up sections with intermediate stiffeners under bending. I: Tests and numerical validation, Journal of Structural Engineering. 142 (2016) 04015150.. https://doi.org/10.1061/(ASCE)ST.1943-541X.0001428

[15] L.Wang and B.Young, Behavior of cold-formed steel built-up sections with intermediate stiffeners under bending. II: Parametric study and design, Journal of Structural Engineering. 142 (2016) 04015151.. https://doi.org/10.1061/(ASCE)ST.1943-541X.0001427

[16] E.M.Hassan, M.H.Serror and S.A.Mourad, Numerical prediction of available rotation capacity of cold-formed steel beams, Journal of Constructional Steel Research. 128 (2017) 84-98.. https://doi.org/10.1016/j.jcsr.2016.08.010

[17] North American specification for the design of cold-formed steel structural members, American Iron and Steel Institute. (2001)

[18] S.Selvaraj and M.Madhavan, Structural design of cold-formed steel face-to-face connected built-up beams using direct strength method, Journal of Constructional Steel Research. 160 (2019) 613-28.. https://doi.org/10.1016/j.jcsr.2019.05.053

[19] B.M.Put, Y-L.Pi and N.Trahair, Lateral buckling tests on cold-formed Z-beams, Journal of Structural Engineering. 125 (1999) 1277-83.. https://doi.org/10.1061/(ASCE)0733-9445(1999)125:11(1277)

[20] C.Yu and B.W.Schafer, Local buckling tests on cold-formed steel beams, Journal of Structural Engineering. 129 (2003) 1596-606.. https://doi.org/10.1061/(ASCE)0733-9445(2003)129:12(1596)

[21] C.Yu and B.W.Schafer, Simulation of cold-formed steel beams in local and distortional buckling with applications to the direct strength method, Journal of Constructional Steel Research .63 (2007) 581-90.. https://doi.org/10.1016/j.jcsr.2006.07.008

[22] M.R.Haidaral and D.A.Nethercot, Finite element modelling of cold-formed steel beams under local buckling or combined local/distortional buckling, Thin-Walled Structures. 49 (2011) 1554-62.. https://doi.org/10.1016/j.tws.2011.08.003

[23] B.M.Put, Y-L.Pi and N.S.Trahair, Lateral buckling tests on cold-formed channel beams, Journal of Structural Engineering .125 (1999) 532-9.. https://doi.org/10.1061/(ASCE)0733-9445(1999)125:5(532)

[24] X-T.Chu, Z-M.Ye, R.Kettle and L-Y.Li,Buckling behaviour of cold-formed channel sections under uniformly distributed loads, Thin-Walled Structures. 43 (2005) 531-42.. https://doi.org/10.1016/j.tws.2004.10.002

[25] S.Cheng, L-Y.Li and B.Kim, Buckling analysis of cold-formed steel channel-section beams at elevated temperatures, Journal of Constructional Steel Research. 104 (2015) 74-80.. https://doi.org/10.1016/j.jcsr.2014.10.004

[26] N.Hadjipantelis, L.Gardner and M.A.Wadee, Prestressed cold-formed steel beams: Concept and mechanical behaviour, Engineering Structures. 172 (2018) 1057-72.. https://doi.org/10.1016/j.engstruct.2018.06.027

[27] N.Hadjipantelis, L.Gardner and M.A.Wadee, Design of prestressed cold-formed steel beams, Thin-Walled Structures. 140 (2019) 565-78.. https://doi.org/10.1016/j.tws.2019.02.029

[28] P.Paczos and P.Wasilewicz, Experimental investigations of buckling of lipped, cold-formed thin-walled beams with I-section, Thin-Walled Structures. 47 (2009) 1354-62.. https://doi.org/10.1016/j.tws.2009.03.009

[29] A.M. Abou-Rayan, N.N.Khalil and A.A.Zaky, Experimental investigation on the flexural behavior of steel cold-formed I-beam with strengthened hollow tubular flanges, Thin-Walled Structures. 155 (2020) 106971.. https://doi.org/10.1016/j.tws.2020.106971

[30] D.Dubina and V.Ungureanu, Effect of imperfections on numerical simulation of instability behaviour of cold-formed steel members, Thin-Walled Structures. 40 (2002) 239-62.. https://doi.org/10.1016/S0263-8231(01)00046-5

[31] P.Gatheeshgar, K.Poologanathan, S.Gunalan, B.Nagaratnam, K.D.Tsavdaridis and J.Ye, Structural behaviour of optimized cold - formed steel beams, Steel Construction. 13 (2020) 294-304.. https://doi.org/10.1002/stco.201900024

[32] B.Nie, S.Xu, Z.hang and R.Gu, Experimental investigation on corroded cold-formed steel beam-columns under compression and major axis bending, Journal of Constructional Steel Research. 169 (2020) 106026.. https://doi.org/10.1016/j.jcsr.2020.106026

[33] J.Samuel, J.Pravin, R.Divahar, P.A.Raj and P.Joanna, Performance enhancement of built-up cold-formed steel beams with diagonal rebars in web, Materials Today: Proceedings. 169 (2020) 106026.. https://doi.org/10.1016/j.matpr.2020.08.767

[34] P.Sangeetha, S.Revathi S, Sudhakar V, D.Swarnavarshini and S.Sweatha, Behaviour of cold-formed steel hollow beam with perforation under flexural loading, Materials Today: Proceedings. 38 (2020) 3103-3109.. https://doi.org/10.1016/j.matpr.2020.09.492

[35] H.Wang and Y.Zhang, Experimental and numerical investigation on cold-formed steel C-section flexural members, Journal of Structural Engineering. 65 (2009) 1225-35.. https://doi.org/10.1016/j.jcsr.2008.08.007

[36] M.R.Haidarali and D.A.Nethercot, Local and distortional buckling of cold-formed steel beams with both edge and intermediate stiffeners in their compression flanges, Thin-Walled Structures. 54 (2012) 106-12.. https://doi.org/10.1016/j.tws.2012.02.013

[37] C.H.Pham and G.J.Hancock, 2013 Experimental investigation and direct strength design of high-strength, complex C-sections in pure bending, Journal of Structural Engineering. 139 (2013) 1842-52.. https://doi.org/10.1061/(ASCE)ST.1943-541X.0000736

[38] L.Wang and B.Young, Design of cold-formed steel channels with stiffened webs subjected to bending, Thin-Walled Structures. 85 (2014) 81-92.. https://doi.org/10.1016/j.tws.2014.08.002

[39] W-B.Yuan, N-T.Yu and L-Y.Li, Distortional buckling of perforated cold-formed steel channel-section beams with circular holes in web, International Journal of Mechanical Sciences. 126 (2017) 255-60.. https://doi.org/10.1016/j.ijmecsci.2017.04.001

[40] N-T.Yu, B.Kim, L-Y.Li, W-J.Hong and W-B.Yuan, Distortional buckling of perforated cold-formed steel beams subject to uniformly distributed transverse loads, Thin-Walled Structures. 148 (2020) 106569.. https://doi.org/10.1016/j.tws.2019.106569

Recent Advancements in Geotechnical Engineering - NCRAG'21
Materials Research Proceedings **19** (2021) 100-107

Materials Research Forum LLC
https://doi.org/10.21741/9781644901618-13

Utilization of Cenosphere in Manufacturing of Fly Ash Brick

R. Premkumar[1,a*], Ramesh Babu Chokkalingam[1], B. Subha[1], S. Pattu Sandhiya[1]

[1]School of Environmental and Construction Technology, Department of Civil Engineering, Kalasalingam Academy of Research and Education, Krishnankoil, Tamil Nadu, India

[a]prem.ce@gmail.com

* corresponding author

Keywords: Cenosphere, Low Density, Compressive Strength, Water Absorption

Abstract. Our project was built with cenosphere material and low-density brick. The cenosphere bricks may be lighter and stronger than traditional fly ash bricks. Cement is used to replace the cenosphere in fly ash bricks in the following proportions: 230mm x 100mm x 75mm sample size for blend percentage of cenosphere, fly ash, and quarry dust. The results show how compressive strength and water absorption vary with curing age for mixed proportions of the materials mentioned previously. Then we can use the 230mm x 100mm x 75mm specimen size to cast bricks with various mix proportions of cenosphere, fly ash, and quarry dust. The weight, compressive strength, and water absorption of the cenosphere with various proportions of fly ash bricks were then compared. Via comprehensive laboratory work, this investigation is primarily based on optimizing the compressive strength of newly formed bricks thus minimizing weight density and water absorption. A definitive goal of undertaking this point as project work is to recognize factors influencing the different properties of bricks.

Introduction

The recognition of factors affecting the different properties of bricks is a clear aim of pursuing this point as project work. Ordinary bricks are made from clay and fired at high temperatures in a kiln, or from normal Portland cement (OPC) concrete. The high-temperature kiln firing not only consumes a lot of energy but also emits a lot of greenhouse gases. Cenospheres are void, unfilled, capable, microscopic rounded particles, composing of silica and alumina as extensive elements loaded with air or gases. Cenospheres are the decision of agitation of shattered coal at high temperature in a thermal power plant. Cenospheres are weightless dormant and empty particles, which are silicon dioxide, aluminum oxide, and iron oxide. The capacity of these particles is beginning in the range of 1to 500μ. They acquire reduce density due to blank and greater strength with, around 300psi as moderate compressive strength. These are the outgrowth in the form of fly-ash of coal-burning power plants. In the process of burning coal in thermal power plants, the fly-ash is rescued as a waste product consists of ceramic particles of alumina and silica. When burning coal has appeared at 1500^0 to 1750^0 C temperatures, these cenosphere particles are composed, through hard physical and chemical transformation. These particles are utilizing by assorted industries in modern days like paints, plastics, ceramics, etc. But their production rate is much larger than its utilization rate. On the other side, fly-ash as well as cenospheres both are air pollutants, whatever element so many adverse impacts on human life. On the support of researches attended on cenospheres, it is realized that cenosphere particles are likewise used in construction industries.

Asad Hanif, Pavithra Parthasararhy (2017) Thermal insulating complex helps to lower total power consumption in a building by inventing a barrier between external and internal environment. This study proposes to produce a weightless cement-based composite for thermal isolating application [1]. Cement is moderately replaced with Silica fume and fly ash cenosphere and used as the weightless filler. Aerogel is used to recover thermal insulating behavior. The concrete mix specimen is also approved for the most temperature difference between the outer face and inner surface. The difference in temperature up to 16.78^0C is accomplished which designated the thermal barrier of the building. The micro structural analysis determined the skillful bonding of fly ash cenospheres and aerogel in a cementitious system.

A. Hanif, (2017), in their preparatory study the effects of various weightless functional abound materials on the properties of cement concrete are checked [2]. They include fly ash cenospheres and glass micro-spheres in various ratios. The refined compounds are proved for compressive, flexure, and tensile strength [3]. The outcome determined that one and other cenospheres and glass micro-sphere are excellent abound materials for the strong weightless compound. They can be occupied for structural goals where higher mechanical strength is appropriate [4]. For the fiber-reinforced compound to effectively apply the tensile properties of fibers, fly ash cenospheres and glass micro-spheres are convenient [5]. Increased porosity is associated with a higher weight fraction of the abundant in composition, which could be the final step in improving their strength [6]. To determine the best mix configuration for achieving maximum compressive strength, water absorption, and weight bricks with low density and lightweight that can be handled easily.

Materials

Figure 1.Cenosphere

Table 1.Cenosphere properties

S.No	Property	Cenosphere
1	Specific Gravity	0.87
2	Blaine surface Area (m^2 /Kg)	310
3	Particle Mean Dia	<100
4	Loss of ignition	1.20%

Cenosphere

Figure 1 shows cenosphere is a lightweight, latent, hollow sphere built mainly of alumina, silica and loaded with inert gas or air, mostly combined as a derivative of coal burning at thermal power plants and properties as shown in table 1. It creates them enormous useful in a collection of products, prominently fillers. Now a day's Cenospheres are used as fillers in concrete to create low-density concrete. Newly, some manufacturers have started filling metals and polymers with cenospheres to produce lightweight composite mechanisms with high strength than other types of foam components.

Fly ash

Fly ash is a result of coal burning in nuclear energy production and comprises essentially SiO_2, Al_2O_3, Fe_2O_3, CaO, and some defilement. As pozzolanic materials are joined, calcium hydroxide $Ca(OH)_2$ is converted to optional calcium silicate hydrate (C-S-H) gel, resulting in the transformation of more pores into better pores due to the pozzolanic reaction of the mineral admixtures. The utilization of mineral admixtures positively affects the idea of cement by restricting the $Ca(OH)_2$. A practical choice for mass use of fly ash can be in the creation of blocks containing fly ash as a more added substance. Because of the low calcium content of the fly debris used in this study, its behavior resembles that of a pozzolanic admixture in the block. In block, it responds with obviously consolidated lime to shape the response compounds.

Table 2.Quarry dust properties

S.No	Property	Quarry Dust
1	Specific Gravity	2.62
2	Water Absorption	0.5%
3	Fineness Modulus	3.324
4	Surface Texture	Rough
5	Particle Shape	Angular
6	Grading Zone	II (IS 2386 (Part I) 1963

Table 3.Mix Proportions

Sample	OPC (%)	Cenosphere (%)	Fly ash (%)	Quarry dust (%)
B0	10	0	60	30
B1	10	10	50	30
B2	10	20	40	30
B3	10	30	30	30
B4	10	40	20	30
B5	10	50	10	30
B6	10	60	0	30

Recent Advancements in Geotechnical Engineering - NCRAG'21   Materials Research Forum LLC
Materials Research Proceedings 19 (2021) 100-107   https://doi.org/10.21741/9781644901618-13

Quarry dust

It is sediment appropriated from a stone quarry. Because of the huge expense of travels from normal sources barely conceivable normal sand is high. Furthermore, natural problems of immense scope are exacerbated by the scarcity of these resources. The use of river sand in construction is becoming less appealing; a repurposed or reclamation product for the solid sector should be created. Some people have started orchestrating difficult issues for the sake of chance, expense, and environmental impact. Quarry rock dust is commonly used as a surface completing material and for installing empty squares and weightless cement pre-assembled Elements on interstates with a wide scope. Following that, fine particles with a diameter of less than 4.75 mm are used in this study, and their properties are mentioned in table 2. First Arriving blend level of cenosphere blocks of OPC(10%), Cenosphere (60%), and Quarry dust (30%). Standard block sizes of 230 mm x 100mm x 75 mm are utilized to project the blocks.

Experimental Investigation

The normal hand form is utilized to project the blocks along with the essential size of 230mm x 100mm x 75mm as shown in figure 2. They were projected to provide for the essential technique with various blend proportions showed up in table 3. The proper limit of Cenosphere, Cement, and Quarry dust is resolved as of now, given that the fixing blended impeccably. At that point dependent on the consistency water was added. At that point, the wet block was kept underneath air relieving for 24 hours, and afterward, blocks were water restored for a term of 7, 28day. Being each extent 12 quantities of blocks are projecting, in that 6 blocks are utilized to finish the compressive strength of block in N/mm^2 at 7days, 28days curing time, and 6 blocks are utilized to decide the water ingestion and Efflorescence test.

Figure 2. Casting and Testing of Bricks

Recent Advancements in Geotechnical Engineering - NCRAG'21   Materials Research Forum LLC
Materials Research Proceedings **19** (2021) 100-107   https://doi.org/10.21741/9781644901618-13

Results and Discussion

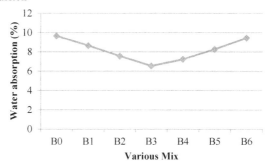

Figure 3. Various mix to Water absorption

Water Absorption
It is necessary to determine the amount of water absorption for new materials such as quarry dust and cenosphere, as it is a key factor in other tests and the production of bricks. It's a straightforward but important test for determining raw material water absorption up to saturation. Water absorption test: In this test, the collected materials were immersed in water for 24 hours and then dried in a laboratory oven at 1005°C for another 24 hours. Water was absorbed by the material in figure 3 to reflect the difference in weight compared to the original weight.

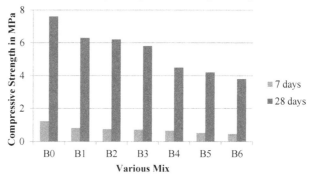

Figure 4: Represents the Compressive strength of the Brick sample

Compressive Strength
The compressive test was carried out on an automated Compression Testing Machine (CTM) with a capacity of 2000kN, with a constant proceeding load of 0.6 kN/sec. The proportion of ultimate failure load to the region of sample horizontal to the direction of load application was used to measure compressive strength (MPa). Figure 4 indicates a higher reduction in strength as cenospheres substitute fly ash compared to standard fly ash bricks as the percentage of cenospheres increases. Compressive intensity is indirectly associated with the cenosphere's ash, as seen in the graph. Higher cenospheres are also associated with lower compressive strength.

Recent Advancements in Geotechnical Engineering - NCRAG'21
Materials Research Proceedings **19** (2021) 100-107

Materials Research Forum LLC
https://doi.org/10.21741/9781644901618-13

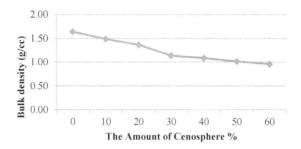

Figure 5: Represents the Bulk density of the Brick sample

Bulk Density
The bulk density was determined by dividing the sample's dry weight by the unfired sample's direct volume measurement (length-height-width). At each age, at least three samples were checked, and the moderate values were defined as the sample's bulk density, as shown in figure 5

Efflorescence
Efflorescence is costly, ivory; as the water evaporates; powdery drops of water-soluble salts disappear from the exterior of bricks. The IS 3495 (Part 3):1992 guidelines were used to coordinate this exam. The sample was fixed in water with one end absorbed for this examination. This was then fixed in a warm (20-30°C) and well-ventilated room until the sample absorbed all of the water and the excess water dispersed. The modification was covered with glass to avoid excessive evaporation. The same process was repeated after the water had fully evaporated. After the second evaporation, the results were registered. According to the IS code, efflorescence was classified as zero (0%), mild (not more than 10%), restricted (up to 50%), strong (more than 50%), and extreme (more than 50%) based on the percentage of naked area covered with a thin deposit of salt as visually authorized (powdering & flaking of the surface). At the age of 28 days, this procedure was carried out. The efflorescence results were both satisfying and encouraging. The bricks made in this study showed no flowering in the arrangement for any of the mixes.

Relationship between density and compressive strength
Figure 6 accord the density and compressive strength of the fly ash bricks as a behave of the cenosphere percentage. The figures demonstrate that as the extension of cenospheres increment, the compressive strength was declined. For this position of the test, the bricks are made beyond air entrainment. Even at the 10% matched of cenospheres, the compressive strength was raised 5MPa, which is dual that recommended by ASTM basic for harsh weather bricks. It can also be leading that the density of the brick goes down with the extension of cenospheres in a precise mode within the test area. The extension cenospheres allow a lighter brick with adequate compressive strength. By calculate 10% cenospheres, the brick density decreased from 2.82 to 2.56g/cc, almost, which is a 10% decrease in density.

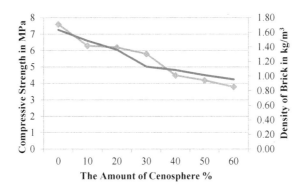

Figure 6: Graphical representation of Compressive Strength Vs bulk density

Conclusion

The following conclusions can be drawn from the findings of this study:

As expected, the expansion of cenospheres to fly ash blocks brings about a huge diminishing in brick density. For example, by adding 10% cenospheres, the brick density lessens by 10%. This is useful for both cost and specialized reasons. The lower weight per block decreases delivery and work costs while simultaneously permitting more prominent structural plan adaptability. While the abatement in density relates to a diminishing in strength, at 60% cenospheres substitution, the compressive strength was as yet 3.56MPa, which is well over the 3MPa needed by ASTM for extreme climate grouping

Also, the utilization of cenospheres in fly ash bricks is relied upon to deliver different advantages, for example, improved warm protecting properties. While the specialized part of adding cenospheres to fly ash block is promising, the current market estimation of cenospheres makes adding them unfeasible. Later on, as the cost of cenospheres diminishes, adding cenospheres may turn into a feasible alternative for creating quality fly ash bricks

References

[1] A. Hanif et al., "Properties Improvement of Fly Ash Cenosphere Modified Cement Pastes using Nano Silica," Cement and Concrete Composites, vol. 81, pp. 35-48, Elsevier Ltd, Aug 2017. https://doi.org/10.1016/j.cemconcomp.2017.04.008

[2] A. Hanif, Z. Lu, and Z. Li, "Utilization of fly ash cenosphere as lightweight filler in cement-based composites-a review,"Construction and Building Materials, vol. 144, pp. 373–384, 2017. https://doi.org/10.1016/j.cemconcomp.2017.04.008

[3] Sumathi, A., and Rajamohan K. S. (2014). "Compressive strength of fly ash brick with the addition of lime, gypsum, and quarry dust." International Journal of ChemTech Research, Vol. 7, No. 1, pp. 28-36

[4] Sutcu, M., Alptekin, H., Erdogmus, E., Yusuf, E., and Gencel, O. (2015). "Characteristics of fired clay bricks with waste marble powder addition as building materials." Construction and Building Materials, Vol. 82, pp.1–8. https://doi.org/10.1016/j.conbuildmat.2015.02.055

[5] Wang, J., Zhang, M., Li, W., Chia, k., and, Liew, R. (2012). "Stability of cenospheres in lightweight cement composites in terms of alkali–silica reaction". Cement and Concrete Research, 42, 721–727. https://doi.org/10.1016/j.cemconres.2012.02.010

[6] Pahroraji, M., Saman, H. M., Rahmat, M. N., and Kamaruddin, K. (2013). "Compressive strength and density of unfired lightweight coal ash brick." International Civil and Infrastructure Engineering Conference, Kuching, Malaysia, pp. 22-24.

[7] IS: 3495 (Part 1): 1992 – Method of tests of burnt clay building bricks., Part 1- Determination of Compressive Strength

[8] IS: 3495 (Part 2): 1992 – Method of tests of burnt clay building bricks., Part 2- Determination of Water Absorption.

Recent Advancements in Geotechnical Engineering - NCRAG'21
Materials Research Proceedings **19** (2021) 108-114

Materials Research Forum LLC
https://doi.org/10.21741/9781644901618-14

A Study on Sustainable Reutilization of C&D Debris in the Construction of Traffic Barrier

S. Janani[1,a*], V. Ranjani[2,b], H. Ram Prithivi[2,c] and R. Poongundran[2,d]

[1]Assistant Professor, Department of Civil Engineering, Kongu Engineering College, Erode, Tamil Nadu, India

[2]UG Scholar, Department of Civil Engineering, Kongu Engineering College, Erode, Tamil Nadu, India

[*a]janani.civil@kongu.edu, [b]ranjaniv.17civil@kongu.edu, [c]ramprithivih.17civil@kongu.edu, [d]poongundranr.17civil@kongu.edu

Keywords: C&D debris, Recycling Techniques, Traffic Barriers, Sustainable Approach, Fine and Coarse Aggregate

Abstract. In India, the construction industry is growing at twice the world average. This leads to a significant accumulation of C&D waste. This typically includes asphalt, steel, concrete, bricks, wood and other building materials. It is estimated on a conservative basis that over 25-30 million tons of C&D waste is generated which clogs rivers, blocks traffic and occupies land / agricultural space which in turn creates pollution, solid waste production, discharge of dust and gas and leads to additional utilization of natural resources including non-renewable resources, thereby depleting the available resources. Only little amount of construction and demolition concrete debris is recycled or reused. Construction and demolition waste generation and handling issues are being focused to achieve sustainable goals. Based on this study, experimental investigations are carried out to evaluate the material properties and to study the strength characteristics and effect of partial replacement (20 %, 30 % and 40 %) of both fine and coarse aggregate obtained from construction and demolition waste (CDW) in the construction of intermediate road traffic concrete barriers.

Introduction

According to the Building Material Promotion Council, India generates an estimated 150 million tonnes of C&D waste every year yet the official recycling capacity is a meagre 6,500 tonnes per day i.e. about one percentage. The growing population in the country and requirement of land for commercial purposes have reduced the availability of land for open dumping. Among the 3R's there-utilization is an important strategy for management of such waste in effective manner.

Role of the Government:

The Bureau of Indian Standards has allowed the use of concrete made from recycled material and processed C&D waste. Also, the Construction and Demolition Waste Rules and Regulations, 2016 mandated the reuse of recycled material wherever possible. The need for C&D waste management is even recognized by the Swatch Bharat Mission. Above all, the fast depleting reserves of conventional natural aggregate and river sand urge us to adopt the recycling technology and material. This mutually paves the way for reduced purchase of raw materials along with low transportation cost, reduced capital investment on raw materials with improved profits and less environmental impact.

Literature overview

Table 1.Literature overview.

<table>
<tr><th colspan="6">LITERATURE STUDY</th></tr>
<tr><th>No.</th><th>NAME OF THE LITERATURE</th><th>YEAR</th><th>RECYCLED PRODUCT</th><th>TESTS CONDUCTED</th><th>TEST RESULTS</th></tr>
<tr>
<td>1</td>
<td>Use of Construction Demolition Waste in Pavement</td>
<td>2017</td>
<td>Feasibility of(CDW) for improving the performance of **sub grade and sub base layers** in the road design</td>
<td>Aggregate Impact Value Test Crushing Value Test Specific Gravity Test Water Absorption Test Loss Angeles Abrasion Test. Marshall stability Test</td>
<td>The aggregates are best suited for the design of road pavement. The Marshall Stability of construction demolition wastes was found10.15 KN which satisfies the requirement for DBM course as per given in MORTH specification.</td>
</tr>
<tr>
<td>2</td>
<td>Reusability of Construction & Demolition waste in bricks</td>
<td>2017</td>
<td>**Bricks** Cement and fly ash - Binder Recycled coarse and fine aggregates</td>
<td>Hardness test Efflorescence test Water absorption test Compressive strength test</td>
<td>Bricks have compressive strength of **9.71N/mm^2** is potentially at par with the conventionally manufactured common burnt clay bricks. Hence highly recommended for non-load bearing structure.</td>
</tr>
<tr>
<td>3</td>
<td>Preparation of Bricks using Construction and Demolition waste and Sludge</td>
<td>2018</td>
<td>**Bricks** with the ratio of 3:2:3:2 Fly ash : cement : sludge : C & D waste.</td>
<td>Compressive strength Bulk Density pH content Water Absorption</td>
<td>This brick (recycled) has a **potential** to be used as instead of normal bricks, except the pH value (6.7 < 8.5)</td>
</tr>
<tr>
<td>4</td>
<td>Experimental investigation on effect of demolished aggregate in paving block</td>
<td>2018</td>
<td>Replacement of coarse and fine aggregates in **Paver blocks**</td>
<td>Flexural strength test Spilt tensile strength Compressive strength test</td>
<td>Use of 50% recycled aggregate paving block shows good results over fully replaced demolished aggregate. Mix : 1 :2.71:2.6 (M30 grade)</td>
</tr>
<tr>
<td>5</td>
<td>Experimental Study on Bricks by Using Demolished Construction Material</td>
<td>2018</td>
<td>**Bricks** with 20 % C and D debris</td>
<td>Water absorption test Compressive test</td>
<td>**23.42 N/mm^2** compressive sttrength is obtained.</td>
</tr>
<tr>
<td>6</td>
<td>Study of Construction and Demolition waste for reuse and recycle</td>
<td>2018</td>
<td>**Recycled aggregates**</td>
<td>Sieve analysis Particle size distribution Impact value test</td>
<td>Recycled aggregate is in workable condition and can be used for the road construction purpose.</td>
</tr>
<tr>
<td>7</td>
<td>Use of Construction and Demolition Waste as Partial Replacement of Fine Aggregate for Development of Paving Block</td>
<td>2018</td>
<td>C & D debris as Partial Replacement of Fine Aggregate for **Paver Block**</td>
<td>Compression strength test Flexural strength test Split tensile Test Abrasion Test</td>
<td>Higher compressive strength was achieved when 40% to 60% fine aggregate was replaced by C&D waste fine aggregate.</td>
</tr>
<tr>
<td>8</td>
<td>Reuse of Clay Brick Waste in Mortar and Concrete</td>
<td>2020</td>
<td>Clay brick powder (CBP) exhibits pozzolanic activity and can be used as cement replacement. Recycled clay brick aggregate (RBA) can be used to substitute natural coarse aggregate.</td>
<td>Flexural strength test Compressive strength</td>
<td>The higher the replacement rates of RBAs are, the greater the strength loss was. The reduction in compressive strength was 44% in RBAC prepared with 50% RBAs after 28 days.</td>
</tr>
</table>

There are numerous way for recycling the waste but the best is again using it without much change in its original form by retaining or strengthening its physical and chemical properties. Based on the literature study, re-utilization is one of the best disposal methods for C and D debris.

The Recycled products are summarized as follows,
- Recycled aggregates
- Bricks
- Paver blocks
- Sub - grade and sub - base layer

By analyzing the characteristics of the recycled products from the journals, it is acceptable to adapt the same methodology for the others construction elements. In our day to day, replacing a element should be economical and efficient and when it comes to Median Rigid Traffic Barrier, it satisfies both the above conditions and their strength criteria will match with the above mentioned products. And as we know roads are like nerves which connects every nodes of the region, the maximum utilization of C and D debris can be adapted through this method of traffic barrier construction.

Standards for Traffic Barrier
As per IRC 119-2015, the role of median traffic barrier is to protect the roadside traffic from both the sides. An important factor in the design of concrete barriers is impact load, the load which is acted suddenly upon the barrier during collision. They are intended to prevent the impact Head-on-collisions caused by out-of-control vehicles jumping across the medians. The main objective is that it must satisfy performance requirements at minimum total cost including initial and maintenance costs. The capability of the traffic barrier is to effectively redirect passenger cars and vans for locations with poor geometrics, high traffic volume and on-going constructions activities.

Discussion
It is evident from the table, that the products produced from C and D waste has the potential and criteria to be reused as per the Standards and IS codes. Impact load is the foremost factor to be considered in the design of concrete barriers, which a vehicle exerts over them upon collision. Jersey type barrier dimensions are as follows

- Height - 813 mm
- Base width - 610 mm
- Top width - 240 mm

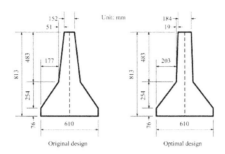

Original design

Optimal design

Figure 1. *Cross section of Traffic Barrier.*

These dimensions ensure the stability of concrete barriers during the collision time. The software utilized to create the analytical models is LS-DYNA as it can effectively simulate vehicle impact on concrete barriers. The key points from literature study are

o It is observed from the previous paper study, that maximum strength is achieved between the ranges when the replacement of fine aggregate is between 20% to 50%.
o It is estimated that reutilization of C and D debris saves about 3.28% cost of concrete.
o It is learned from previous literature that the paver interlocks with demolished concrete waste along with 3 cm copper wire (e-waste) gave maximum compressive strength and least percentage water absorption.

The Strength characteristics are mainly governed by the mix design and proportions of the recycled material along with proper casting techniques. It is suggested that the minimum 28 day compressive strength of traffic barrier should be around 3000 lb/in2 (approximately 20 N/mm^2). This strength can be determined by applying compressive load over the cubical specimen of size150mm x 150mm x 150 mm.

Experimental tests and results
The C and D debris is collected from casting yard and crushed to required size. The debris is collected and segregated using IS 4.75 mm and 2.36 mm sieves. After this process, the specimen is tested for its specific gravity, particle size, aggregate strength test and water absorption test.

Specific gravity test results:

Table 2. *Specific gravity test results.*

	COARSE AGG.	FINE AGG.
NORMAL AGGREGATE	2.9	2.69
RE-UTILIZED AGGREGATE	2.94	2.8
STANDARD AGG.	2.9	2.8

Particle Size Distribution Analysis:

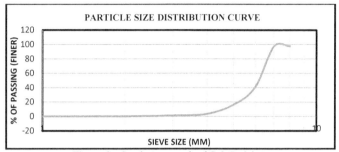

Figure 2. *Gradation graph of C & D debris.*

This curve indicates that the particles are in dense gradation which refers to a sample that is approximately of equal amounts of various sizes of aggregate i.e. An even curve on the gradation graph resulting in maximum Grain-to-grain contact.

Table 3. *Particle size distribution analysis.*

SIEVE SIZE	% FINER
0 mm	0.1
0.15 mm	1.2
0.30 mm	3.4
0.45 mm	16
1.18 mm	41.1
2.36 mm	97
4.75 mm	97.5

Aggregate strength test result:

Table 4. *Aggregate Impact & Crushing test Results.*

	IMPACT VALUE	CRUSHING VALUE
NORMAL AGGREGATE	11.02	8.9
RE-UTILIZED AGGREGATE	20.44	18.03
AS PER IS 383:1970	45	45

Water Absorption Test:

Table 5. *Water Absorption test Results.*

	REUTILISED AGG. (g)	NORMAL AGG. (g)
TOTAL DRY WEIGHT OF THE AGGREGATES (W1)	342	200
WEIGHT OF THE SATURATED SPECIMEN (W2)	348	202
WEIGHT OF WATER ABSORBED (W2-W1)	6	2
% OF THE WATER ABSORPTION (W3/W1) *100	1.75	1

After the preliminary test, the materials are segregated separately. The M-40 grade of concrete is selected for cubical specimen testing. The mix design calculation is done as per IS 10262:2009. The cubes are casted with three different proportions of fine and coarse aggregates replacement with C&D debris aggregates and they will be tested for its compressive strength at 7 and 14 days. The following table contains the volume of each mix for three cubes of dimensions 150mm.

Table 6. *Mix Proportion (M40 grade & Ratio - 1 : 2.3 : 3.8) Details.*

Percentage replacement of coarse and fine aggregate	Mix design M40 GRADE [kg]				
	CEMENT	NORMAL FINE AGGREGATE	NORMAL COARSE AGGREGATE	CDW FINE AGG.	CDW COARSE AGG.
0%	4.7385	10.803	18.057	0	0
20%	4.7385	8.6424	14.445	2.1606	3.6114
30%	4.7385	7.5621	12.6399	3.2409	5.4171
40%	4.7385	6.4818	10.8342	4.3212	7.2228

The Slump value is between 80-100 mm. Since we can assure the strength characteristics from the previous literature study, we can adapt the same process for the construction of Median Rigid Traffic Barrier.

Conclusion
The best way to reduce the impact of C and D waste is to re-utilize it in construction sector itself so as to minimize its effect over natural resources. The major demerit noted during literature study is the age of the concrete debris i.e., the age of building from which the CDW is extracted as it plays a vital role in achieving the strength characteristics. In order to eliminate this demerit, debris from the building built during past decade is to considered for analysis &experimental test procedures. The above factor and experimental inferences will be considered while casting the cubical specimens even though the merits outweigh the demerits. The cubical specimens pertained to

Recent Advancements in Geotechnical Engineering - NCRAG'21   Materials Research Forum LLC
Materials Research Proceedings **19** (2021) 108-114   https://doi.org/10.21741/9781644901618-14

above mix proportions will be tested for its compressive strength (7 &14 days strength) and future analysis will be done accordingly.

References

[1] Avinash M, Vishal K, Dnyaneshwar G, Vikram G, Sachin M and Prof Nigade Y M 2018 *Preparation of Bricks using Construction and Demolition waste and Sludge*   Vol. 6 Issue 3 IJIRCCE *ISSN (Online): 2320-9801*[2]   Shivkumar H, Rohit M. Shinde, Vaishnavi B and Tejashree G 2018 Experimental Investigation On Effect Of Demolished Aggregate In Paving Block Vol. 5 Issue 7 JETIR (ISSN-2349-5162)

[3] Vishal V P, Vinayak B K, Avadhut K and Akash K 2017 *Use of Construction Demolition Waste in Pavement* Vol. 4 Issue 12 IJIRCCE *ISSN: 2350-0328*

[4] Mohit A and Amit K 2017 Reusability of Construction & Demolition waste in bricks Vol.4 Issue 12 IRJET e-ISSN: 2395-0056

[5] Yeotikar V U, Kulkarni G A, Syed Nadeem , Bhosale N M and Kokare D R 2018 *Experimental Study on Bricks by Using Demolished Construction Material* Vol.15 Issue2 JASRAE E-ISSN: 2230-7540. https://doi.org/10.29070/15/56790

[6] Makegaonkar A R, Dange P S and Waghmode R B 2018 Study of Construction and Demolition waste for reuse and recycleVol. 5 Issue 07 IRJET e-ISSN: 2395-0056

[7] Mahesh T, Krutika P, Priyanka N and Aditya P 2018 Use of Construction and Demolition Waste as Partial Replacement of Fine Aggregate for Development of Paving BlockVol.15Issue 2 JASRAE E-ISSN : 2230 -7540

[8] IRC 119 2015 - Guidelines for traffic safety barrier

Recent Advancements in Geotechnical Engineering - NCRAG'21
Materials Research Proceedings 19 (2021) 115-122

Materials Research Forum LLC
https://doi.org/10.21741/9781644901618-15

Self-Compacting Concrete Properties of Recycled Coarse Aggregate

R. Premkumar[1,a*], Ramesh Babu Chokkalingam[1], Vemula Jayanth Kumar[1]

[1]School of Environmental and Construction Technology, Department of Civil Engineering, Kalasalingam Academy of Research and Education, Krishnankoil, Tamil Nadu, India.

[a]prem.ce@gmail.com

* Corresponding author

Keywords: Self-Compacting Concrete, Recycled Coarse Aggregate, Mechanical, Durability

Abstract. Self-compacting concrete, which is characterized by its capacity to flow, can also consolidate under its weight. Hardened concrete from concrete building demolition can be used to partially replace natural coarse aggregate in self-compacting concrete. The current study compares the properties of self-compacting concrete with 0 percent, 25%, 50%, 75%, and 100% substitution of recycled coarse aggregate in the fresh and hardened states. The evolution of passing ability properties using the L-box test, filling ability properties using the slump cone test, and segregation properties using the V-funnel test are also included. Compression, tension, and flexural strength are all checked for hardened properties. Rapid chloride permeability and sorptivity tests are used to assess durability. The experimental program revealed that at RCA utilization levels of 25% to 50%, little to no negative impact on power, workability, or durability properties was observed.

Introduction

The use of sustainable materials has become increasingly common in recent years. By that the use of nonrenewable natural resources, sustainability benefits the ecosystem. Concrete, the world's second most used commodity after water, consumes a large amount of non-renewable energy. As a result, several studies have looked into the use of recycled materials in the manufacturing process. The use of sustainable materials has become increasingly common in recent years [1]. By that the use of nonrenewable natural resources, sustainability benefits the ecosystem. Concrete, the world's second most used commodity after water, consumes a large amount of non-renewable energy. Accordingly, a few investigations have investigated the utilization of reused materials in the assembling interaction [2]. The utilization of reused totals in the creation of new cement seems to have a great deal of guarantee. It considers the goal of issues identified with the assortment, transportation, and removal of building and destruction squander, just as adding to a conceivably more feasible environment through an improvement in the estimation of such squanders, accordingly lessening the utilization of common aggregate [3]. The examination of self-compacting concrete (SCC) with RA, yet then again, should prompt a compelling assessment between the R&D zones and the genuine requirements from both the development business and its last customers because the capacity to customer needs and the relationship execution quality-cost is the key distinctive components of sound rivalry in the development business. It can be difficult to ensure that the formwork is properly stacked, that is, completely compacted without voids or honeycombs, when a large amount of generous assistance is to be put in a shaped cement (RC) section.

Compaction with a manual or electronic vibrator is extremely difficult in this case. Underwater concreting necessitated the use of fresh concrete that could be installed without the need for compaction; vibration was simply not an option in such circumstances [4]. This problem can now be solved with self-compacting concrete. This research will look at the long-term properties of SCC with recycled coarse and fine aggregates, as a follow-up to a previous study that looked at the long-term behaviour of structural concrete with coarse and fine aggregates [5]. Accordingly, the impacts of different plans on SCC properties in both new and solidified states are examined to evaluate the practicality of SCC with incredible mechanical obstruction [6]. As a result, when compared to standard aggregate concrete, RAC structural components typically have poor mechanical and physical properties, such as weak mechanical low productivity, and poor durability behavior [7]. RAC concrete made entirely of recycled aggregates was said to have a lower compressive strength [8]. Previous research studies have shown that some of the disadvantages of recycled aggregate concrete include greater drying shrinkage and creep, as well as chemical resistance to chloride-ion penetration when compared to standard concrete. However, this weakness can be mitigated by applying a small amount of fly ash to the concrete mix, as fly ash is known to minimize drying shrinkage, creep, and chloride ion penetration in concrete [9]. This study aims to fill a significant gap in the current literature by investigating the versatile properties of SCCs with characteristic coarse total subbed with RCA at levels of 0% (control), 25%, half, 75%, and 100%. To better understand the impact of RCA on these properties, SCC intensity characteristics are analyzed at each of the RCA utilization stages.

Materials
Ordinary Portland cement (Grade 53) conforming to IS12269:1987 was used in all of the formulations. After 28 days, it weighed 3.23 specific gravity, 380 m^2/kg specific surface area, and 58 MPa compressive pressures. To increase the powder content in SCC, Elkem Company's grade 920D silica fume with a specific gravity of 2.3 was used. As the natural aggregate, crushed basalt with a maximum size of 10 mm was collected from a nearby stone quarry. Crushed concrete rubbles from building demolition campaigns made up almost all of the recycled aggregate. Demolished concrete aggregates were crushed in a laboratory jaw crusher to produce a cumulative grain size distribution curve that looked close to that of natural coarse aggregates. The aggregates used were crushed granite with a nominal maximum size of 10 mm and properties described in table 2. The fine aggregate in the concrete mixtures was river sand.

Mix Proportion
Five different concrete mixtures were created for the experiment. The following proportions of recycled coarse aggregate were used to replace natural coarse aggregate in each mixture: 0%, 25%, 50%, 75%, and 100% by volume. Table 2 shows the specifics of the blended template for each of these five blends. Following the initial mix design, EFNARC guidelines were followed to prepare and test the trial mixes for SCC fresh properties. Because of slightly higher water absorption and minor variations in the amount of superplasticizer used to achieve comparable quality for all blends, the number of components used to manufacture 1 m3 of concrete remained constant. The specimens were then put in the curing tank to cure after they were de-moulded. In this analysis, compression, flexure, and split tensile strength measuring mechanical properties were cast and stored for 28 days before being tested for strength. The effects of different recycled aggregate concrete on the solidity of SCC were measured using toughness properties including water sorptivity and chloride particle penetration of recycled aggregate concrete above SCC and compared to standard aggregate concrete.

Table 1..Properties of Aggregate

S.No	Property	Natural Aggregate	Recycle Aggregate
1	Specific Gravity	2.657	2.469
2	Water Absorption	0.311%	2.24%
3	Fineness Modulus	6.25	5.45
4	Bulk Density	1.404kg/l	1.31 kg/l
5	Crushing Value	28%	28%
6	Impact Value	21%	30%

Table 2.Mix Proportion

Mix code	w/b ratio	Water (kg/m³)	Cement (kg/m³)	Fly ash(kg/ m³)	Silica Fume (kg/ m³)	10mm aggregate (kg/m³)	Quarry dust (kg/m³)	Recycled 10mm (kg/m³)	(%) of RCA	SP (l/m³)
RC0	0.35	220	450	150	30	650	825	0	0	4.5
RC25	0.35	220	450	150	30	488	825	162	25	4.5
RC50	0.35	220	450	150	30	325	825	325	50	4.5
RC75	0.35	220	450	150	30	162	825	488	75	4.5
RC100	0.35	220	450	150	30	0	825	650	100	4.5

Results and Discussion

Table 3 shows the droop stream, hindering proportion, and sifter isolation test results for the control SCC and SCCs with various degrees of RCA use. This finding shows that all SCCs have similar flow ability, but that increasing RCA content increases viscosity. Slump flow experiments performed one hour after concrete mixing revealed a similar trend. The t500 times, on the other hand, increased by a greater percentage as the RCA content increased; for example, when moving from control to 100% RCA, the t500 times increased by 45 percent at initial measurement and 92 percent after 1 hour (see Table 3). The obvious thickness with developing RCA substance could be because of the RCA's rakish structure, while the time-subordinate move in droop stream results could be because of the reused aggregate proceeded with water ingestion despite being presoaked and dried for one hour before utilizing. Table 3 shows the consequences of the L-box assessment. As referenced in the past section, this test evaluates the SCC's reasonableness for use in a part with blocked support by estimating its passing capacity. In the L-box test one hour after blending, the divergence between the control SCC and the SCCs comprising 75 percent RCA and 100 percent RCA increments. In this study, the obstructing proportions of the 75 percent and 100 percent RCA SCCs were reduced by around 8% and 10%, respectively, as compared to the normal SCC. Table 3 shows that as the RCA content of the SCCs increased, so did the SCCs' isolation obstruction. This is probably because of the reused aggregate's higher water ingestion capacity. As indicated by each SCC mix falling into the strainer isolation opposition class SR2 (isolation part <=15%), the entirety of the SCCs were considered adequate.

Table 3. *Fresh Concrete Properties*

Mix code	Wet density (kg/m3)	Slump flow test					L-box			Sieve segregation P (%)
		Initial		After 1 hr		Variation	Initial	After 1 hr	Variation	
		S0 (mm)	T500 (s)	S1 (mm)	T500 (s)	(S0– S1) hr)/S0(%)	B0 (ratio)	B1hr (ratio)	(B0– B1 hr)/B0(%)	
RC0	2375	710	2.9	640	3.9	9.86	0.94	0.89	5.32	9.90
RC25	2360	700	3.7	610	5.9	12.86	0.95	0.88	7.37	7.70
RC50	2345	720	3.9	640	6.4	11.11	0.97	0.89	8.25	6.30
RC75	2332	710	4.1	610	6.9	14.08	0.92	0.82	10.87	6.00
RC100	2325	700	4.3	580	7.6	17.14	0.93	0.80	13.98	5.20

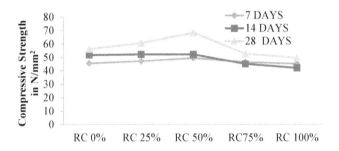

Figure 1.Compressive Strength

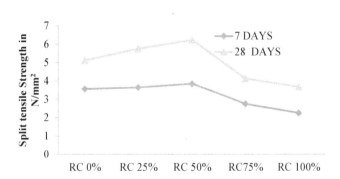

Figure 2.Split tensile strength

Compressive Strength

As demonstrated in Figure 1, the compressive strength of 7, 14, and 28 days was a particular rate replacement of coarse total in SCC. The normal strength in three 150mm x 150mm x 150mm solid shape examples of each blend extent was utilized to acquire the entirety of the test outcomes. RCA0 percent had a compressive strength of $56N/mm^2$ after 28 days; RCA25 percent, 50 percent, 75 percent, and 100 percent concrete mixes with recycling aggregate had compressive strengths of $60N/mm^2$, $68N/mm^2$, $52N/mm^2$, and $49N/mm^2$, respectively. When taking a gander at the compressive strength of examples, it was discovered that as the level of reuse coarse aggregate replacement was expanded, the compressive strength of the examples diminished after half substitution. In any case, since silica fume was accustomed to restricting substance, the compressive strength was additionally diminished. Aside from RCA25% and RCA50% reuse total superseded concrete, the compressive strength of a wide range of cement blends was discovered to be more noteworthy than the plan estimation of solidarity.

Split Tensile Strength

The ASTM norm was used to calculate the splitting tensile strength of each concrete sequence. As suggested by the ASTM standard, the stacking was applied at a consistent pace of 0.7–1.4 MPa each moment. At a concrete age of 28 days, three 150 x 300 mm cylinders were checked for each combination. After a 50 percent replacement mix proportion, raising the amount of recycled aggregate in the concrete mix reduces the concrete's fracturing tensile strength. Silica fume is commonly used to improve the pozzolanic action of SCC concrete. As a result, we've been able to boost all of concrete's mechanical properties. However, applying mineral admixtures to recycled aggregate concrete does not improve its mechanical properties, according to this report. Ordinary concrete has an elasticity of 8–14% of its compressive power, according to the split tensile measure.

As demonstrated in Figure 3, the level of rigidity comparative with the compressive strength of the relating reuse aggregate cement went from 8-14 percent to 50 percent coarse aggregate substitutions. After more than half of the aggregate was reused, the compressive strength was reduced to less than 8% of its original value.

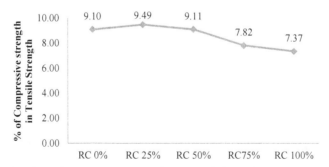

Figure 3. The relation between Percentage of Split Tensile Strength to Compressive Strength

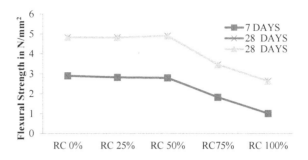

Figure 4.Flexural strength

Flexural Strength

A universal testing machine with a stacking limit of 1000 kN was utilized to evaluate the flexural qualities of concrete. As shown by the ASTM, the stacking was applied at a rate that expanded the most extreme pressure gave an account of the strained surface between 0.9 MPa each moment. At the ages of 7, and 28 days, the flexural strength is estimated. When contrasted with other blend extents of the percentage of silica fume, 0% replacement of reused aggregate was the cutoff. This distinction can be because of a diminishing in the consistency of the hard and fast mortar interfacial exchange zone as the extent of reused aggregate in the example increments, bringing about a lower mechanical strength under turning conditions.

Rapid Chloride Permeability Test

According to ASTM C1202, a 50 mm thick, 100 mm thick gauge solid model is exposed to a DC voltage of 60 V for 6 hours as part of an ASTM C1202 evaluation. As demonstrated in figure 5, one compartment had a 3.0 percent NaCl course of action and the other had a 0.3 M NaOH strategy. The aftereffects of this test have appeared in Table 4. The chloride goes through the solid example in this investigation, which was required following 28 days of restoring, demonstrating the penetrability of the solid. The charge transferred by coloumbs values is derived from the hardware screen, and these characteristics are compared to the ASTM C1202 standard characteristics.

Figure 5. Rapid Chloride Permeability Test

Sorptivity Test

The hair like rising level of consistency on generally homogeneous material can be utilized to dispense with sorptivity. The test liquid was comprised of water. After throwing, the chambers were lowered in water for 28 days to direct. Following drying in a holder at a temperature of 100 + 10 °C, the model was gagged with a water level close to 5 mm over the surface. As shown in the test result table 5, this demonstrates that reused coarse aggregate has infinitely better pore structures, vehicles, and transcendent volumes than the normal coarse aggregate.

Table 4. Rapid Chloride Permeability Test

S.No	Mix Id	Charge Pass In Coloumbs (C)	As Per ASTM
1	RC 0%	2605	Moderate
2	RC25%	2414	Moderate
3	RC50%	2245	Moderate
4	RC75%	2010	Moderate
5	RC100%	1715	LOW

Table 5. Sorptivity Test

S.No	Mix Id	Sorptivity x 10^{-6} mm/ min	Rate of Absorption I mm
1	RC 0%	4.50	101.62
2	RC25%	5.36	111.23
3	RC50%	6.28	125.60
4	RC75%	6.72	131.49
5	RC100%	7.36	143.56

Conclusion

The research paper contributed to the current SCC literature by examining the effects of different levels of RCA integration on workability, strength, and, most importantly, durability.

- According to the workability checks, the viscosity of the SCCs increased as the RCA material was increased, as did sieve segregation resistance. When RCA usage exceeded 50%, the SCC's passing capacity was found to be substantially reduced; however, the 75 percent RCA and 100 percent RCA SCCs were still within reasonable passing ability limits.
- However, with the aid of silica fume and fly ash, it was possible to manufacture good quality RAC that met the concrete strength requirements.

- The coulomb reduction identified in the chloride diffusion test for the fly ash and silica fume concretes was related to micro structural changes and might even be due to the decline in pore solution conductivity.
- The safety from chloride molecule passageway deteriorated as the reused concrete material grew longer. In either case, the opposition was strengthened by mixing silica fume residues in concrete mixers. However, these properties are inferior to those of ordinary aggregate concrete with the same volume and variety of recycled concrete

References

[1] Sherif A. Khafaga (2014) "Production of High strength self compacting concrete using recycled concrete as fine and /or coarse aggregates". World applied sciences journal 29 940: 465-474.

[2] Ozbakkaloglu, T.; Gholampour, A.; Xie, T.Y. "Mechanical and durability properties of recycled aggregate concrete: Effect of recycled aggregate size and content on the behaviour". J. Mater. Civ. Eng. vol. 30, pp. 04017275, 2017. https://doi.org/10.1061/(ASCE)MT.1943-5533.0002142

[3] B. Gonza´ lez-Fonteboa , F. Martı´nez-Abella, "Concretes with aggregates from demolition waste and silica fume Materials and mechanical properties," Building and Environment, vol 43, pp. 429–437, 2008. https://doi.org/10.1016/j.buildenv.2007.01.008

[4] Isaia, G. C., Gastaldini, A. L. G., and Moraes, R."Physical and pozzolanic action of mineral additions on the mechanical strength of high-performance concrete." Cem. Concr. Vol. 25, pp. 69–76, 2003. https://doi.org/10.1016/S0958-9465(01)00057-9

[5] Kamal M.M, Safan M.A.,Etman Z.A and Eldaboly E.A(2013)."Evaluating the prolonged properties of fresh self compacting concrete incorporating recycled aggregates."International journal of current engineering and technology ISSN 2277-4106. Vol :3 issue :2. https://doi.org/10.21608/erjm.2013.67433

[6] Nwzad Abduljabar Abdulla1," Effect of Recycled Coarse Aggregate Type on Concrete". J. Mater. Civ. Eng. vol. 27(10), pp. 04014273, 2015. https://doi.org/10.1061/(ASCE)MT.1943-5533.0001247

[7] Moslem Mohammadi Jatani, Ali delnavaz(2017)." A study on strength and durability of self compacting concretes made of recycled aggregates. "Journal of structural engineering and Geotechnics

[8] P. Saravana Kumar and G. Dhinakaran, "Effect of Admixed Recycled Aggregate Concrete on Properties of Fresh and Hardened Concrete", Journal of Materials in Civil Engineering, vol. 24, pp. 494-498, 2012. https://doi.org/10.1061/(ASCE)MT.1943-5533.0000393

[9] Premkumar R, Ramesh BabuChokkalingam and M Shanmugasundaram, "Durability Performance of Fly Ash and Steatite Powder Based Geopolymer Concrete", IOP Conference Series: Materials Science and Engineering, vol. 561, 012055, 2019, Available from: https://doi.org/10.1088/1757-899X/561/1/012055

Recent Advancements in Geotechnical Engineering - NCRAG'21
Materials Research Proceedings **19** (2021) 123-132

Materials Research Forum LLC
https://doi.org/10.21741/9781644901618-16

Basic Experimental Studies on Coconut Shell Charcoal Ash in Modified Bitumen

Dr. S. Suchithra[1,a*], S. Madhankumar[2,b], M. GowshicPrasanna[2,c],
V. Nandhakumar[2,d] and S. Jayashree[3,e]

[1]Associate Professor, Department of civil enginerring, Kongu Engineering College, Perundurai, Erode, Tamilnadu, India

[2]U.G Students, Department of civil engineering, Kongu Engineering College, Perundurai, Erode, Tamilnadu, India

[3]P.G Student, Department of civil engineering, Kongu Engineering College, Perundurai, Erode, Tamilnadu, India

[a*]suchithra@kongu.ac.in, [b]madhankumarvedha@gmail.com, [c]gowshicprasannakec57@gmail.com, [d]venkateshnandhakumar@gmail.com, [e]jayashreesiva22@gmail.com

Keywords: Bitumen, Aggregate, Coconut Shell Charcoal, Filler, Marshall Test

Abstract. For reducing the cost in bitumen roads and also increasing the efficiency of bituminuous roads, varieties of materials are used for improving the road by using coconut shell charcoal ash as fillers in the flexible pavement. In the literature work, the main descriptive of the work is to compare the results with different percentages of coconut shell charcoal ash in bitumen. The Properties of the coconut shell charcoal possesses are resistance to breaking the materials, absorbing the heat, moisture content of surface, grading, heating and synthetic resin glues which is important for pavement of bitumen roads. Therefore, its stability of Marshall stability test and flow value in Marshall stability and air void ratio are obtained. So that it can be compared with different modified percentage as 4.5%, 5%, 5.5% and 6% in test on Bitumen. From this test we can establish so that it can be useful as a substitute as a coconut shell charcoal ash for improving the strength, quality and durability of bitumnious road. For carrying out these experiments, Marshall stability test is used for obtaining better results for normal mix and modified mix for the bitumen.

Introduction

A proper mixture of bitumen and aggregates were heated, which is laid on the road and compacted well on the granular layer bed to form a flexible pavement. A flexible pavement consists of a base course, a sub base course and a bituminous surface course. Base course of a flexible pavement is the one which lies below the surface course or wearing course and above thesub base course. And this layer provides some additional load distribution, drainage layer and frost resistance in flexible pavement. Base course are usually constructed out of Hot Mix Asphaltand as well as aggregate [1].

Coconut shell charcoal ash is a product of agriculture obtained by burning coconut shells in a limited supply of oxygen. It is widely known for its use as a domestic and industrial fuel. Coconut Shell Charcoal Ash as filler material can be used as addition of different percentages in Bitumen for the construction of flexible pavement[1].

Coconut shell is the agricultural waste product and the coconut fiber can be easily removed if the coconut shell fiber is allowed for sun-dry. In the coconut shell removed waste things and washed unwanted waste materials. To change some properties of charcoal, the coconut shells can be subjected to the heating process for five minutes at the temperature of 400 to $450°C$ using furnace[1]. Coconut shell charcoal after heating at certain temperature and allowed them to cool down the temperature before doing its crushing the coconut shell charcoal. Coconut shell charcoal ash grinded out after the cooling process is over and crushed them manually or physically. Coconut shell charcoal ash was sieved in sieve size passing through 2.36mm sieve and retained in 0.075mm sieve. Coconut Shell charcoal Ash was then weighted 4.5%, 5%, 5.5%, and 6% by weighting the bitumen for testing the bitumen conducted.

Methodology
Literature review paper was studied and the sample was collected from agricultural waste and the material properties of Bitumen, Coarse aggregate and Coconut shell charcoal was collected. After that aggregate tests and experimental work on bitumen are done in the laboratory and after that discussions and conclusion was completed.

Material properties
Bitumen
- It is obtained from coal and tar. The properties and chemical composition of coal tar and bitumen are similar like, both are black in color and sticky. Heating the coal at very high temperature give coal tar and it is the by-product of coke and gas[2].
- The bitumen is used as a binding agent for the road construction. It has been produced by asphalt replacement of about 30-70%.The bitumen was used in the highway department[2].

Aggregate
- An aggregate is used for construction purpose, which provides greater strength for the construction. The aggregates can give good characteristic performance for giving strength. About 95% of the mixture by weight is covered by aggregates[2]. The good physical property and good quality of the aggregates ensures the good pavement. The aggregate was using 10mm graded aggregate and 20mm grade aggregate to use for mix in the bitumen.

Coconut shell charcoal
1. Coconut shell charcoal gives the strength and high property for the other fillers and dueto its low specific weight and hardness[3].
2. It shows property of high modulus.
3. It has high resistance to different weather as High lignin content and it is suitable forconstruction purpose[3].
4. It has good durability and abrasion resistance Characteristics in the charcoal ash[3].
5. It has low Cellulose Content.

Figure 1. *Coconut shell charcoal ash*

Recent Advancements in Geotechnical Engineering - NCRAG'21
Materials Research Proceedings **19** (2021) 123-132

Materials Research Forum LLC
https://doi.org/10.21741/9781644901618-16

Experimental work on aggregates

Specific gravity test on Coarse aggregate
This test on coarse aggregate in specific gravity and it is used to check the quality and strength of the material. The aggregates having high specific gravity possess greater strength compared that of the aggregates having low specific gravity. The strength was identified helps with the specific gravity test. The aggregates used for construction work should have the specific gravity about 2.6 to 2.9. The specific gravity of the aggregates obtained as 2.87, hence it is acceptable[4]. The figure 2 consists of Specific gravity test on coarse aggregate.

Figure 2.Specific Gravity test on coarse aggregate

Water absorption test on coarse aggregate
This test gives an idea for checking the quality and different strength of rock. The aggregates having more water absorption and having more porous in nature and based on the strength, impact and hardness and found to be acceptable. The aggregates may have water absorption values between 1.0 to 2.0 percent for surface dressing. As we done the water absorption test on coarse aggregate is 2% and it can be used for construction work purpose[4]. The figure 3 consistsof Water absorption test on coarse aggregate.

Figure 3.Water absorption test on coarse aggregate

Sieve analysis & Fineness modulus test on coarse aggregate
In Sieve analysis test and fineness modulus test of coarse aggregate and the sieve sizes are arranged in the order such as 80 mm, 63mm, 50mm, 40mm,31.5mm, 25mm, 20mm, 16mm, 12.5mm, 10mm, 6.3mm and 4.75 mm. The fineness modulus value is calculated by using (Cumulative percentage retained / 100). From the graph we can follow some specifications. Straight curve implies uniformly graded aggregates which can be used in base course. S curve implies well graded aggregates which can be used in drainage layers and sub base course. Combination of straight and S curve implies gap graded aggregates which can be used in sub base.

Recent Advancements in Geotechnical Engineering - NCRAG'21   Materials Research Forum LLC
Materials Research Proceedings 19 (2021) 123-132   https://doi.org/10.21741/9781644901618-16

If none of the above conditions occur, aggregate may be graded as poorly graded[4]. The figure 4 consists of Sieve Analysis test on coarse aggregate.

Figure 4.Sieve analysis test on coarse aggregate

Impact value test on coarse aggregate
Toughness means the property of a material to resist the sudden load. Since the movement of vehicle provides impact load on the aggregates, it is necessary to determine the impact value i.e., crushing value of aggregates. The impact value of aggregates is based on the sudden break applied by the vehicle and the load of the vehicle which acts as the compressive load on the aggregates, due to sudden break. The impact value of aggregates should not exceed 30% and 45% for the wearing course and base course respectively as per IS 2383-1963[5]. Hence the given aggregate can be used for subgrade, base and surface course. As we done the aggregate impact value of coarse aggregate is 8.54%.The type of pavement where the aggregate can be used is wearing course and Base course. The figure 5 consists of Impact value test on coarse aggregate.

Figure 5.Impact value test on coarse aggregate

Crushing value test on coarse aggregate

The crushing value of coarse aggregate it gives a relative measure and it is crushing an aggregate under gradually applying compressive load. This coarse aggregate gives more strength for the road construction. Aggregate with lower crushing value and it give long service life to the road. The broken coarse aggregate or crushed aggregate can be used for the highway. The aggregate used in the road construction should be strong bonder roller traffic. According to IS: 9376-1979 the crushing value of good quality aggregates to be used in base course and surface course shall not exceed 45% and shall not be less than 30%respectively[6]. As we done the crushing strength of given aggregate sample is 6.14%.The figure 6 shows crushing value test on coarse aggregate.

Figure 6. *Crushing value test on coarse aggregate*

Attrition value test on coarse aggregate

Attrition test is a combination of the impact test and the abrasion test, because the stones are impacted due to the drop during rotation of the cylinder and the stone dust formed acts as an abrasive between the metal pieces. This property is quite essential in a road stone to be used in water bound macadam road and bitumen painted roads. Aggregate attrition value is below 2% and the quality is very good, the value is 2 to2.5% and the quality is good, the value is 2.5 to 3.1% and the quality is fairly, the value is 3.1 to 4.0% and the quality is poor and the value is

over 4% and the quality is very poor[9]. As we done the Attrition aggregate test and the value is 1.1% and the quality of the aggregate is very good. The figure 7 shows attrition value test on coarse aggregate.

Figure 7. Attrition value test on coarse aggregate

Abrasion value test on coarse aggregate

Abrasion Value of the aggregates is determined in order to determine their resistance against wearing due to the movement of traffic. When fast moving traffic fitted with pneumatic tyres on the wheels move on the road, the soil particles present between the road surface and the tyres cause abrasion of the road surface. As per IS: 10070 - 1982 the abrasion value should not be more than 30% and 50% for wearing surfaces and concrete other than wearing surface respectively[7]. As we done the abrasion test the value is 0.57% and it can be used for wearing courses and for concrete. Abrasion testing machine is shown in figure 8 on coarse aggregate.

Figure 8 .*Abrasion value test on coarse aggregate*

Flakiness index of coarse aggregate

The aggregates are flaky and are not desirable because the large number of flaky aggregates creates more voids, which in turn requires large amount of water and fine materials for the same workability, since such shapes offer more surface area for lubrication. It also tends to harm durability and the particles tend to causing limitations. Flakiness index or elongation index is the weight of flaky of elongated particles measured as percentage of the total weight of the sample. Flakiness index in excess of 35 to 40 percent is considered undesirable. No limits for elongation index are known to have been prescribed as yet. According to IS: 383-2016 the flakiness index should not exceed 40%. As we done the flakiness index of the aggregates the value is 1.13%. The figure 9 consists of Flakiness index of coarse aggregate [8].

Figure 9.*Flakiness index of coarse aggregate*

Elongation index of coarse aggregate
The elongation index of coarse aggregate is the percentage by weight of particles whose greatest dimension or length is greater than 1.8 times their mean dimension. This test is not applicable to aggregates of size smaller than 6.3 mm. According to IS: 383-2016 the Elongation index should not exceed 40%[8]. As we done the Elongation index of the aggregates the value is 20.26%. The figure 10 consists of Elongation index of coarse aggregate.

Figure 10.Elongation index of coarse aggregate

Experimental work on bitumen
Specific gravity test on bitumen
A knowledge of the correct specific gravity of bituminous materials have mainly two application convert the specified bitumen content by weight of volume basis when the binder is measured by volume is necessary to know the coefficient of expansion or the specific gravity values at different temperatures. Second, the specific gravity is useful to identify the source of a bituminous binder. Pure bitumen has a specific gravity in the range from 0.97 to 1.02[4]. Thus it is possible for a qualitative estimation of mineral impurity in bitumen. Table 1 gives the specific gravity values of different samples. The figure 11 & 12 consists of Specific gravity test on Bitumen.

Penetration test on bitumen
To determine the consistency, this test is conducted on the bitumen. It is expressed as the distance in tenths of a millimeter that a standard needle it penetrates through vertically in to specimen of penetration test of a specified temperature. Penetration values of different proportions of coconut shell charcoal ash in bitumen. The penetration test followed by IS code 1203-1978. The figure 13 & 14 consists of penetration test on bitumen [9]. Table 2 gives the corresponding values for different samples.

Table 1 specific gravity values of different samples

Test samples	Value
100 % of Bitumen	1.1
Bitumen + 4.5% Coconut Shell Charcoal ash	1.05
Bitumen + 5% Coconut Shell Charcoal ash	1.06
Bitumen + 5.5% Coconut Shell Charcoal ash	1.08
Bitumen + 6% Coconut Shell Charcoal ash	1.1

Figure 11.Specific gravity test on bitumen

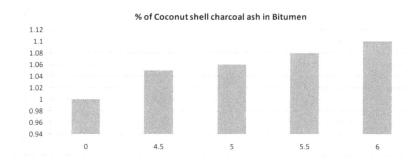

Figure 12.Specific gravity test on bitumen

Table 2 Penetration test values of different samples

Test samples	Value
100 % of Bitumen	70
Bitumen + 4.5% Coconut Shell Charcoal ash	83
Bitumen + 5% Coconut Shell Charcoal ash	91
Bitumen + 5.5% Coconut Shell Charcoal ash	95
Bitumen + 6% Coconut Shell Charcoal ash	99

Figure 13.Penetration test on bitumen

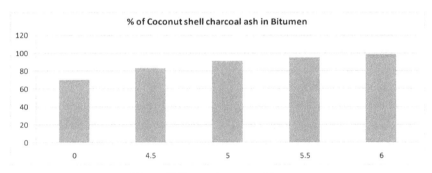

Figure 14.Penetration test on bitumen

Conclusion

From the test results, it is concluded that by using coconut shell charcoal ash as a filler materialin bitumen for the road construction shall be 0%, 4.5%, 5%, 5.5%, 6%. Laboratory tests were conducted for the modified bitumen and compared with the 100% bitumen test results. The addition of coconut shell ash in the bitumen improves the properties of bitumen in all aspects, which helps to improve the lifespan of the bitumen. After analyzing the tests, it has been inferenced that the results of modified bitumen have more workability than 100 percent bitumen. From the properties of all modified bitumen, we conclude that the values are increasing and giving better strength and has better to be used in highway construction.

References

[1] M. Mohan, K.M. Hussaina, I. Easa, M.K. Faisal, M.A.K. A, Bitumen Modification Using Crumb Rubber and Partial Replacement of Fine Aggregates Using Coconut Shell, Int. J. Innovative Research. Managem. Eng. Technol. 4 (2019).

[2] R.P. Jaya, M.R. Hainin, K.A. Masri, Performance of Charcoal Coconut Shell Ash in the Asphalt Mixture under Long Term Aging, Int. J. Recent Technol. Eng. 8 (2019) 383–387. https://doi.org/10.35940/ijrte.C1010.1183S319

[3] S. Dung Dung, Assessment of the Suitability of Coconut Shell Charcoal As Filler in Stone Matrix Asphalt, (2014).

[4] S.K. Dr.Khanna, C.E.. Dr.Justo, A. Dr.Veeraragavan, Highway Engineering, 2015.

[5] IS 2386- Part III, Method of Test for aggregate for concrete. Part III- Specific gravity, density, voids, absorption and bulking, Bur. Indian Stand. New Delhi. (1963) (Reaffirmed2002).

[6] M. Kisan, S.Sangathan, J. Nehru, S.G. Pitroda, मानक, (1979).

[7] M. Kisan, S. Sangathan, J. Nehru, S.G. Pitroda, मानक, (1982).

[8] Bureau of Indian Standards (BIS), Concrete Mix Proportioning- Guidelines, Bur. IndianStand. Second Rev (2019) 1–40. https://doi.org/10.1201/9780429285196-1

[9] IS: 1201-1220, Indian standard methods for testing tar and bituminous materials., Bur.Indian Stand. (1978) 1st Revision.

Model Tests on Use of Tyre Chips and Fly Ash Chips as a Replacement of Aggregate in Stone Columns

V. Naveenraj[1,a*], P. Kulanthaivel[1, b], S. Velmurugan[3, c], M. Arun Kumar[1, d*]and Prabakaran[2, e]

[1*] Assistant Professor, Department of Civil Engineering, Kongu Engineering College, Perundurai, Erode, Tamil Nadu, India

[2] PG Scholar, Department of Civil Engineering, Kongu Engineering College, Perundurai, Erode, Tamil Nadu, India

[3] Assistant Professor, Department of Civil Engineering, Bannari Amman Institute of Technology, Sathyamangalam, Erode, Tamil Nadu, India

[a]naveenraj.civil@kongu.edu,[b]pkulanthaicivil@gmail.com,[c]velmurugan@bitsathy.ac.in, [d]rsmanoharun@gmail.com, [e]praba_27@icloud.com

Keywords: Tyre Chips, Fly Ash Brick Chips, Aggregates, Soft Clay, Stone Columns, Load Carrying Capacity, Settlements, Comparison

Abstract. In order to reduce the generated waste in industry the concept of reusability is adopted as an application in the civil engineering field. In this study, the experiments were performed by using shredded tyre chips, chips of fly ash bricks in partial replacement with aggregates passing through 12.5 mm sieve and retaining on 10 mm sieve (IS-Indian standard). The experiments with partial replacement of stone columns were carried out at various proportions of tyre chips and fly ash brick chips in soft clay. Corresponding settlement rate was noted by loading the stone column gradually through a hydraulic jack for various L/D ratios. On comparison the final results it was concluded that the stone column with replacement of 75% tyre chips and 25% coarse aggregate proved good to carry maximum load and with lower settlement rate than ordinary stone column without replacement.

Introduction

Tyre chips are one of the major wastes generated from the industries now-a-days which alarms to environmental pollution. As major environmental thread is caused by Land filling and burning of tyres, researches are being undergoing to use the tyre chips in effective manner. From survey of the tyres that were scrapped, 43% were burnt as tire-derived fuel, with cement manufacturing the largest user, in another 25% were used to make ground rubber, 8% were used in civil engineering projects, 17% were disposed of in landfills and 8% had other uses In geotechnical engineering perspective the waste tyre chips [1] has low density, high strength, low thermal conductivity, durability, resilience, high frictional strength and hydrophobic nature.

Reviews about the use of scrap tyres, shredded tyres as a soil mixtures and various evaluation of chemical compositions, sorption capacity, environmental sustainability and reusability of waste tyres in geotechnics has been viewed [2]. When coarse aggregate is partially replaced with waste tyre chips and fly ash chips it helps to improve the strength parameter like load bearing capacity and reduce the settlement characteristics of the Clay soil [3].

Soil sample collection and tests
Soil sample for test is collected from Vellode of erode district. The sample is then distorted to certain range from its solidity and the basic tests were carried out in laboratory. Sieve analysis is done for the collected sample for gradation of the soil and it is classified as fine grained soil of size less than .002mm which belongs to Clay type soil[4].

Characteristics of materials used
Clayey soil
For the study, the soil is taken as Soft Clay. The various index properties of Soft clay such as moisture content, liquid limit, plasticity [5], specific gravity, density and engineering properties such as compressibility, consolidation [6] was carried out in the laboratory as per the procedures recommended by Indian Standards (IS) Codes. The properties of Soft clay is studied [7] and values are showed in the table 1.

Table 1. Properties of Soil

Property of soil	Vellode clay soil
Soil Classification	CI
Specific Gravity	2.5
Liquid Limit (%)	37
Plastic Limit (%)	16
Plastic Index (%)	21

Tyre chips
Radial tyre is used for taking the tyre chips for the experiments shown in Figure1. The scaling Factor used in test is 1/10 .Tyre chips which passes through 12.5 mm sieve and retains on 10mm sieve as per IS codes was taken [8].The properties of Tyre chips is showed in the table 2. Various tests for tyre chips has been carried in laboratory such as water absorption, tensile strength, compression and Specific gravity. For carrying the test with soft clay, various comparative study has been made through the existing researches and experiments [9].Thus the usage of tyre chips not only reduces the waste but it also helps in saving the natural resources, energy and to increase the stability of soft soil[1].

Figure 1. Tyrechips

Table2. Tyrechipsproperties

Specific Gravity of tyre chips	1.14%
Water absorption of tyre chips	4%

Coarse aggregate
As the comparison is made with tyre chips and fly ash brick chips the similar size is taken for the coarse aggregate also. The coarse aggregate of size passing through 12.5 mm sieve and retains on 10mm sieve was taken [4]. Flakiness and Elongation properties of coarse aggregates were found.The properties of coarse aggregate [10] is showed in the table 3.

Table3.Coarse aggregate properties

Specific gravity of coarse aggregate	2.6
Water absorption of coarse aggregate	2.5%
Crushing value of aggregate	12.18

Fly ash brick chips
Fly ash brick chips of size passing through 12.5 mm sieve and which retains on 10mm sieve was taken as an alternate replacement material for coarse aggregate [5]. Basic tests for Fly ash brick chips are carried out at Laboratory [10] and material sizes are shown in table 4.

Table 4. Sizes of materials used

Materials	Size (mm)
Coarse aggregate	10
Tyre chips	10
Fly Ash Brick chips	10
Clay Soil	4.25

Test setup
The Cylinder tank made of cast iron having height of 410 mm was used. It is shown in figure 2 and mould dimensions are shown in table 5 .The wall thickness of the tank was 3mm and diameter of the tank is 250mm.The scaling factor used in test model was 1/10.The diameter of the stone column is 45 mm with the height of 270mm placed at the center of the tank corresponding to L/D ratio(Length of the column to diameter of the column equal to 6).The load was given through the proving ring at a constant rate of 25mm/min vertically over the stone column by placing a circular disc over the column for uniform distribution of load.

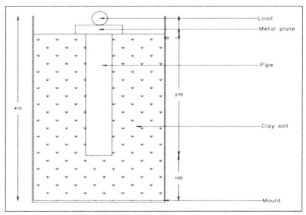

Figure 2. Mould

Table 5. Mould dimensions

Mould Dimensions in mm	
Height	410
Inner diameter of mould	250
Outer diameter of mould	256
Thickness of mould	3
Material of mould	Cast iron

Formation of clay bed
The empty tank is first filled by grease around the inner wall in order to reduce the friction between the clay and cylinder. The water content of soft clay is maintained properly and periodical test was carried.

The soft clay is placed as layers in tank [11] and compacted manually by hands to ensure the even spread of soil inside the tank without Air traps. The clay is filled up to certain height in the tank.

Formation of stone column
The centre of the tank is marked in proper position so that Load can be distributed uniformly. The column is designed in such a way that it can reused. The material used for the pipe column is Polyvinyl chloride (PVC) of diameter 45mm and thickness of 3mm diameter.

The PVC pipe is applied by greases on both sides for friction purpose. At base 100 mm is filled with clay. Then the PVC Pipe column is placed at the centre and tyre chips are placed layer by layer with well compaction with great care to ensure proper compaction [12].

The pipe is fully filled and surrounded with clay uniformly up to height of 270 mm and the pipe was slowly taken out at each layer when outside clay soil is filled uniformly and its behavior is notes [13]. This procedure is carried out for other proportions of tyre chips, fly ash aggregates and coarse aggregates [14].

Procedure for Testing

The apparatus is placed on the testing machine for testing. The Load is given at center of the column. The L/D ratio considered for the test is 6.

The load was given and respective settlement values are noted[3] shown in figure 3.

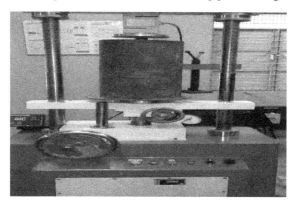

Figure 3. A shows the loading of clay soil through hydraulic jack with constantly increasing loading.

Result and discussion

The behavior of Tyre chips, Stone Aggregate and Fly ash brick chips are compared and shown in following bar chart .From the chart it is noted that the load settlement behavior of the proportion is not in linear form. All the test were carried out at carried the same compacted density of 5-7 KN/m3 .The graph of all proportions shows various rates of settlement with respect to load. The proportions are made in order to reuse the waste materials in construction field. As a result of using coarse aggregate as a column filler it gives raise in cost which does not leads to efficiency.

The graph shows the settlement rate of each proportion. It helps to compare the proportions for better usage in construction. On comparison 50% proportions shows good capacity of load bearing. But on specific 75% coarse and 25% tyre chips shows high load bearing capacity along with cost efficiency which make the soft clay more stable than other composition. It is noted that the mechanical properties of coarse and tyre chips with proper proportion shows a better bearing capacity of load as they could withstand for higher load. The crushing properties of coarse and tyre seems to hold good for the soft clay soil.80% of combinations of Coarse Aggregate (80%) with Fly Ash brick chips (20 %) shows that the proportion could hold load better but not as of 75% proportion.

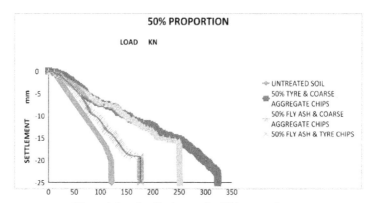

Figure 4. Load vs Settlement for 50% proportion

The above figure 4 shows the various combinations of 50% proportions such as 50%tyre chips and coarse aggregate, 50%fly ash and coarse aggregate, 50% fly ash and tyre chips. The graph gives a clear view of comparison between three proportions with untreated soil with respect to load and settlement. It shows the load increment given to the column and respective settlement rate of the proportion.

From the graph it is inferred that the rate of settlement of coarse aggregate with fly ash proportion withstand high load than fly ash with coarse aggregate proportion. The untreated soil has lesser strength to bear the load given to it due to its nature. The proportion of fly ash and tyre chips fails sooner than other proportion since the fly ash initially crushes faster than coarse aggregate. Along with tyre chips, fly ash combination shows greater settlement at initial stage itself.

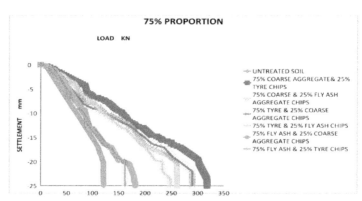

Figure 5. Load vs Settlement for 75% proportion

The figure 5 shows the various combinations of 75% proportions such as Tyre chips (75%) with Coarse Aggregate (25 %), Coarse Aggregate (25%) with Fly Ash brick chips (75 %), Aggregate

(75%) with Fly Ash brick chips (25 %), Tyre chips (25%) with Fly Ash brick chips (75 %), Tyre chips (75%) with Fly Ash brick chips (25 %) and Tyre chips (25%) with Coarse Aggregate (75 %).

The graph gives a clear view of comparison between three proportions with untreated soil .It shows the load increment given to the column and respective settlement rate of the proportion. From the graph it is inferred that the rate of settlement of coarse aggregate with tyre chips proportion withstand high load than other proportions. The untreated soil fails soon as it could not carry load further.

From this it is noted that the mechanical properties of coarse and tyre chips with proper proportion shows a better bearing capacity of load as they could withstand for higher load. The crushing properties of the coarse and tyre seems to hold good for the test shown in figure 6.

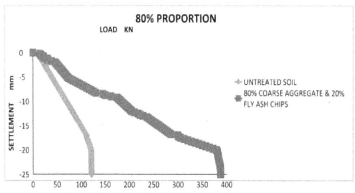

Figure 6. Load vs Settlement for 80 % proportion

The graph shows the combinations of 80% of combinations of Coarse Aggregate (80%) with Fly Ash brick chips (20 %).The graph gives a clear view of comparison between three proportions with untreated soil and the proportion. It shows the load increment given to the column and respective settlement rate of the proportion.

From the graph it is inferred that the rate of settlement of coarse aggregate and fly ash chips is higher than the untreated soil loading capacity shown in figure 6. The untreated soil fails since the soil has lesser strength to bear the load given to it due to its nature.

The figure 7 shows the combinations of 100% proportions such as 100% tyre chips, 100% coarse aggregate, 100% fly ash chips. The graph gives a comparison between three proportions with untreated soil .It shows the load increment given to the column and respective settlement rate of the proportion. From the graph it is inferred that 100% coarse aggregate carries approximately 420 KN load than other proportion. When untreated soil is loaded it gets settled at minimum load due to its property. Next to coarse aggregate, the tyre chips of considered size prove to hold good to withstand load up to certain level.

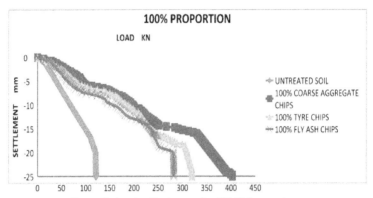

Figure 7. Load vs Settlement for 100 % Proportion

Conclusion

From overall Model test it is observed and noted that the combination 75% tyre chips and 25% coarse aggregate when compared with other combination such as 50% tyre chips and 50% coarse aggregate, 75 % coarse aggregate and 25% tyre chips, 100% tyre chips, 100% coarse aggregate chips, 100 % fly ash brick chips shows a better result and Load Carrying Capacity with lesser settlement rate. From the inferred result, replacement of stone aggregate with specific range will reduce the construction cost and can enhance the strength and settlement capacity of the column [15]. Thus usage of tyre chips does not affect the quality of groundwater and pollute the environment. It can be a better way to reduce the waste material. The graph and the settlements values are based on the test carried out in the laboratory with the objective of reusability of waste materials in construction practice.

References

[1] A. Al-Tabbaa, O. Blackwell, S. Porter, An investigation into the geotechnical properties of soil-tyre mixtures, Environmental technology. 18 (1997) 855-860. https://doi.org/10.1080/09593331808616605

[2] D. Tapas, S. Baleshwar, Benefits and impacts of scrap tyre use in geotechnical engineering, J. Environ. Res. Develop. 7 (2013) 1262-1271.

[3] S. Malarvizhi, K. Ilamparuthi, Load versus settlement of clay bed stabilized with stone and reinforced stone columns, Proceeding of the 3rd Asian Regional Conference on Geosynthetics, GEOASIA Seoul, Korea, 2004. pp. 322-329.

[4] S. Verma, S. Akhtar, S. Shrivastava, Assessment of Particles of Varied Soil By Grain Size Analysis–A Case Study in Jabalpur MP, International Journal of Engineering Research and Application. 7 (2017) 32-37. https://doi.org/10.9790/9622-0707093237

[5] A. Sridharan, H. Nagaraj, Plastic limit and compaction characteristics of finegrained soils, Proceedings of the institution of civil engineers-ground improvement. 9 (2005) 17-22. https://doi.org/10.1680/grim.2005.9.1.17

[6] S.-A. Tan, T.-S. Tan, L.C. Ting, K.-Y. Yong, G. Karunaratne, S.-L. Lee, Determination of consolidation properties for very soft clay, Geotechnical Testing Journal. 11 (1988) 233-240. https://doi.org/10.1520/GTJ10653J

[7] T. Kokusho, Y. Yoshida, Y. Esashi, Dynamic properties of soft clay for wide strain range, Soils and Foundations. 22 (1982) 1-18. https://doi.org/10.3208/sandf1972.22.4_1

[8] H. Moo-Young, K. Sellasie, D. Zeroka, G. Sabnis, Physical and chemical properties of recycled tire shreds for use in construction, Journal of Environmental Engineering. 129 (2003) 921-929. https://doi.org/10.1061/(ASCE)0733-9372(2003)129:10(921)

[9] A. Priyadarshee, D. Gupta, V. Kumar, V. Sharma, Comparative study on performance of tire crumbles with fly ash and kaolin clay, International Journal of Geosynthetics and Ground Engineering. 1 (2015) 1-7. https://doi.org/10.1007/s40891-015-0033-3

[10] H. Liu, S.K. Banerji, W.J. Burkett, J. Van Engelenhoven, Environmental properties of fly ash bricks, World of Coal Ash, USA, (2009).

[11] R. Shivashankar, M.D. Babu, S. Nayak, V. Rajathkumar, Experimental studies on behaviour of stone columns in layered soils, Geotechnical and Geological Engineering. 29 (2011) 749. https://doi.org/10.1007/s10706-011-9414-0

[12] A. Zahmatkesh, A. Choobbasti, Settlement evaluation of soft clay reinforced by stone columns, considering the effect of soil compaction, International Journal of Research and Reviews in Applied Sciences. 3 (2010) 159-166.

[13] W.-S. Bae, B.-W. Shin, B.-C. An, J.-S. Kim, Behaviors of foundation system improved with stone columns, The Twelfth International Offshore and Polar Engineering Conference, International Society of Offshore and Polar Engineers, 2002.

[14] R. Ayothiraman, S. Soumya, Model tests on the use of tyre chips as aggregate in stone columns, Proceedings of the Institution of Civil Engineers-Ground Improvement. 168 (2015) 187-193. https://doi.org/10.1680/grim.13.00006

[15] J. Castro, M. Karstunen, N. Sivasithamparam, Influence of stone column installation on settlement reduction, Computers and Geotechnics. 59 (2014) 87-97. https://doi.org/10.1016/j.compgeo.2014.03.003

Recent Advancements in Geotechnical Engineering - NCRAG'21   Materials Research Forum LLC
Materials Research Proceedings **19** (2021) 142-149   https://doi.org/10.21741/9781644901618-18

Mechanical Strength Study on C&D Aggregates Replaced Concrete

S. Suchithra[1,a] and S. Jayashree[2,b*]

[1]Associate Professor, Department of Civil Engineering, Kongu Engineering College, Erode, Tamilnadu, India

[2]PG Student, Department of Civil Engineering, Kongu Engineering College, Erode, Tamilnadu, India

[a]suchithra.civil@kongu.edu, [b]jayashreesiva22@gmail.com

Keywords: Recycled Coarse Aggregates, Accelerated Steam Curing, Water Absorption, Construction and Demolition Waste

Abstract. Recycled concrete was produced to overcome the problem of disposal of construction and demolition waste and lack of availability of natural materials. To improve the characteristics of recycled concrete, new treatments and suggestions were given by the researchers. This paper investigates the compressive strength of recycled aggregate concrete having the replacement of 0, 30, 40, 50 & 60% recycled coarse aggregates. The compressive strength of recycled concrete in water curing is compared with steam curing. The compressive strength of concrete is not much affected because of the use of large size recycled aggregates. The use of saturated dried surface large size recycled aggregates improves the strength of concrete.

Introduction

Day by day technology and innovations were improving, which helps mankind to save their energy. On the other side, the originality of the materials was becoming down. To replace natural products, many artificial products were introduced by mankind. Likewise, the lack of availability of natural materials was replaced by recycled materials. Generally, these recycled materials don't provide the 100% originality and purity of the corresponding natural materials. By implementing some methods, the recycled materials shall meet the properties of natural materials closely. The recycling process will be carried out using the waste materials. This process also helps to reduce the disposal of wastes. In this way, Construction and Demolition Waste (C&DW) is one of the major wastes carried out for disposal regularly in the disposal site areas [1]. Some of these wastes are used as embankments, landfills, road fills. But the quantity of these wastes cannot be reduced greatly. To overcome the problem of lack of availability of natural materials and reduction of disposal wastes, the production of recycled concrete is the better solution. The recycled concrete had existed for research work in 90's, but for the usage in real-time structures till now it is not boomed. The main reason is the lack of confidence among the people in the recycled materials[2]. Recycled concrete shall be produced by adding or replacing one or more materials in the concrete. The use of recycled materials is more if the replacement is carried out in the coarse aggregates other than the replacement in cement or fine aggregates. Also, the replacement of natural coarse aggregates with recycled coarse aggregates provides better results [3]. Many researchers suggested that the natural coarse and fine aggregates in the concrete shall be replaced with 25-30% of the C&D waste, which will not provide the greater difference in the strength aspects of the conventional concrete [4–6]. But to replace more than the suggested quantity, some of the treatments should be carried out for the recycled materials. The main drawback for the strength

Recent Advancements in Geotechnical Engineering - NCRAG'21   Materials Research Forum LLC
Materials Research Proceedings 19 (2021) 142-149   https://doi.org/10.21741/9781644901618-18

loss in the recycled coarse aggregate concrete (RCAC) is the attached mortar of recycled materials [7]. Hence the use of well-washed recycled materials improves the characteristics of the recycled concrete [8]. This paper investigates the workability and compressive strength of the washed RCAC. Also, the compressive strength behaviour of recycled concrete with water curing and accelerated steam chamber curing is compared.

Materials
Cement
The type of cement used for this study is the Ordinary Portland Cement (grade 53).

Fine aggregates
The fine aggregates obtained from the river sand having the size of 4.75mm sieve passed are used.

Coarse aggregates
The well-graded natural aggregates are obtained from the quarry. The recycled aggregates that are obtained from the concrete laboratory wastes shown in fig.1 and the demolition waste of residential buildings. These wastes are crushed using the hammer and heavy materials to separate the aggregates. The use of large size recycled aggregates doesn't affect the strength properties greatly [9]. Hence, the size of the recycled aggregates used in the concrete mix is passed in a 20mm sieve and retained in a 12.5mm sieve. The attached mortar and dust are removed partially.

Fig.1 Crushed recycled coarse aggregates

Superplasticizer
The grade of concrete adopted was M30. Hence as per IS 10262:2019, the superplasticizer (sp) should be used for a high grade of concrete [10]. The sp used in this study was a polycarboxylic ether-based superplasticizer.

Concrete Mixture
Five different concrete mix was prepared, they are conventional concrete (CC), recycled aggregate concrete with the replacement of 30% natural aggregates (RAC-1), recycled aggregate concrete with replacement of 40% natural aggregates (RAC-2), recycled aggregate concrete with 50% recycled aggregates (RAC-3), recycled aggregate concrete with 60% recycled aggregates

(RAC-4). The hand mix is carried out for concrete. The adopted Water-Cement ratio is 0.4. The coarse aggregates were added in saturated dried surface condition, hence the amount of water to be used for all the mix is the same. The concrete mix proportion per cubic meter is tabulated in Table.1.

Table.1 – Concrete mix proportion

Description	Cement (kg/m^3)	Natural coarse aggregates (kg/m^3)	Recycled coarse aggregates (kg/m^3)	Fine aggregates (kg/m^3)	W/C ratio	Superplasticizer (kg/m^3)
CC	415	1049.3	0	852.08	0.4	4.12
RAC-1	415	734.51	314.79	852.08	0.4	4.12
RAC-2	415	629.58	419.72	852.08	0.4	4.12
RAC-3	415	524.65	524.65	852.08	0.4	4.12
RAC-4	415	419.72	629.58	852.08	0.4	4.12

Test of Coarse aggregates
Water absorption test
The test is carried out between the 4 different coarse aggregates. Natural coarse aggregates - NA, recycled coarse aggregates procured from concrete laboratory - RAL, recycled coarse aggregates procured from the demolition wastes - RAD, a combination of recycled coarse aggregates procured from concrete laboratory and demolition waste - CRA were tested.

Specific gravity test
The specific gravity test on natural aggregates and recycled coarse aggregates - CRA wereconducted.

Test on Concrete
Workability test
The fresh concrete test is carried out with a slump cone. A slump cone test was carried out for all five concrete mixes.

Compressive strength test
The test is carried out using a 150x150x150mm cube. Curing of concrete is carried out in twoways – water curing and accelerated steam curing. The 7-day and 28-day compressive strength was tested. And the steam curing is carried in the accelerated steam curing chamber at 100°C for 3 hours.

Results and Discussion
Tests on Coarse aggregates
The water absorption rate of RCA's was greater than the natural coarse aggregates. Compared to all other aggregates the combined recycled coarse aggregates – CRA absorbs more water. The water absorption capacity is more in recycled aggregates due to the presence of attached mortar and pores. This absorption rate of aggregates may affect the concrete at later ages. Table.2 shows

Recent Advancements in Geotechnical Engineering - NCRAG'21   Materials Research Forum LLC
Materials Research Proceedings **19** (2021) 142-149   https://doi.org/10.21741/9781644901618-18

the water absorption rate and a specific gravity of all four types of aggregates. The specific gravity of natural and recycled aggregates does not show much variation.

Table.2 – Water absorption and a specific gravity of samples

Description	Water absorption rate	Specific gravity
NA	1.96	2.79
RAL	8.42	2.65
RAD	6.38	2.69
CRA	9.67	2.67

Workability test
The result of the workability test on all five concrete mixes was shown in Fig.2. Since all the aggregates are allowed to absorb enough water before mixing, the workability of concrete is not affected greatly. The workability of the conventional concrete is good enough for casting. Likewise, the workability of other concrete mixes does not vary much.

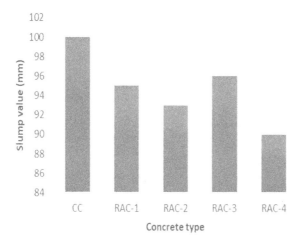

Fig.2 – Workability of conventional and recycled concrete

Compressive strength
The 7-day and 28-day compressive strength of the different types of concrete are shown in Fig.3.

Recent Advancements in Geotechnical Engineering - NCRAG'21
Materials Research Proceedings **19** (2021) 142-149

Materials Research Forum LLC
https://doi.org/10.21741/9781644901618-18

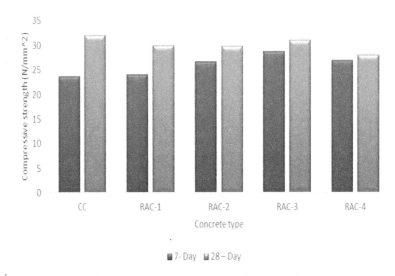

Fig.3 – Compressive strength of concrete

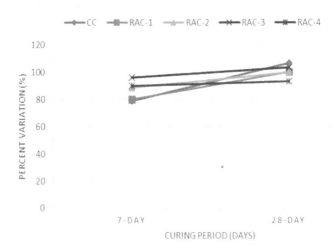

Fig.4 – Comparison between 7-d and 28-d compression strength

Recent Advancements in Geotechnical Engineering - NCRAG'21   Materials Research Forum LLC
Materials Research Proceedings **19** (2021) 142-149   https://doi.org/10.21741/9781644901618-18

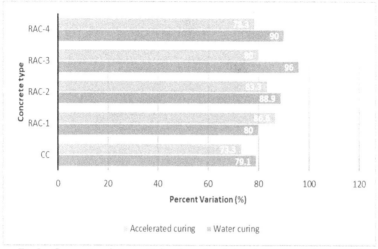

Fig.5 – Comparison between 7-d and accelerated curing compressive strength

From the above graph, it is well-known that the strength of 7-day curing and accelerated curing provides almost the same results. Through accelerated steam curing for 3 hours, the concrete shall attain 7-day compressive strength. Changes had been observed in 28-day compressive strength, when compared with 7-day and accelerated curing. The strength of conventional concrete achieved its 28-day compressive strength. As the curing period increases, the strength of all types of concrete is increased. Also, the compressive strength of concrete generally decreases with an increase in the replacement percent. Here the compressive strength of the recycled concrete increases with an increase in replacement percent to 50%. In RAC-4, the compressive strength decreases again. From fig.4, it is observed that the strength of conventional concrete increases from 79% to 106% as the curing period increases. Whereas, RAC-1, RAC-2, RAC-3 and RAC-4 shows the strength variation 80 to 100%, 88.9 to 99.6%, 96 to 103.3% and 90 to 93.3% respectively. Until the RAC-3 concrete mix, the concrete achieves its target mean strength. Compared to accelerated curing, the water curing compressive strength of concrete provides greater strength as shown in fig.5. But generally, steam curing provides better results if the curing period is increased. Because of less duration for curing, all the concrete mix attains the 7-day compressive strength nearly. The 50% replacement of RCA's in the concrete attains the target strength i.e., attains the strength of conventional concrete. Fig.6 exhibits the crack that propagated in the recycled aggregate concrete after the compression test.

Materials Research Forum LLC
https://doi.org/10.21741/9781644901618-18

Fig.6 – Compression test on Concrete

Conclusion

From the experimental investigation on RCAC and RCA's following conclusions were made,

- Due to the presence of more voids, the water absorption rate is greater in the recycled aggregates than the natural aggregates.
- The removal of specks of dust and attached mortar of recycled aggregates improves the properties of aggregates.
- The workability of concrete does not affect greatly because of the use of a superplasticizer.
- The use of large-size saturated dried-surface recycled aggregates helps to improve the compressive strength of concrete and also 50% replacement shall be carried out. Replacement of natural aggregates more than 50% reduces the strength of concrete.
- For non-structural applications, more than 50% replacement shall be done. For structural applications, 50% replacement shall be carried out along with the addition of sp and the use of large size recycled aggregates.
- Since the usage of recycled aggregates is more, it is better to implement mechanical equipment to separate the recycled aggregates from Demolition wastes and Concrete wastes.

References

[1] M.R. Ponnada, K. P, Construction and Demolition Waste Management – A Review, Int. J. Adv. Sci. Technol. 84 (2015) 19–46. https://doi.org/10.14257/ijast.2015.84.03.

[2] R. V. Silva, R. Neves, J. De Brito, R.K. Dhir, Carbonation behaviour of recycled aggregate concrete, Cem. Concr. Compos. 62 (2015) 22–32. https://doi.org/10.1016/j.cemconcomp.2015.04.017.

[3] C. Liang, H. Ma, Y. Pan, Z. Ma, Z. Duan, Z. He, Chloride permeability and the caused steel corrosion in the concrete with carbonated recycled aggregate, Constr. Build. Mater. 218 (2019) 506–518. https://doi.org/10.1016/j.conbuildmat.2019.05.136.

[4] B. Cantero, I.F. Sáez del Bosque, A. Matías, M.I. Sánchez de Rojas, C. Medina, Inclusion of construction and demolition waste as a coarse aggregate and a cement addition in structural concrete design, Arch. Civ. Mech. Eng. 19 (2019) 1338–1352. https://doi.org/10.1016/j.acme.2019.08.004.

[5] A. Juan-Valdés, D. Rodríguez-Robles, J. García-González, M.I. Sánchez de Rojas Gómez, M.

Recent Advancements in Geotechnical Engineering - NCRAG'21   Materials Research Forum LLC
Materials Research Proceedings **19** (2021) 142-149   https://doi.org/10.21741/9781644901618-18

Ignacio Guerra-Romero, N. De Belie, J.M. Morán-del Pozo, Mechanical and microstructural properties of recycled concretes mixed with ceramic recycled cement and secondary recycled aggregates. A viable option for future concrete, Constr. Build. Mater. (2020). https://doi.org/10.1016/j.conbuildmat.2020.121455.

[6] Z. Ma, W. Li, H. Wu, C. Cao, Chloride permeability of concrete mixed with activity recycled powder obtained from C&D waste, Constr. Build. Mater. 199 (2019) 652–663. https://doi.org/10.1016/j.conbuildmat.2018.12.065.

[7] A. Adessina, A. Ben Fraj, J.F. Barthélémy, C. Chateau, D. Garnier, Experimental and micromechanical investigation on the mechanical and durability properties of recycled aggregates concrete, Cem. Concr. Res. 126 (2019) 105900. https://doi.org/10.1016/j.cemconres.2019.105900.

[8] L. Restuccia, C. Spoto, G.A. Ferro, J.M. Tulliani, Recycled Mortars with C&D Waste, Procedia Struct. Integr. 2 (2016) 2896–2904. https://doi.org/10.1016/j.prostr.2016.06.362.

[9] R. Rao, Q. Deng, J. Fu, C. Liu, X. Ouyang, Y. Huang, Improvement of mechanical strength of recycled blend concrete with secondary vibrating approach, Constr. Build. Mater. 237 (2020) 117661. https://doi.org/10.1016/j.conbuildmat.2019.117661.

[10]   Bureau of Indian Standards (BIS), Concrete Mix Proportioning- Guidelines, Bur. Indian Stand. Second Rev (2019) 1–40.

Recent Advancements in Geotechnical Engineering - NCRAG'21
Materials Research Proceedings **19** (2021) 150-160

Materials Research Forum LLC
https://doi.org/10.21741/9781644901618-19

Investigation on Retrofitting of Reinforced Concrete Beam with Glass Fiber and Banana Fiber Mat

M. Rajendran[1,a] *, S. Sanjaygandhi[1,b], V. Senthilkumar[2,c] and
S. Ramakrishnan[3,d]

[1]Department of Civil Engineering, Bannari Amman Institute of Technology,
Sathyamangalam-638401, India

[2]Department of Civil Engineering, Sri Shakthi Institute of Engineering & Technology,
Coimbatore-641062, India

[3]Department of Civil Engineering, Sri Krishna College of Engineering and Technology,
Coimbatore-641008, India

[a]*rajendranm@bitsathy.ac.in, [b]sanjaygandhi.st19@bitsathy.ac.in, [c]civilvsk@gmail.com,
[d]ramakrishnans@skcet.ac.in

Keywords: Retrofitting, Reinforced Concrete Beam, Glass Fiber, Banana Fiber, Ultimate Load Carrying Capacity

Abstract. Concrete is the predominant material in the construction industry. To be sustainable, the old Reinforced Concrete (RC) buildings should be retrofitted, and the life of the building should be extended. Experimental study has been attempted to investigate the load carrying capacity of concrete beam strengthened with glass fiber and banana fiber mat. The primary aim of this study is to retrofit the RC beam specimen to enhance the load carrying capacity. All the beams were casted with the same grade of concrete (M30) and same structural detailing. Two-point symmetrical loading were given to the control beams to obtain load at initial crack and ultimate load. Then the beams other than control beams were loaded till it showes initial crack and then retrofitted with banana fiber and glass fiber bonded externally with resin. The retrofitted beams were tested for ultimate load performance. Load carrying capacity was higher for both retrofitting but the beam retrofitter with glass fiber showed significant improvement in the ultimate load carrying capacity.

Introduction

Reinforced concrete is one of the most important materials in the construction field. Concrete related structures are to be damaged due to several reasons after their life time. In such cases the damaged portion of the structures is difficult to replace because of financial issues and time duration. The alternative remedy for repairing the damaged structure is retrofitting instead of replacing the structure.

Retrofitting is all about the process of strengthening the older buildings, damaged structures such as heritage buildings, bridges etc., It lowers the risk of damage to an existing structure. Retrofitted specimen helps to minimize the further damage of the structure. This paper reports about the strengthening of reinforced concrete beam using glass fiber and banana fiber mat.

There are various types of glass fiber which differ only in the proportioning of their contents[1]. Synthetic fiber is added to the concrete mix to avoid the shrinkage cracking of plain concrete[2]. Concrete with self-curing agents would be a new development in the concrete construction industry[3]. Application of carbon fiber brings about very good improvement in strength but the failure is usually explosive in nature[4]. Melt spinning techniques are used in producing E-Glass fibers[5].

A comparative study on flexural strength of wrapped and unwrapped beams and found a higher ultimate load carrying capacity and initial crack load for wrapped beams compared to unwrapped beams[6]. Similar to the internal flexural steel reinforcement, the principal tensile fibers are oriented in the longitudinal axis of the beam[7]. The addition of polypropylene fibers to concrete reduces its unit weight while increasing its strength[8]. FRP sheets or plates are added to the tension face of the member for flexural strengthening[9].

Steel fiber reinforcement not only improves the material's hardness, impact and fatigue resistance, but it also improves the material's resistance against cracking[10]. Also, the weakness of plain concrete can be removed by inclusion of fibers in the mix[11]. Retrofitting with FRP sheets, especially GFRP sheets, was found to be the most suitable and cost-effective way to extend the service life of the beam[12]. The contribution of fibers in concrete towards flexural strength is smaller compared to the strength given by the rebar[13].

Various government bodies and academic institutions have consistently advocated the use of waste materials as an alternative construction material, such as fly ash, glass powder, and ground granular blast furnace slag (GGBS)[15].

There are various types of techniques to be followed for retrofitting the beam. Externally bonded glass fiber and banana fiber mat are used to retrofit the beam specimen. Uni-directional woven glass fiber sheet is utilized in current research and non-corrosive in nature.

Banana fiber is generally lignocelluloses material, consisting of helically wound cellulose micro fibers in amorphous matrix of lignin and hemi cellulose. Banana fibers have desirable mechanical properties due to their high cellulose content and low micro fibril angle. Lignin's are bound with hemicellulose and play an important role in lignocellulose materials' natural decay resistance.

In present investigation, M30 concrete grade is used. Mix design was done as per IS 10262: 2009 "Indian Standard Concrete Mix Proportioning – Guideline"[16]. Based on the above practice, a concrete proportion with a characteristics target compressive strength is designed. Experimental investigations have been carried out to find outthe enhancement of flexural strength of M30 grade concrete specimen. Thetests were conducted as per IScodalspecifications.

Materials

Cement, Fine and Coarse aggregate

Ordinary Portland Cement (OPC) of grade 53 was used in this study. Fine aggregate which only passes through 4.75mm sieve was sieved and selected. Manufacturing sand (M sand) derived from the granite stone quarry was used instead of natural river sand due to its scarcity. As far as coarse aggregate was concerned, 60 percent 20mm aggregate and 40 percent 12mm aggregate was used.

Glass fiber and Banana fiber mat

The glass fiber is an artificial thin material bonded with huge number of extremely fine fiber of glass (Refer with: Figure 1). Banana fiber is natural fiber obtained from pseudo stem of banana plant relatively with good mechanical properties (Refer with: Figure 1). The properties of glass fiber and banana fiber are given in the table 1.

Figure 1.Glass fiber   *Figure 2.Banana fiber mat*

Table 1. *Properties of Glass fiber and Banana fiber*

	Properties of glass fiber			Properties of banana fiber	
S.No	Test	Standard Value	Observed Value	Test	Observed Value
1	Width (cm)	100 ± 3	100	Tenacity	29.98g/Denier
2	Moisture content (%/mass)	0.2 max	0.15	Fineness	17.15
3	Loss on ignition (%/mass)	4.0 ± 2.20	4.05	Moisture regain	13.00%
4	Average mass/unit are (g/m^2)	450 ± 7	440	Elongation	6.54
5	%^{age} variation in mass per range	<19	8.90	Alcoben extractives	1.70%
6	Flexural strength of laminate Dry Wet	180 mint 135 mint	234 195	Total cellulose	81.80%
7	-	-	-	Alpha cellulose	61.50%
8	-	-	-	Residual gum	41.90%
9	-	-	-	Lignin	15.00%

GP Resin

General purpose polyester resign is unsaturated chemical which was mixed together with cobalt, catalyst (MKEP) forms a polyester resin. Mix proportion proposed for this resin to retrofit the beam is 1Kg of resin added with 10 ml of cobalt and 15 ml of catalyst (Refer with: Figure 3).

Figure 3. GP Resin

MixDesignofM30GradeConcreteUsingIs10262:2009 [13].
Mixproportion of conventional concrete of M30 grade.

Cement	=	497kg/m³
Fine aggregate	=	674 kg/m³
Coarse aggregate	=	1099kg/m³
Water	=	197kg/m³

Casting of Beams

Form work of mould and Beam casting

A wooden mould of dimension 150mm wide, 250mm deep and 1000mm length was used to cast the beam.Generally, concrete's tensile strength is neglected. 2 numbers of 12mm diameter Fe500 steel reinforcement were used in the tension and as well as compression zone. The stirrups will be 8mm diameter provided at 150 mm center to center spacing for the entire length. The structural detailing is shown in figure 4.a and 4.b.

All dimensions are in cm unless otherwise mentioned.

Figure 4(a). Reinforcement details

Figure 4(b).Beam reinforcement and casting

Curing

The casting of beam was done by placing the concrete in to the mould and compacted well for removing the voids. The curing was done for the time period of 28-day in curing tank(Refer with: Figure 5).

Figure 5. Curing of the specimen

Testing of beams

For testing of specimen, loading frame was used. The loading frame consists of steel column, beams, hydraulic jack, linear vertical displacement transducer and supports. The loading frame capacity was 750 kN. The beam placed over the two-point roller support leaving 50 mm from the ends of the beam. From the beam span remaining 900 mm was equally divided and three (Linear Variable Differential Transformer) LVDT were placed to determine the deflection of the beam. 2 numbers of LVDT were placed at $1/3^{rd}$ distance and one LVDT were placed at mid-point(Refer with: Figure 6). Initially the control beams were tested under two-point loading conditions to obtain the initial crack(Refer with: Figure 7.a), then the test was continued to determine the ultimate load carrying capacity of the beam and the type of failure occurred in the beam[14].

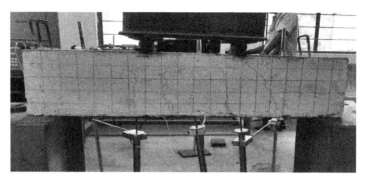

Figure 6. *Testing setup of the specimen*

Retrofitting of beams and Testing

The retrofitting on beams was carried out by pasting the fiber mat with the help of resin. The single layer wrapping technique is followed to retrofit the beam. All the beam specimens were loaded to get the initial cracks and then the experiment was stopped. Before wrapping the beam, the surface should be cleaned to make rough surface so that the resin sticks well in the surface of beam. After that the beam was coated with polystyrene resin and the fiber mat was wrapped well (Refer with: Figure 7.b & 7.c). Similar test was carried out for all the retrofitted beam specimens. From this retrofitted beam test, ultimate load and the maximum deflection of the beam was obtained(Refer with: Figure 7.d& 7.e).

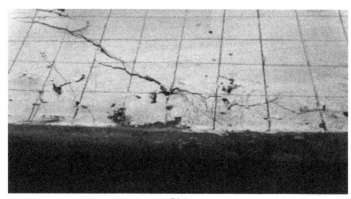

7(a)

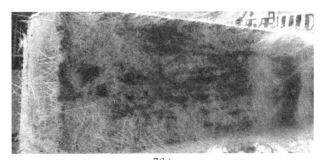

7(b)

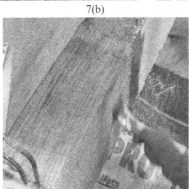

7(c)

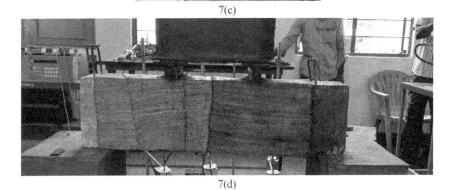

7(d)

7(e)

Figure 7. *(a) Beam with shear cracks, (b) Beam wrapped with glass fiber mat, (c) Beam wrapped with banana fiber mat, (d) Retrofitted banana fiber mat beam testing, (e) Retrofitted glass fiber mat beam testing.*

Result and Discussion

Load carrying capacity of control beam

Table 2 shows the Initial crack load in kN, Ultimate load in kN and maximum deflection in mm of control beam specimen. Throughout the study beam 1 and beam 2 is subjected to bending failure and shear failure respectively.

Table 2. Control Specimen results

S.no	Type of beam	Initial crack load in KN	Ultimate load in KN	Maximum deflection in mm
1	Control beam 1	90.0	200	3.2
2	Control beam 2	83.5	193	2.8

Load carrying capacity of retrofitted beam

Concrete beam are subjected to loading until it got initial cracks to replicate the damaged beam at site. Then the beams have retrofitted with wrapping of glass fiber and banana fiber on the periphery of the beam. Table 3 shows the Initial crack load in kN, Ultimate load in kN and maximum deflection in mm of retrofitted beam specimen.

Table 3. *Retrofitted Beam Specimens results*

S.no	Type of beam	Ultimate load inKN	Maximum deflection in mm	Average deflection in mm
1	Glass fiber 1	278	6.16	
2	Glass fiber 2	255	5.84	6
3	Banana fiber 1	245	3.5	
4	Banana fiber 2	232	4.5	4

Wrapping method of retrofitting significantly improved the ultimate load carrying capacity of beams irrespective of the type of fibers. Figure 8 indicates the load versus deflection graph of the control beam. The significant improvement was observed in the glass fiber mat wrapped beam with 39% and 32% in their ultimate load carrying capacity of the retrofitted beam(Refer with: Figure 9.a). Whereas only 22.5% and 20% increase was observed in banana natural fiber retrofitted beam specimen(Refer with: Figure 9.b).

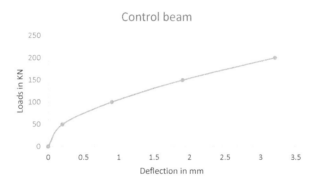

Figure 8.*Load vs. Deflection graph of control beam*

Even though natural banana fiber wrapping method of retrofitting has not shown the significant butt still it has around 20 % increase in the ultimate load carrying capacity of beam. For sustainable way of retrofitting, banana fiber mat method is adopted.

It is clear from the above graph that the flexibility of the reinforced concrete beam has increased along with its load carrying capacity after wrapping retrofitting. Especially the beam retrofitted with glass fiber's deflection has increased twice than that of the control beam.

Materials Research Forum LLC
https://doi.org/10.21741/9781644901618-19

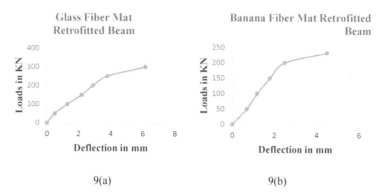

9(a)   9(b)

Figure 9. Load vs. Deflection graph of retrofitted beam of (a) Glass fiber mat, (b) Banana fiber mat.

Conclusion

This experimental study has been carried out to ascertain the performance of the wrapping retrofitting method with glass fiber and natural banana fiber mat.

1. This investigation indicates that externally wrapped glass fiber mat and banana fiber mat are an effective method to increase the structural load carrying capacity.

2. Significant increase in ultimate load carrying capacity was found in both the fiber mat retrofitted method, but Ultimate load carrying capacity of glass fiber wrapping retrofitted beam specimen has average of around 35% increase compared to the conventional beam.

3. Similarly significant improvement in the beam's flexibility was found and especially the beam retrofitted with glass fiber has twice the amount of deflection of control beam before it fails.

4. In allsituations, glass fiber mat wrapping retrofitted method has great performance compared to the natural banana fiber wrapping retrofitted method, but the natural banana fiber mat retrofitting method can be adopted in case of ecofriendly and sustainable situation.

References

[1] Sandeep G. Sawant, A. B. Sawant, M. B. Kumthekar, Strengthening of R.C.C. Beam-Using Different Glass Fiber, International Journal of Inventive Engineering and Sciences (IJIES) Volume 1, Issue 2(2013).

[2] T.Sirisha, A.V.S Sai kumar , B.Madhanna, Use of Discrete Fiber in Construction, International Journal of Innovative Research in Science, Engineering and Technology,Volume 5, Issue 8 (2016),pp. 15249-15253.

[3] Mohanraj A, Rajendran M, Ramesh A S, Mahalakshmi M, Manoj Prabhakar S, An Experimental Investigation of Eco-Friendly Self-Curing Concrete Incorporated with Polyethylene Glycol, International Advanced Research Journal in Science, Engineering andTechnology,Volume 1, Issue 2 (2014), pp. 85-89.

[4] Rahul Dev Bharti, Prof. Nitesh Khuswaha, Comparative Study on RCC Beams with & without Carbon Fiber Reinforced Polymer Using Ansys Software, International Journal of Trend in Scientific Research and Development (IJTSRD),Volume 4, Issue 1(2019), pp.478-482.

[5] P. Arulsivanantham, Experimental Study on usage of Class-E Glass Fiber in the Cement Concrete, International Journal of Engineering Research & Technology (IJERT), Volume 4, Issue 6 (2015), pp. 116-121. https://doi.org/10.17577/IJERTV4IS060183

[6] K.M. Mini, Rini John Alapatt, Anjana Elizabeth David, Aswathy Radhakrishnan, Minu Maria Cyriac and R. Ramakrishnan, Experimental study on strengthening of R.C beam using glass fiber reinforced composite, Structural Engineering and Mechanics, Volume 50, Number 3 (2014), pp.275-286. https://doi.org/10.12989/sem.2014.50.3.275

[7] T.P. Meikandaan, Dr. A. Ramachandra murthy, Retrofitting of reinforced concrete beams using GFRP overlays, International Journal of Civil Engineering and Technology (IJCIET), Volume 8, Issue 2 (2017), pp.423-439.

[8] Saman Khan, Roohul Abad Khan, Amadur Rahman Khan, Misbahul Islam, Saman Nayal, Mechanical properties of polypropylene fiber reinforced concrete for M25 & M30m mixes: a comparative study, International Journal of ScientificEngineering and Applied Science (IJSEAS), Volume 1, Issue 6 (2015).

[9] D.N. Shinde, Pudale Yojana M, Nair Veena V, Flexural Behaviour of Reinforced Cement Concrete Beam Wrapped with GFRP sheet, International Journal of Research in Engineering and Technology, Volume 3, Issue 30 (2014), pp.760-763. https://doi.org/10.15623/ijret.2014.0315143

[10] K.Srinivasa Rao, S.Rakesh kumar, A.Laxmi Narayana, Comparison of Performanceof Standard Concrete and Fiber Reinforced Standard Concrete Exposed to Elevated Temperatures, American Journal of Engineering Research (AJER), Volume 2, Issue 3 (2010), pp 20-26.

[11] Kavita S Kene, Vikrant S Vairagade and Satish Sathawane, Experimental Study on Behavior of Steel and Glass Fiber Reinforced Concrete Composites,Bonfring International Journal of Industrial Engineering and Management Science Volume 2, Number 4 (2012), pp. 125-130. https://doi.org/10.9756/BIJIEMS.1617

[12] T.P. Meikandaan, Dr. A. Ramachandra murthy, Retrofitting of Reinforced Concrete Beams using GFRP Overlays, International Journal of Civil Engineering and Technology (IJCIET),Volume 8, Issue 2 (2017), pp.423-439.

[13] Nanditha Mandava, Kallempudi Murali, M. Srinadh Reddy, M Narendranatha Reddy, Investigation of Reinforced Concrete Beams by Incorporating Polypropylene Fiber Reinforced Polymer Composites, International Journal of Civil Engineering and Technology (IJCIET),Volume 9, Issue 1, (2018), pp. 423-430.

[14] IS: 516-1959 (2006),Indian Standard Methods of Tests for Strength of Concrete, Bureau of Indian Standards, New Delhi, India.

[15] S. Shankarananth, B. Jaivignesh, Experimental Study on the use of Glass Powder, GGBS & Perlite in Flyash Bricks,International Journal of AdvancedResearch,Volume 4 (2016), pp 1381-1387. https://doi.org/10.21474/IJAR01/292

[16] IS:10262 (2009),Concrete Mix Proportioning-Guidelines, Bureau of Indian Standards, New Delhi, India.

Recent Advancements in Geotechnical Engineering - NCRAG'21
Materials Research Proceedings 19 (2021) 161-165

Materials Research Forum LLC
https://doi.org/10.21741/9781644901618-20

Investigation of Eco – Friendly Interlocking Masonry Units

M. Veerapathran[1,a], S. Arnesh[2,b*], M. Kishore Kumar[2,c], S. Rakeshwaran[2,d] and A. Sarankarthi[2,e]

[1]Assistant Professor (SG), Department of Civil Engineering, Dr.N.G.P Institute of Technology, Coimbatore-641 048, Tamil Nadu, India

[2]Final Year UG Students, Department of Civil Engineering, Dr.N.G.P Institute of Technology, Coimbatore-641 048, Tamil Nadu, India

[a]veerapathranm@drngpit.ac.in, [b*]smartsoundararnesh@gmail.com, [c]kishorekumarm17ce@drngpit.ac.in, [d]rakeshwarans17ce@drngpit.ac.in, [e]sarankarthia17ce@drngpit.ac.in

Keywords: Masonry Units, Interlocking Bricks, Soil, Male and Female Joints

Abstract. This project reveals about the detailed investigation of eco-friendly interlocking masonry units. Interlocking between individual units is enabled by providing grooves, male and female joint on them. Hence less mortar is required for construction of masonry units while using these interlocking bricks. Various trails and tests will be conducted on these interlocking bricks by addition of various materials such as E-wastes, coir pith and saw dust in clay soil. Hence the cost of these masonry units will be reduced. All these various mixtures are mixed at different proportions and ideal mixture are to be found then the grooves are to be altered by male and female joints. Further in addition of clay and sand, wooden powder and coir pith are to be added so that while burning of these masonry units results in good colour and more strength (35% improved strength while comparing to an A-Class brick). Optimum ratio with minimal cost and max efficiency with sustainability to the environment is recommended to the market. In the past year there was a spread of pandemic COVID 19. Precautious measures are taken to avoid the spread of this pandemic. By considering this situation a chemical is to be added in this masonry unit which will be acting as an disinfectious agent which will avoid the entry of various common viruses and bacteria like rhino viruses, salmonella. This ability of the masonry unit will last more than 24 months and beyond. And this can also be replenished after specific period of time. These masonry units have less mortar consumption (70% less mortar consumption while comparing to an A-Class brick), more workability, disinfectious and accommodates waste materials. Hence it is considered to be eco-friendly and sustainable.

Introduction

Masonry units covered by most standards include those made from normal and light weight concretes, calcium silicate, natural stone, fired clay, interlocking blocks etc., these masonry units are one of the most important part of the building. Nowadays these masonry units cost are costlier as the quality increases. To deal with this major problem an effective idea has been proposed to achieve all the qualities of the masonry unit such as strength, workability and weight.

This project reveals the detailed investigation of general interlocking bricks and grooves made of cementatious substance and fly ash and further various trails and tests will be conducted on these interlocking bricks by addition of various materials such as plastic wastes, foundry wastes, clay soils which are used for making bricks. All these various mixtures are mixed and at different proportions and ideal mixture are to be found then the grooves are to be altered by male and female joints. Further in addition of clay sand wooden powder and coir pith are to be added so that while burning the burning of these masonry units are complete which gives good colour and more strength while comparing to an A-Class brick. All these ratios are to be found and tested and the mixture with minimal cost and max efficiency with sustainability to the environment is to be adopted for the market.

In the past year there was a spread of pandemic COVID 19 although there is various discussions on cure various precautious measures are taken to avoid the spread of this pandemic. By considering this situation a chemical is to be added in this masonry unit which will be acting as an disinfectious agent which will avoid the entry of various common viruses and bacteria like rhino viruses, salmonella, shigella. This ability of the masonry will last more than 24 months and beyond. And this can also be replenished after specific period of time. Since these masonry units don't need any plastering work and painting work as they come in desirable colours the disinfectious ability of the unit works more efficiently.

This investigation is to be done in the district of Coimbatore (11.0168°N, 76.9558°E) in the Kongu Nadu region of the Indian state of Tamil Nadu with an area of 246.8 km^2 and with Metropolitan area as 642.1km^2 which ranks as second largest district in the state of Tamil Nadu with respect to the area. Coimbatore is the Manchester of south India and is considered as one of the most developing city in Tamil Nadu. Coimbatore is one of the selected cities for the scheme of smart city development. By introduction of these masonry units the will become smarter and ecologically more efficient.

Materials
Material
Clay soil, Sawdust, E-Wastes are collected from the local regions of Coimbatore. Clay soil is sieved and graded. The Atterberg limits are checked for the soil. E-Wastes are also tested and thermoplast temperatures of the E-Wastes are also found. And saw powder is grinned finely.

Mould making
The mould is made in cast iron by providing male and female joints ate the top and bottom and also grooves are provided at the lateral parts of the mould. The base is provided with the plate and tensioned using a spring for better workability during casting.

Mixture
The clay soil is mixed with the optimum moisture content. While addition of saw dust it is mixed with the clay soil at 3:1 ratio. This mixture is followed as such in addition of E-Waste also.

Methodology
Casting
The water is mixed with the clay soil at the optimum ratio and then mixed well before the day of casting and then placed undisturbed for a day. During the day of casting it is again, mixed well then the soil is pressed with a great force into the mould and then it is pushed to the ground then the brick is removed from the mould with the help of the tensioned spring. The brick is left undisturbed for drying for minimum of 14 days at normal room temperature. Then the brick is burnt at the kiln at One thousand and two hundred (1200) degree Celsius. Similarly the same process is done while addition of E-Waste and saw dust with different ratios.

Results and discussions

Crushing strength of Masonry unit

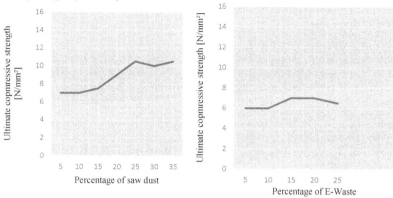

Figure 1: *Compressive strength while addition of saw dust.*

Figure 2: *Compressive strength while addition of E-Waste*

The crushing strength of the interlocking clay brick masonry unit is comparatively high while comparing the normal brick and it is almost equivalent to the conventional interlocking brick. The strength is more when it is tested for both individual brick as well as masonry unit. While testing in the compressive testing machine (CTM) the average compressive strength is above 7.5 N/mm² and the average compressive strength of 10.5 N/mm². Addition of saw dust by 30 percent increases the compressive strength upto 35 percent (Fig.1). Similarly by addition of E waste by 25 percent increases strength by 40 percent (Fig.2).

Water absorption of masonry unit

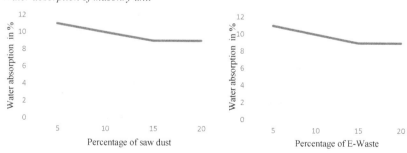

Figure 3:*Water absorption while addition of saw dust*

Figure 4:*Water absorption while addition of E-Waste*

Recent Advancements in Geotechnical Engineering - NCRAG'21   Materials Research Forum LLC
Materials Research Proceedings **19** (2021) 161-165   https://doi.org/10.21741/9781644901618-20

The water absorption of the interlocking clay brick is as similar to the normal brick and a bit more than conventional interlocking block. By addition of saw dust upto 30 percent reduces the water absorption by 3 percent (Fig.3). And by addition of E waste decreases the water absorption by 4 percent (Fig.4).

Efflorescence of masonry unit
The efflorescence of the masonry unit is less than 10 percent in bricks, interlocking clay bricks, and conventional interlocking bricks. By addition of saw dust and E wastes does not alter the efflorescence as the efflorescence depends mainly upon the soil.

Hardness, Soundness, Dimension tests
The hardness of the normal brick and interlocking clay bricks is similar. The soundness test on the interlocking clay brick gives the clear indication about the burning of brick. A well burnt clay brick gives clear bell sound. The dimensions of a normal clay is 4.5*2.75*9 (in inches), while the conventional interlocking bricks are 16*6*5 (in inches) and whereas clay interlocking brick are 5.5*3.75*10 (in inches).

Decrease in mortar content
While comparing to normal clay bricks the usage of mortar for the interlocking brick masonry is less about 60 to 70 percentage (Fig.4). Conventional interlocking brick also consumes less mortar when compared to the normal clay brick.

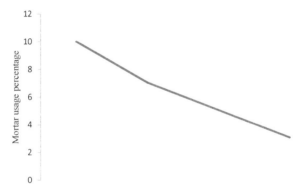

Figure 5:￼*Decrease in mortar usage*

Airdal spray
Airdal spray is sprayed over the masonry unit during the transport so that it would reduce transmission of contagious pathogens through the masonry units. A litre of the spray is used for about 500 bricks and above for the disinfection period of 24+ months.

Conclusion

The interlocking masonry units made up of clay soil by addition of both E waste and saw dust is a new material recommended for the market as they have more workability and less labour needed. As there is increase in need for the modern technique for the field of construction. The addition of saw dust makes the masonry unit lighter and stronger while introduced into the kiln as they are completely burnt and creates pores which reduces the weight if the masonry unit. The E wastes are also burnt well which turns into thermoplast fills the pores thereby increasing the bonding but increase in weight. In addition to that the airdal spray is used to get rid of common bacteria to avoid contagious spread through the unit during the transport and handling of the masonry unit. And in further investigation more study should be done to get more desired results.

Reference

[1] Shivakumar. K et.al., Limestone Dust and Wood Saw As a Brick Material, International Journal of Engineering Trends and Application (IJETA) Vol.5 Issue 2 (2008).

[2] Amin Al-Fakih et.al., Development of Interlocking Masonry Bricks and its' Structural Behaviour, A Review Paper IOP Conf. Series: Earth and Environmental Science 140 (2018). https://doi.org/10.1088/1755-1315/140/1/012127

[3] Emmanuel Nana Jackson et.al.,Comparative cost analysis between interlocking bricks and sandcret blocks for residential buildings, Ghana MedCarve World of Research Vol.4 Issue 4(2018). https://doi.org/10.15406/mojce.2018.04.00120

[4] Dipakphapale et.al., Fly ash interlocking brick geo polymer concrete, International Research Journal of Engineering and Technology (IRJET) Vol.07 Issue 03 (2020).

[5] Simion Hosea Kintingu, Design of Interlocking Bricks for Enhanced Wall Construction Flexibility, Alignment Accuracy and Load Bearing, A thesis submitted to The University of Warwick, School of Engineering (2000).

[6] S.V. GiriBabu and Dr. S. Krishnaiah, Manufacturing of Eco-Friendly Brick: A Critical Review, International Journal of Computational Engineering Research (IJCER) Vol.08, Issue 02 (2018).

[7] Halima Chemani and BachirChemnai, Valorization of wood sawdust in making porous clay brick, Academic journals Vol.8, Issue 15,(2013) pp 609 – 614.

[8] Kiel Industries Germany, Airdal User guide: Ideal protection against viruses and bacteria, (2010).

[9] PeriRaghava Ravi Teja, Studies on Mechanical Properties of Brick Masonry, A thesis submitted to National Institute of Technology Rourkela, (2015).

Recent Advancements in Geotechnical Engineering - NCRAG'21
Materials Research Proceedings **19** (2021) 166-174

Materials Research Forum LLC
https://doi.org/10.21741/9781644901618-21

Experimental Study on Fly-Ash Aggregate as a Lightweight Filler in a Structural Element

S. Deepasree[1,a*], V. Raguraman[2,b] and R. Anuradha[3,c]

[1]Student- Department of Civil Engineereing Sri Shakthi Institute of Engineering and Technology, Coimbatore, Tamilnadu, India

[2]Assistant Professor- Department of Civil Engineereing Sri Shakthi Institute of Engineering and Technology, Coimbatore, Tamilnadu, India

[3]Professor and Head- Department of Civil Engineereing Sri Shakthi Institute of Engineering and Technology, Coimbatore, Tamilnadu, India

[a*]deepuscool2@gmail.com, [b]svs.vrr49@gmail.com, [c]hodcivil@siet.ac.in

Keywords: Lightweight Structure, Fly-Ash Aggregate, Sintering Effect, Compressive Strength, Split Tensile Strength, Flexural Strength

Abstract. Light-weight structures are widely used in the construction field. Light-weight fillers such as aggregates can be used to improve weightless structures. Generally, standard aggregates cannot be used to attain the desired weight for light-weight structures. To determine a light-weight filler, the aggregates are made by using fly-ash along with cement mortar. Fly ash was collected from the Mettur Thermal power plant. Cement and fly-ash were mixed in a concrete mixer in a proportion of 30:70 with a water-cement ratio of 0.3 and it is mixed until the pellets are formed. The aggregates are replaced at different percentages such as 0%, 10%, 20%, and 30% respectively to the coarse aggregate. The properties such as compressive strength, split tensile strength and flexural strength were taken. The maximum strength was attained at 30% of fly-ash aggregate with a compressive strength of 46.47 N/mm^2, split tensile strength of 14.85 N/mm^2 and flexural strength of 3.80 N/mm^2.

Introduction

From the coal combustion plant, the production of fly-ash is nearly 80%, and bottom ash of 20% which results in nearly 500 tons [1]. The production of materials requires a large land area for disposal which results in soil contamination, water and air pollution [2–6]. In the construction field, there is a demand for utilizing a new application and technology. Likewise, industrial waste products are being used in the construction field [7–12]. The utilization of waste is generally perceived as one of the favored alternatives towards the accomplishment of a feasible turn of events [13]. Light-weight structures are preferably used than the high self-weight of concrete since such high weight units become a limiting factor in some construction fields [14–17]. Light-weight structures possess various advantages such as thinner structure and footing, reduced dimensional column and beams with the availability of large space, and easy handling of precast elements [18]. Fly ash has been used in various sectors such as cellular concrete, stabilization of soil, manufacturing of bricks, and lightweight aggregate [19]. Fly ash is effectively utilized in many construction applications such as abrasives, backfills. Manufacturing of soil products, drainage media, road base, subbase, and structural fill [20]. To advance the properties of ash, thermal methods such as autoclaving, steam process, and sintering are applied. Sintering suggests the openness of the pellet to high temperature. It has a typical source in the production of aggregates regardless of being an energy-concentrated cycle [21–25]. Fly debris can be conveyed by accepting palletization as a technique of joining better particles into a strong material without the application of external force which brings about the low-density weight as a result of the presence of pores [26,27]. The pellets are produced with fly debris because of the occurrence of airborne voids and these airborne voids are answerable for their retentiveness. Retentiveness has a huge role in a blend and the exhibition of the concrete [28]. Fly ash aggregates not only used for protection of environment by recycling the waste resource also to produce a light weight structure in improving the concrete properties. Bottom ash was utilized for the most part on road construction and concrete block and also applied as light weight in cement mortar [28]. In addition to that, it can also be used in coarse aggregate and fine aggregate mainly in high performance concrete [29]. High permeable bottom ash elements may lessen the shrinkage due to the utilization of those elements as a light weight in concrete. The creation of solid utilizing these aggregate is around 22% lighter and simultaneously 20% more grounded than the standard weight aggregate concrete. Drying shrinkage is found to be 32% comparatively reduced than that of ordinary concrete. This study is the first attempt in using a fly-ash pellet as a light-weight filler for the replacement of coarse aggregate.

Materials and experimental methods
Materials
Cement
The concrete paste was set up from ordinary Portland cement (OPC) with a specific gravity of 3.12. The consistent water-binder ratio of 0.55 was utilized for all blends.

Fly-debris
Fly-debris was obtained from the Mettur Thermal power plant. In addition to some potential benefits to the concrete itself, the application of fly debris as a light-weight pellet in place of natural aggregate offers a wealth of benefits both economically and environmentally.

Preparation of Fly-ash pellet
Fly Ash was obtained from Mettur nuclear energy station. Fly debris has been generated from an electrostatic precipitator in the nuclear energy station which was taken straightforwardly from the container in a dry state. It has been classified under class C-fly debris. Fly debris is usually delivered by consuming lignite or sub-bituminous coal. Concrete and fly debris were blended in a concrete blender in a proportion of 30:70 with a water binder ratio of 0.3 and the mixture is blended until the pellets are shaped. The pellets are continued drying for 3 days. After the drying stage, the pellets ought to be on restoring for 7 days. The preparation of fly ash aggregate is shown in figure 1.

Materials Research Forum LLC
https://doi.org/10.21741/9781644901618-21

Fig. 1 Preparation of fly ash aggregate

Mix Proportion
The samples are cast in different sizes for the compressive, split tensile and flexural test in sizes of 150x150x150 mm, 150x300 mm, and 150x150x700 mm respectively with a water-binder ratio of 0.55. The fly ash aggregate was replaced in different proportions such as 0%, 10%, 20%,and 30% to the coarse aggregate.

Materials Research Forum LLC
https://doi.org/10.21741/9781644901618-21

Fig. 2 Fly ash aggregate

Experimental results

Compressive strength

The concrete cube of size 150x150x150 mm was cast. The fly-ash pellets were replaced with coarse aggregate at a proportion of 0%, 10.0%, 20.0%, and 30.0% respectively. The properties of concrete were tested at 7 days and 28 days. At 7 days of strength, the strength parameter was increased by 31.2%, 49.7%, 50.8% for a mix proportion of 10.0%, 20.0%, and 30.0% respectively compared to the conventional mix. At 28 days of strength, the compressive strength was increased by 7.5%, 17.1%, 53.7% for 10.0%, 20.0%, and 30.0% respectively compared to conventional mix as discussed in table1. The pictorial representation of the compressive strength was shown in figure 3.

Table 1 Compressive strength of concrete

S.No	Percentage of pellet	Compressive strength N/mm²	
		7 day	**28 day**
1	0	15.97	30.33
2	10	20.96	32.5
3	20	23.91	35.4
4	30	24.01	46.47

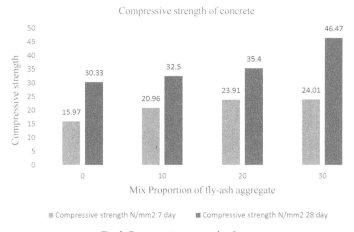

Fig.3 Compressive strength of concrete

Split tensile strength
The concrete cylinder of size 150x300 mm was cast. The fly-ash pellets were replaced with coarse aggregate at a proportion of 0%, 10.0%, 20.0%, and 30.0% respectively. The graphical representation of the split tensile strength was shown in figure 4. The strength parameter was tested at 7 days and 28 days. At 7 days of testing, the split tensile strength was increased by 16.7%, 31.7%, 70% for a mix proportion of 10.0%, 20.0%, and 30.0% respectively compared to the conventional mix. At 28 days of testing, the compressive strength was increased by 13.3%, 14.9%, 51.5% for 10.0%, 20.0%, and 30.0% respectively compared to the control mix as discussed in table 2.

Table 2 Split tensile strength of concrete

S.No	Percentage of pellet	Split tensile strength N/mm²	
		7 day	**28 day**
1	0	6	9.8
2	10	7	11.1
3	20	7.9	11.26
4	30	10.2	14.85

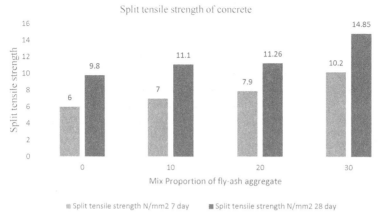

Fig.4 Split tensile strength of concrete

Flexural strength
The beam of size 750x150x150 mm was cast. The fly-ash pellets were replaced with coarse aggregate at a proportion of 0%, 10.0%, 20.0%, and 30.0% respectively. The strength parameter was tested at 7 days and 28 days. At 7 days of testing, the flexural strength was increased by 4.9%, 9.7%, 66.4% for a mix proportion of 10.0%, 20.0%, and 30.0% respectively compared to the conventional mix. At 28 days of testing, the flexural strength was increased by 9.4%, 19.2%, 62.4% for 10.0%, 20.0%, and 30.0% respectively compared to the conventional mix as discussed in table 3. The graphical representation of the flexural strength was shown in figure 5.

Table 3 Flexural strength of the beam

S.No	Percentage of pellet	Flexural strength N/mm^2	
		7 day	**28 day**
1	0	2.26	2.34
2	10	2.37	2.56
3	20	2.48	2.79
4	30	3.76	3.8

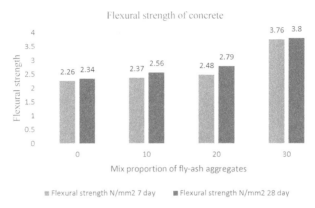

Fig. 5 Flexural strength of concrete

Conclusions

The following are the accomplishment of the study:

- Lightweight concrete is made by using a fly ash aggregate as a lightweight filler.
- The sintering effect is used to make fly-ash aggregate. Cement and fly-ash were added in a proportion of 30:70.
- The fly-ash aggregate is replaced with coarse aggregate at different proportions such as 0%, 10%, 20%, and 30% respectively.
- The optimum strength was obtained at a substitution of 30% of fly-ash pellet to the coarse aggregate.

References

[1] Acar, I.; Atalay, M.U. Characterization of sintered class F fly ashes. *Fuel* **2013**, *106*, 195–203. https://doi.org/10.1016/j.fuel.2012.10.057

[2] Sokolar, R.; Smetanova, L. Dry pressed ceramic tiles based on fly ash–clay body: influence of fly ash granulometry and pentasodium triphosphate addition. *Ceram. Int.* **2010**, *36*, 215–221. https://doi.org/10.1016/j.ceramint.2009.07.009

[3] Medina, A.; Gamero, P.; Querol, X.; Moreno, N.; De León, B.; Almanza, M.; Vargas, G.; Izquierdo, M.; Font, O. Fly ash from a Mexican mineral coal I: Mineralogical and chemical characterization. *J. Hazard. Mater.* **2010**, *181*, 82–90. https://doi.org/10.1016/j.jhazmat.2010.04.096

[4] Sočo, E.; Kalembkiewicz, J. Investigations of sequential leaching behaviour of Cu and Zn from coal fly ash and their mobility in environmental conditions. *J. Hazard. Mater.* **2007**, *145*, 482–487. https://doi.org/10.1016/j.jhazmat.2006.11.046

[5] Terzić, A.; Pavlović, L.; Miličić, L. Evaluation of lignite fly ash for utilization as component in construction materials. *Int. J. Coal Prep. Util.***2013**, *33*, 159–180. https://doi.org/10.1080/19392699.2013.776960

[6] Chen, X.; Lu, A.; Qu, G. Preparation and characterization of foam ceramics from red mud and fly ash using sodium silicate as foaming agent. *Ceram. Int.***2013**, *39*, 1923–1929. https://doi.org/10.1016/j.ceramint.2012.08.042

[7] Terzić, A.; Andrić, L.; Mitić, V. Mechanically activated coal ash as refractory bauxite shotcrete microfiller: Thermal interactions mechanism investigation. *Ceram. Int.***2014**, *40*, 12055–12065. https://doi.org/10.1016/j.ceramint.2014.04.045

[8] Yilmaz, A.; Degirmenci, N. Possibility of using waste tire rubber and fly ash with Portland cement as construction materials. *Waste Manag.***2009**, *29*, 1541–1546. https://doi.org/10.1016/j.wasman.2008.11.002

[9] Erol, M.; Küçükbayrak, S.; Ersoy-Mericboyu, A. The influence of the binder on the properties of sintered glass-ceramics produced from industrial wastes. *Ceram. Int.***2009**, *35*, 2609–2617. https://doi.org/10.1016/j.ceramint.2009.02.028

[10] El-Didamony, H.; Abd El-Rahman, E.; Osman, R.M. Fire resistance of fired clay bricks–fly ash composite cement pastes. *Ceram. Int.***2012**, *38*, 201–209. https://doi.org/10.1016/j.ceramint.2011.06.050

[11] Mukhopadhyay, T.K.; Ghosh, S.; Ghosh, J.; Ghatak, S.; Maiti, H.S. Effect of fly ash on the physico-chemical and mechanical properties of a porcelain composition. *Ceram. Int.***2010**, *36*, 1055–1062. https://doi.org/10.1016/j.ceramint.2009.12.012

[12] Chandra, N.; Sharma, P.; Pashkov, G.L.; Voskresenskaya, E.N.; Amritphale, S.S.; Baghel, N.S. Coal fly ash utilization: Low temperature sintering of wall tiles. *Waste Manag.***2008**, *28*, 1993–2002. https://doi.org/10.1016/j.wasman.2007.09.001

[13] Snelson, D.G.; Kinuthia, J.M. Characterisation of an unprocessed landfill ash for application in concrete. *J. Environ. Manage.***2010**, *91*, 2117–2125. https://doi.org/10.1016/j.jenvman.2010.04.015

[14] Kılıç, A.; Atiş, C.D.; Yaşar, E.; Özcan, F. High-strength lightweight concrete made with scoria aggregate containing mineral admixtures. *Cem. Concr. Res.***2003**, *33*, 1595–1599. https://doi.org/10.1016/S0008-8846(03)00131-5

[15] Bentur, A.; Igarashi, S.; Kovler, K. Prevention of autogenous shrinkage in high-strength concrete by internal curing using wet lightweight aggregates. *Cem. Concr. Res.***2001**, *31*, 1587–1591. https://doi.org/10.1016/S0008-8846(01)00608-1

[16] Kim, Y.J.; Choi, Y.W.; Lachemi, M. Characteristics of self-consolidating concrete using two types of lightweight coarse aggregates. *Constr. Build. Mater.***2010**, *24*, 11–16. https://doi.org/10.1016/j.conbuildmat.2009.08.004

[17] Gesoğlu, M.; Güneyisi, E.; Özturan, T.; Öz, H.Ö.; Asaad, D.S. Self-consolidating characteristics of concrete composites including rounded fine and coarse fly ash lightweight aggregates. *Compos. Part B Eng.***2014**, *60*, 757–763. https://doi.org/10.1016/j.compositesb.2014.01.008

[18]Kayali, O. Fly ash lightweight aggregates in high performance concrete. *Constr. Build. Mater.***2008**, *22*, 2393–2399. https://doi.org/10.1016/j.conbuildmat.2007.09.001

[19]GÖRHAN, G.; KAHRAMAN, E.; BAŞPINAR, M.S.; Demir, İ. Uçucu Kül Bölüm I: Oluşumu, Sınıflandırılması ve Kullanım Alanları. *Yapı Teknol. Elektron. Derg.***2008**, *4*, 85–94.

[20]Singh, M.; Siddique, R. Effect of coal bottom ash as partial replacement of sand on properties of concrete. *Resour. Conserv. Recycl.***2013**, *72*, 20–32. https://doi.org/10.1016/j.resconrec.2012.12.006

[21]Cheeseman, C.R.; Virdi, G.S. Properties and microstructure of lightweight aggregate produced from sintered sewage sludge ash. *Resour. Conserv. Recycl.***2005**, *45*, 18–30. https://doi.org/10.1016/j.resconrec.2004.12.006

[22]Ramamurthy, K.; Harikrishnan, K.I. Influence of binders on properties of sintered fly ash aggregate. *Cem. Concr. Compos.***2006**, *28*, 33–38. https://doi.org/10.1016/j.cemconcomp.2005.06.005

[23]Kockal, N.U.; Ozturan, T. Characteristics of lightweight fly ash aggregates produced with different binders and heat treatments. *Cem. Concr. Compos.***2011**, *33*, 61–67. https://doi.org/10.1016/j.cemconcomp.2010.09.007

[24]Cheeseman, C.R.; Sollars, C.J.; McEntee, S. Properties, microstructure and leaching of sintered sewage sludge ash. *Resour. Conserv. Recycl.***2003**, *40*, 13–25. https://doi.org/10.1016/S0921-3449(03)00022-3

[25]Geetha, S.; Ramamurthy, K. Properties of sintered low calcium bottom ash aggregate with clay binders. *Constr. Build. Mater.***2011**, *25*, 2002–2013. https://doi.org/10.1016/j.conbuildmat.2010.11.051

[26]Manikandan, R.; Ramamurthy, K. Effect of curing method on characteristics of cold bonded fly ash aggregates. *Cem. Concr. Compos.***2008**, *30*, 848–853. https://doi.org/10.1016/j.cemconcomp.2008.06.006

[27]Baykal, G.; Döven, A.G. Utilization of fly ash by pelletization process; theory, application areas and research results. *Resour. Conserv. Recycl.***2000**, *30*, 59–77. https://doi.org/10.1016/S0921-3449(00)00042-2

[28]Johnsen, H.; Helland, S.; Hemdal, E. Construction of Stovset Free Cantilever Bridge and the Nordhordland Cable Stayer Bridge. In Proceedings of the Proceedings of International symposium on structural lightweight aggregate concrete. Sandefiord; 1995; pp. 373–379.

[29]Lee, H.-K.; Kim, H.-K.; Hwang, E.A. Utilization of power plant bottom ash as aggregates in fiber-reinforced cellular concrete. *Waste Manag.***2010**, *30*, 274–284. https://doi.org/10.1016/j.wasman.2009.09.043

Recent Advancements in Geotechnical Engineering - NCRAG'21
Materials Research Proceedings 19 (2021) 175-180

Materials Research Forum LLC
https://doi.org/10.21741/9781644901618-22

Experimental Investigations on Eco-Friendly Helium-Mist Near-Dry Wire-Cut EDM of M2-HSS Material

Boopathi Sampath[1, a *], M. Sureshkumar[2,b], T. Yuvaraj[1,c], D. Velmurugan[1,d]

[1]Department of Mechanical Engineering, Muthayammal Engineering College, Rasipuram, Tamil Nadu 637408

[2]Department of Mechanical Engineering, Bannariamman Institute of Technology, Sathyamangalam, Tamil Nadu 638401

[a]boopasangee@gmail.com, [b]sureshkumarm@bitsathy.ac.in, [c]yuvaraj.t.mech@mec.edu.in, [d]velmurugan.d.mech@mec.edu.in

Keywords: Near Dry WEDM, Helium, M2-HSS, Minimum Quantity Lubrication, Taguchi Method

Abstract. In this paper, helium-assisted near-dry wire-cut electrical discharge machining (NDWEDM) method molybdenum wire has been used to reduce the environmental impact and to cut M2-HSS material. The pressurized non-reacting helium gas mixed with a small amount of water (Helium-mist) is used as the dielectric fluid to accomplish adequate cooling and flush-out debris. The new experimental setup has been developed to conduct the near-dry WEDM tests using the L9 orthogonal array of the Taguchi technique. The input parameters such as voltage (V), pulse-width (PW), pulse-interval (PI), and flow rate (F) of mixing water and output variables are the material removal rate (MRR) and surface roughness (Ra). It was observed that MRR and Ra are amplified by the rise in voltage and pulse-width, and flow rate conversely, the pulse interval minimizes the responses. The percentage of contribution of pulse width, voltage, pulse interval and flow rate are 24.06%, 32.98%, 12.75% and 30.21% on MRR and 20.94%, 22.22%, 47.86% and 8.97% on Ra respectively. Finally, the confirmation trials have been accomplished to validate the foreseen best parameter sets on optimal responses.

Introduction

In the WEDM process, manufacturing characters and environmental influence are deliberated to analyze the machining mechanics, tool change, minimum rejections in production, and effects of cutting-fluid flow[1]. The environmental effect of machining should be analyzed for minimizing environmental impacts by modification of existing technology and the development of new manufacturing methods[2]. In these aspects, research on the modification of EDM and WEDM processes was developed to make the trade-off techniques between machining performance and machining pollutions.

The many experimental research on dry and near-dry EDM processes have previously been studied to find the analytical relationship for tool wear, MRR, the influence of dielectric fluid, and environmental impacts such as toxicity and flammability[2,3]. However, the dry and near-dry WEDM process, the investigations had so far been studied to improve the cutting performances as follows. The first systematic study in near-dry WEDM was carried out to investigate the air-mist dielectric fluid to cut the HSS-M2 steel materials. The optimal parameters for best machining performance had been predicted using the evolutionary optimization method[4]. The conventional tap water missed with air as dielectric has been tried to analyze the influences on cutting factors[5]. The oxygen-mist NDWEDM process has been investigated by using the response surface method to reveal the effect of oxygen-mist in WEDM Process[6]. It was observed from comparative studies, the oxygen-mist near-dry WEDM process has better performance than the air-mist near-dry process [7]. The Monel metal, EN-31 die steel, ANSI-D3 steel, and Tungsten carbide (WC) as work materials and air/ gas-mist as dielectric fluids had been investigated in near-dry WEDM processes[8,9]. It was also tried to investigate the near-dry WEDM process to cut various alloy materials by few researchers. Thus, there is no attempt found in the helium-mist near-dry WEDM process to cut the HSS-M2 materials.

In this research, the helium gas -water as dielectric and molybdenum wire electrode are used as key factors to investigate the machining performance by Taguchi L9 orthogonal array. The significant factors and percentage of contributions on machining performance are discussed.

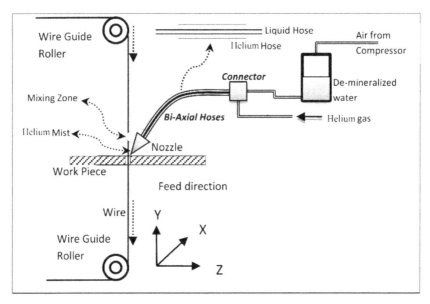

Figure 1. Experimental Setup of Helium assisted near-dry WEDM

Experimental setup and Experimentation

The 5 mm thickness of M2-HSS was used as work material for helium-mist near dry WEDM processes. The investigational setup of Helium-assisted near-dry WEDM is exposed in Figure 1. The helium gas was supplied outside the hose and a small quantity of water is flowing through the inner hose. Both fluids are mixed at the end of co-axial hoses to the nozzle. Helium-mist was acting as a working medium in reciprocating NDWEDM machine. The voltage, pulse width, and pulse interval can be adjusted from Fuzzy controlled WEDM. The mixing flow rate of small water was controlled and measured by a new experimental setup. The surface roughness of WEDM was directly measured along with four different passes over the workpiece surface by the roughness tester. The material removal rate (MRR) can be premeditated by the ratio of the volume of debris removed with a period using Equations (1) and (2).

$$Kerf = wire\ diameter + 2 \times times\ of\ parking\ gap = 0.20mm \qquad (1)$$

$$MRR = (thickness * Kerf * length \ of \ cut)/time \quad mm^3/min \tag{2}$$

Based on the trial test, the inputs and their required levels are recognized. The levels of each process variable are arranged in Table 1. The experimentations are steered using the L9 orthogonal array of the Taguchi method[10] and the MRR and Ra values observed over the trials are shown in Table 2.

Table 1. Helium assisted Near-dry WEDM levels of input variables

Symbol	Input factor	Units	Level 1	Level 2	Level 3
V	Gap-Voltage	V	3	5	4
PW	Pulse width	μs	15	25	20
PI	Pulse interval	μs	45	75	60
F	Mixing water Flow Rate	ml/min	10	20	15

Table 2. Experimental observation using L9 design of experiment

S.N.	Input factors				Mean Responses	
	V	PW	PI	F	MRR (mm³/min)	Ra (μm)
1.	3	15	45	10	4.14	1.17
2.	3	20	60	15	7.065	1.08
3.	3	25	75	20	9.414	1.26
4.	4	15	60	20	7.596	1.17
5.	4	20	75	10	6.003	1.08
6.	4	25	45	15	11.619	1.89
7.	5	15	75	15	7.281	1.08
8.	5	20	45	20	13.896	2.16
9.	5	25	60	10	9.504	1.53

Table 3. Taguchi analysis for MRR to predict the percentage of contribution

Input	Degree of Freedom	The sequential sum of square	Percentage of contribution	Rank
V	2	16.9154	24.06	3
PW	2	23.1813	32.98	1
PI	2	8.9658	12.75	4
F	2	21.2329	30.21	2
Total	8	70.2954	-	-

Table 4. Taguchi analysis for Ra to predict the percentage of contribution

Input	Degree of Freedom	The sequential sum of square	Percentage of contribution	Rank
V	2	0.2646	20.94	3
PW	2	0.2808	22.22	1
PI	2	0.6048	47.86	4
F	2	0.1134	8.97	2
Total	2	1.2636	-	-

Result analysis

Taguchi's analysis for MRR and Ra are shown in Tables 3 and 4 respectively. The contribution (%) of gap voltage, pulse width, pulse interval, and flow rate on MRR is 24.06%, 32.98%, 12.75%, and 30.21% respectively. Similarly, the percentage of contribution of gap voltage, pulse width, pulse interval, and flow rate on Ra is 20.94%, 22.22%, 47.86%, and 8.97% respectively. The pulse width is the most significant factor on MRR due to an increase in spark strength[4,6]. The flow rate is the second important factor on both MRR and Ra due to provide sufficient cooling in the plasma zone and flush out debris. The pulse interval is the more dominant factor on surface roughness due to discrete spark by long pulse pause time[5,11]. While increasing MRR by controlling factors, the surface roughness also getting increased due to the coarse of debris. The percentage of contributions of input variables on MRR and Ra are illustrated in Figure 2.

Percentage of Contribution on MRR and Ra

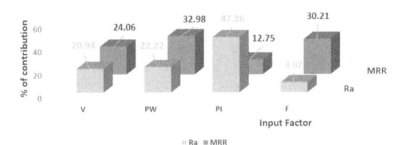

Figure 2. Input factors Contributions on Machining Responses

Figures 3(a) &(b) are illustrating the mean effects on the MRR and Ra respectively. The plots show that the MRR and Ra are significantly amplified due to the growth in gap voltage, pulse width, and flow rate. Conversely, MRR and Ra values are condensed by growing pulse interval[4,5]. Taguchi analysis tests and the percentage of contribution of process factors are illustrated for MRR and Ra are shown in Tables 3 and 4 respectively. It was revealed that pulse-width is a very significant contribution to MRR and pulse interval has more contribution on Ra. The plots show that voltage, pulse width, and flow rate have a more momentous consequence on MRR and Ra than pulse-interval[8,9,12–14]. The validation tests are used to authorize the predicted outcomes from the Taguchi Method. The proof tests are completed by steering the experimentations with an exact influence of the levels as shown in Table 5. The following Equation (3) is applied to estimate the best of the MRR and Ra[4].

$$\delta_{opt} = \delta_{tot} + \sum_{j=1}^{n}(\delta_j - \delta_{tot}) \qquad (3)$$

Table 5. Validation of Taguchi Prediction results.

Response	Process Parameters				Predicted Value	Experiment Value	Unit
	V	PW	PI	F			
MRR	5	25	45	20	15.08	15.45	mm³/min
Ra	3	15	75	10	0.57	0.60	μm

The best response values are predicted using the Taguchi technique using the trial version of MINITAB® software. The input factor combination ($V_3PW_3PI_1F_3$) for the maximization of MRR is shown in Figures 2(a). Similarly, the input factor combination ($V_1PW_1PI_3F_1$) for minimization of is Ra showed in Figures 2(b). The maximum of MRR (15.09mm^3/min) has been found with the grouping of input factors of $V_3PW_3PI_1F_3$ from the validation test. Similarly, the smallest value of Ra (0.57µm) has been found with the grouping of input factors of $V_1PW_1PI_1F_3$ by evaluation test. While increasing pulse width and gap voltage, the MRR and Ra are maximized due to the high intensity of spark between wire and work material[6]. The highest MRR and Ra are achieved by the maximum flow rate of the dielectric medium due to quick flushing of debrides components[15].

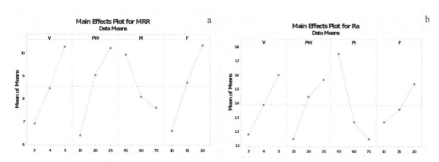

Figure 3 Input factor's influences on (a) MRR (b) Ra

Conclusions

The new helium-mist Near-dry WEDM experiments were conducted to cut M2-HSS material and estimate the optimal process variables for machining responses. As per the Taguchi analysis, the following conclusions were obtained.

- The percentage of contribution of gap voltage, pulse width, pulse interval, and flow rate on MRR is 24.06%, 32.98%, 12.75%, and 30.21% respectively. Similarly, the percentage of contribution of gap voltage, pulse width, pulse interval, and flow rate on Ra is 20.94%, 22.22%, 47.86%, and 8.97% respectively.
- The maximum of MRR (15.09mm^3/min) has been found with the grouping of input factors of $V_3PW_3PI_1F_3$ from the validation test. Similarly, the smallest value of Ra (0.57µm) has been found with the grouping of input factors of $V_1PW_1PI_3F_1$ by evaluation test.
- While increasing gap voltage, pulse width, and flow rate the MRR and Ra are maximized due to the high intensity of heat between the wire and work material. The highest MRR and Ra are found by the maximum flow rate of the dielectric medium due to quick flushing of debrides components. However, the Ra is proportionally increased with increasing MRR.
- The poor MRR and Ra were obtained by increasing pulse interval due to the expansion of spark-free time.

References

[1] A.A. Munoz, P. Sheng, An analytical approach for determining the environmental impact of machining processes, J. Mater. Process. Tech., 53 (1995) 736–758. https://doi.org/10.1016/0924-0136(94)01764-R

[2] S.H. Yeo, H.C. Tan, A.K. New, Assessment of waste streams in electric-discharge machining for environmental impact analysis, Proc. Inst. Mech. Eng. Part B J. Eng. Manuf., 212 (1998) 393–400. https://doi.org/10.1243/0954405981515996

[3] M.S. Hewidy, T.A. El-Taweel, M.F. El-Safty, Modelling the machining parameters of wire electrical discharge machining of Inconel 601 using RSM, J. Mater. Process. Technol., 169 (2005) 328–336. https://doi.org/10.1016/j.jmatprotec.2005.04.078

[4] S. Boopathi, K. Sivakumar, Experimental investigation and parameter optimization of near-dry wire-cut electrical discharge machining using multi-objective evolutionary algorithm, Int. J. Adv. Manuf. Technol., 67 (2013) 2639–2655. https://doi.org/10.1007/s00170-012-4680-4

[5] S. Boopathi, K. Sivakumar, Study of water assisted dry wire-cut electrical discharge machining, Indian J. Eng. Mater. Sci., 21 (2014) 75–82.

[6] S. Boopathi, K. Sivakumar, Optimal parameter prediction of oxygen-mist near-dry Wire-cut EDM, Int. J. Manuf. Technol. Manag., 30 (2016) 164–178. https://doi.org/10.1504/IJMTM.2016.077812

[7] S. Boopathi, K. Sivakumar, Experimental comparative study of near-dry wire-cut electrical discharge machining (WEDM), Eur. J. Sci. Res., 75 (2012) 472–481.

[8] S. Boopathi, S. Myilsamy, Material removal rate and surface roughness study on Near-dry wire electrical discharge Machining process, Mater. Today Proc., xx (2021) xx–xx. https://doi.org/10.1016/j.matpr.2021.02.267

[9] Y. Jia, B.S. Kim, D.J. Hu, J. Ni, Parametric study on near-dry wire electrodischarge machining of polycrystalline diamond-coated tungsten carbide material, Proc. Inst. Mech. Eng. Part B J. Eng. Manuf., 224 (2010) 185–193. https://doi.org/10.1243/09544054JEM1602

[10] S. Boopathi, Experimental investigation and parameter analysis of LPG refrigeration system using Taguchi method, SN Appl. Sci., 1 (2019) 892. https://doi.org/10.1007/s42452-019-0925-2

[11] S.K. Saha, S.K. Choudhury, Experimental investigation and empirical modeling of the dry electric discharge machining process, Int. J. Mach. Tools Manuf., 49 (2009) 297–308. https://doi.org/10.1016/j.ijmachtools.2008.10.012

[12] C.C. Kao, J. Tao, S. Lee, A.J. Shih, Dry wire electrical discharge machining of thin workpiece, in: Trans. North Am. Manuf. Res. Inst. SME, 2006: pp. 253–260.

[13] C.C. Kao, J. Tao, A.J. Shih, Near dry electrical discharge machining, Int. J. Mach. Tools Manuf., 47 (2007) 2273–2281. https://doi.org/10.1016/j.ijmachtools.2007.06.001

[14] S. Abdulkareem, A.A. Khan, M. Konneh, Reducing electrode wear ratio using cryogenic cooling during electrical discharge machining, Int. J. Adv. Manuf. Technol., 45 (2009) 1146–1151. https://doi.org/10.1007/s00170-009-2060-5

[15] S. Boopathi, Experimental Comparative Study of Near-Dry Wire-Cut Electrical Discharge Machining (WEDM), 75 (2012) 472–481.

Recent Advancements in Geotechnical Engineering - NCRAG'21
Materials Research Proceedings 19 (2021) 181-190

Materials Research Forum LLC
https://doi.org/10.21741/9781644901618-23

Performance of Additive Blended High Volume Fly Ash Concrete - A Systematic Literature Study

T.S. Mukesh[1,a*], R.K. Shobakiruthika[2,b], S. Sowmini[2,c], M. Subaash[2,d]

[1]Assistant Professor, Department of Civil Engineering, Kongu Engineering College, Perundurai, Erode, Tamilnadu, India

[2]Student, Department of Civil Engineering, Kongu Engineering College, Perundurai, Erode, Tamilnadu, India

[a*]mukesh.sakthivel@gmail.com, [b]shobakiruthikark@gmail.com, [c]sowminisri2017@gmail.com, [d]subaashm.17civil@kongu.edu

Keywords: Fly Ash, Compressive Strength, Super Plasticizer, Nano-SiO2, Splitting Tensile Strength, Flexural Rigidity

Abstract. Replacing cement with fly ash has recently created huge popularity among the construction field because of its huge production, efficient resources and sustainability aspect. This study is made to determine the High-Volume fly-ash concrete (HVFC) performance by adding additives. The general used concrete mixture is prepared by proportioning fly ash (40-50%) as a replacement. The concrete specimen was found to have better compressive strengths and hence, passed the strength tests. By incorporating additive Nano-SiO$_2$ and superplasticizer the following compression, flexural rigidity, splitting tensile strength and elasticity modulus were observed in the specimen to establish the cement and fly ash bond. The concrete performance mix with replacement fly ash at different percent was found to have good compressive strength during test and stayed undamaged during the entire period of exposure.

Introduction

The gigantic increment of populace alongside the enormous improvement these days prompted the extraordinary demand for concrete these days. Kanvic's recommended that the Cement request will raise by around 660 MMT (million metric tons) in India by 2030. Cement which is the essential constituent of concrete contributes the significant CO$_2$ discharge into the climate and furthermore an unnatural weather change. To satisfy the emerging need, in this paper the high-volume fly ash solid execution joining added substances is to be broke down. Fly-ash is collected as residue of coal obtained from power stations. Cement is more expense and important part of concrete. The Cement cost for a unit can be decreased by fractional supplanting of concrete by fly-ash. Fly-ash which is the remains collected from ignition of pummeled coal and gathered from electrostatic power stations wherein coal is used as main fuel source. Fly-ash removal is an important issue as unloading of fly ash as residue might lead to serious ecological issues/risks[1]. The fly ash usage as opposed to unloading it as a non-use material can be mostly utilized on monetary grounds as cement for incomplete substitution of concrete and somewhat in view of its gainful impacts, for example, lower water interest for comparable usefulness, decreased dying and last lower development of warmth. It is being utilized especially in huge applications of solids cum enormous volume situation aiming at controlling development because of hydration warmth and furthermore helps at decreasing breaking at initial ages. HVFC has arisen as development material with its self-potential right. This sort of cement typically contains over half fly-ash by a mass having absolute cement materials nature. Numerous specialists have utilized Class-C and Class-F

Materials Research Forum LLC
https://doi.org/10.21741/9781644901618-23

fly-ash in concrete. In the study, an exertion is carried out to introduce the consequences of conducting an examination completed to contemplate the impact of supplanting concrete with HVFC on the properties of cement and an exertion is made to examine the impact of nano-SiO_2 in improving the properties of high strength high HVFC.

Experimental details
Materials
Cement material used here is Ordinary Portland (grade 43). It adjusted to the prerequisites of IS: 8112-1989, and Table 1, shows the results. The cement utilized here is Type-I cement (ASTM C-150). Fly-ash type Class-F (gravity 2.72) is utilized in this examination. It is tried for compound creation per ASTM C-311, and result is presented in Table 2. Natural sand having a 4.75-mm nominal greatest size is utilized as FA[6]. The coarse aggregate utilized was 12.5 mm size. The two totals which was tried per IS: 383-1970, and the actual properties along with strainer examination is given in Table 3 and Table 4, individually. A monetarily accessible superplasticizer which is melamine-based was utilized. Nano-SiO_2 utilized in this paper was purchased from alpha composites, its real properties are given in Table 5.

TABLE 1: Portland cement characteristics

Test conducted	Obtained Results	IS: 8112-1989 Requirements
Cement Fineness which is retained on 90-Am sieve	7.7	Maximum of 10
Cement Fineness: specific surface (m²/kg)	266	Minimum of 225
Normal consistency	30 %	–
Vicat setting time (minutes) Initial time Final time	107 197	Minimum of 30 Maximum of 600
Strength due to Compression (MPa) 7 days 28 days	34.9 45.1	Minimum of 33.0 Minimum of 43.0
Specific gravity	3.15	–

TABLE 2: Fly-ash composition

Chemical parameters	% of Fly ash	ASTM C 618 (%) Requirements
Silicon-dioxide, SiO_2	54.2	-
Aluminum-oxide, Al_2O_3	25.6	-
Ferric-oxide, Fe_2O_3	5.0	-
$SiO_2 + Al_2O_3 = Fe_2O_3$	84.7	Minimum of 70.0
Calcium-oxide	5.2	-
Magnesium-oxide	2.0	Maximum of 5.0
Titanium-oxide	1.27	-
Potassium-oxide	.58	-
Sodium-oxide	.43	Maximum of 1.5
Sulphur-trioxide	1.28	Maximum of 5.0
Ignition loss (1000 °C)	1.68	Maximum of 6.0
Moisture	.26	Maximum of 3.0

Mixture proportions
In the study, a combination M1 is planned per, IS:10262-1982 is casted and found with 28th day strength of compression as 37.2 MPa as a conventional concrete. The other three specimens are casted by substituting cement in concrete by 40, 45 and 50% mass of Class-F fly-ash with differing superplasticizer measurements for every example projecting. Maintaining the constant quantity of additive nano-SiO2 for every sample mixture ratio. In doing as such, water-cement material proportions were kept practically same, so as to explore concrete impacts due to the substitution with high Class-F fly-ash when different boundaries are nearly maintained same. Table 6 represents the mix proportion of concrete. The Fig.1 represents the material mixing.

Fig. 1: Materials mixing

TABLE 3: Aggregates physical properties

Property	Fine aggregate	Coarse aggregate
Specific gravity of aggregate	2.61	2.79
Fineness modulus	2.27	6.59
SSD absorption	0.86%	1.10%
Voids	36.0%	39.8%
Unit-weight (kg/m^3)	1680	1613

Preparing and specimens casting

Compression strength is tested with 150×150mm size concrete cubes. Cylinders of size 150×300-mm is tested for split tensile strength, beams of 101.4×101.4× 508-mm is tested for flexural strength and cylinders of size 150×300-mm is used for testing elasticity modulus. Every concrete example was set up as per IS: 516-1959. In the wake of projecting, specimens are covered using plastic sheets, they are left free in projecting space for a period 24 hrs with 24 ±1 °C temperature. They are demoulded after a day (24 hrs) and are immersed into the water-storing room till the test hour. The casted specimens are shown in the Fig.2.

TABLE 4: Sieve analysis of aggregates

Fine aggregate			Coarse aggregate		
Sieve number	% passing	IS: 383-1970 Requirements	Sieve sizes	% passing	IS: 383-1970 Requirements
4.75 mm	95.4	90-100	12.5 mm	97	95-100
2.36 mm	92.7	85-100	10 mm	69	40-85
1.18 mm	77.0	75-100	4.75 mm	5	0-10
600 mm	61.1	60-79			
300 mm	34.3	12-40			
150 mm	5.7	0-10			

TABLE 5: The physical properties of nano-Sio$_2$

Type	Total surface area/unit mass (m^2/g)	pH-value	Average size of the particle (nm)	SiO$_2$ content (%)	Density of Surface (g/ml)
Class F	100±25	6.5-7.5	10-25	≥ 99.7	≤ 0.15

Properties of fresh concrete

Properties of Freshly casted concrete namely Slump, temperature, unit weight is determined per IS: 1199-1959. The results are tabulated in Table 6.

Recent Advancements in Geotechnical Engineering - NCRAG'21
Materials Research Proceedings **19** (2021) 181-190
Materials Research Forum LLC
https://doi.org/10.21741/9781644901618-23

TABLE 6: *Concrete mixture proportion*

Mixture number	M1	M2	M3	M4
Fly-ash	0 %	40 %	45%	50 %
Cement in kg/m³	405	230	210	200
Fly-ash in kg/m³	0	170	185	190
Water in kg/m³	165	161	165	161
W/ (FA+C)	.41	.40	.41	.40
SSD aggregate (kg/m³)	615	613	609	615
CA (kg/m³)	1227	1225	1227	1226
SP(Superplasticizer) (l/m³)	2	2.2	2.4	2.5
Nano-Sio₂	20	20	20	20
Slump in mm	60	80	85	95
Air-content in %	3.1	3.5	3.4	3.5
Air-temperature in °C	26	25	27	25
Temperature of concrete (°C)	29	27	28	29
Density of Concrete (kg/m3)	2405	2397	2401	2400

Specimen testing

Compressive strength is tested for concrete cubes of 150 mm normal size, split tensile strength is tested with cylinders of size 150×300-mm, beams with size, 101.4×101.4× 508-mm is used for testing flexural strength, finally cylinder with size 150×300-mm is again used for testing the elasticity modulus in the concrete specimen as per IS:516-1959[3].

Fig. 2: *Casted specimens*

Recent Advancements in Geotechnical Engineering - NCRAG'21   Materials Research Forum LLC
Materials Research Proceedings **19** (2021) 181-190   https://doi.org/10.21741/9781644901618-23

Discussion and results

Compressive strength

Concrete mixture having various ages like 7,21 and 91 days were tested for compressive strength. Result obtained are tabulated in Table 7 and in Fig.3[4]. The specimen compressive strength was found to be 37.2 MPa at the 28th day followed by 27.5,24.3 and 22.1MPa at the fly-ash replacement with percent reduction of 26%,35% and 41% respectively comparing to the strength of the concrete of control mixture M1(with fly-ash 0%). Results of compressive strength by the day 91 was found to increase gradually beyond day 28 with a varying strength increase between 21% and 26%. The continued cement hydration is the main reason for the strength increase. The chemical reaction occurring by adding of pozzolans with fly-ash present in concrete is the main significant cause for the steady increase of compressive strength of HVFC. Though reduction of compressive strength occurs due to fly-ash replacement at end of 28 days the mixture M4(50% fly-ash) might be used for the construction of concrete, M3(45% fly-ash) and M2 (40% fly-ash) can be used well for the structural construction of concrete[2]. This shows that the HVFC can maintain a very long-term retaining of strength.

TABLE 7: Compression test result

Mix ratio	Compressive strength (MPa)		
	7th day	28th day	91th day
M1 (0% fly-ash)	25.9	37.1	40.2
M2 (40% fly-ash)	18	27.5	34.6
M3 (45% fly-ash)	15.5	24.3	30.2
M4 (50% fly-ash)	14.2	22.1	26.7

TABLE 8: Result of Splitting tensile strength

Mix ratio	Splitting tensile strength (MPa)		
	7th day	28th day	91th day
M1 (0% fly-ash)	2.6	4.1	4.3
M2 (40% fly-ash)	1.7	3.2	3.9
M3 (45% fly-ash)	1.5	2.7	3.4
M4 (50% fly-ash)	1.4	2.1	2.7

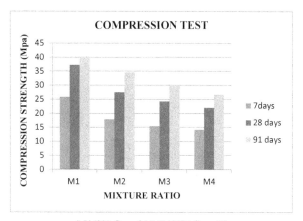

M1(0% fly-ash) M3(45% fly-ash)
M2(40% fly ash) M4 (50% fly-ash)
Fig. 3: *Compressive strength vs mix proportion*

Splitting tensile strength:
The splitting tensile strength of the specimen is calculated for the ages 7th, 28th and 91st days and the results were tabulated in Table 8 and Fig. 4. The strength difference depending on ages are analysed similar to the compressive strength analysis [5]. At age 28 days the splitting tensile strength of the cylinders at M1(0% fly-ash) was found to be 4.1 MPa followed by 3.2,2.7 and 2.1MPa for M2(40% fly-ash), M3(45% fly-ash) and M4 (50% fly-ash) which shows the reduced strength of about 22%, 34% and 49% respectively. At 91th day the strength increased to be 4.3, 3.9, 3.4 and 2.7 for M1(0% fly-ash), for M2(40% fly-ash), M3(45% fly-ash) and M4 (50% fly-ash) respectively which showed an increase of about 5%, 21%, 26% and 29% respectively when compared to the age of 28th day. It can be observed there is a % increase in strength is much higher during 91 days and for concrete mixture M1 compared to early strength at 28th day. This can cause pozzolanic action because of the presence of fly ash.

TABLE 9: *Flexural strength results*

Mix ratio	Flexural strength (MPa)		
	7th day	28th day	91th day
M1 (0% fly-ash)	3.7	5.4	5.6
M2 (40% fly-ash)	2.4	3.7	4.5
M3 (45% fly-ash)	2	3.0	3.9
M4 (50% fly-ash)	1.9	2.8	3.2

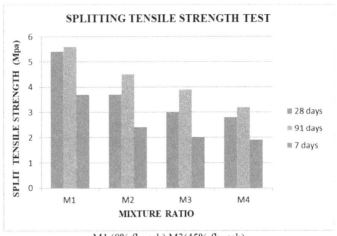

M1 (0% fly-ash) M3(45% fly-ash)
M2(40% fly ash) M4 (50% fly-ash)
Fig. 4: *Splitting tensile strength vs mix proportion*

Flexural strength:
The flexural strength of the concrete specimen for 7th, 28th and 91st days are analysed and results are presented in Table 9 and Fig. 5. Similar to the compressive and splitting tensile there is also an increase in the flexural strength with age. Control mixture M1(0% fly-ash) was observed to have a strength of 5.4 MPa at 28 days and %.6 MPa at 91 days which is an increase of strength. M2(40% fly ash), M3(45% fly-ash) and M4(50% fly-ash) were observed with 3.7, 3 and 2.6 MPa respectively at 28 days respectively. The strength of M2(40% fly-ash), M3(45% fly-ash) and M4 (50% fly-ash) was found to possess 4.5,4,3.2 MPa respectively at 91 days which is observed to have a successive increase of strength compared to the 28th day. It is finally observed from the results that there is a consecutive strength increase beyond 28th day. The flexural strength of concrete from day 28-91 were found to have continuous increase between 14% and 30%, depending on fly ash replacement.

TABLE 10: *Results of Modulus of elasticity*

Mix ratio	Modulus of elasticity (GPa)	
	28th day	91th day
M1 (0% fly-ash)	29.7	30.9
M2 (40% fly-ash)	19.8	22.2
M3 (45% fly-ash)	19.6	20.8
M4 (50% fly-ash)	18.9	19.1

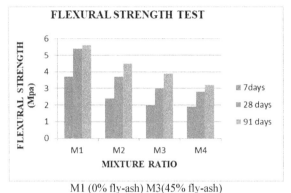

M1 (0% fly-ash) M3(45% fly-ash)
M2(40% fly ash) M4 (50% fly-ash)
Fig. 5: *Flexural strength vs mix proportion*

Modulus of elasticity:
In the examination, the elasticity modulus, that additionally called secant modulus, is taken as the slant of harmony from cause to some discretionary point on the stress – strain curve. The secant modulus determined in this examination is for 33% of the most extreme pressure. Elasticity modulus for day 7,28 and 91 were observed and the results are presented in Table 10 and Fig. 6. The test results indicated that the increasing amount of fly ash decreases the modulus strength compared to that of M1 concrete mixture. The modulus value of at age 28 for M1(0% fly-ash), M2(40% fly-ash), M3(45% fly-ash) and M4(50% fly-ash) was calculated to be 29.7, 19.8,19.6,18.9 MPa respectively. However, there is a successive increase in the modulus strength with ages.

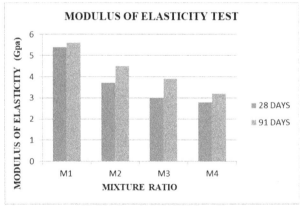

M1 (0% fly-ash) M3(45% fly-ash)
M2(40% fly ash) M4 (50% fly-ash)
Fig.6: *Modulus of elasticity vs mix proportion*

Conclusion

The conclusion obtained from the investigation:

1. The replacement of fly ash in three different percentage at initial stage caused the decrease in strength of compression, Split tensile strength, Flexural strength and modulus of elasticity at 28th day. But still strength gradually increased beyond 28th day.
2. Though the concrete strength gradually decreases at 40%,45% and 50% fly ash replaced concrete at 28 days has much good strength for construction of concrete structure.
3. Incorporation of nano-SiO$_2$ into the HVFC increases both the short and long-term concrete strength.
4. Fly-ash causes high porosity at short time of curing whereas the accelerating additive nano SiO$_2$ produce compact structure even at the shorter time of curing.

References

[1] Rafat Siddique. "Performance characteristics of high volume Class F fly ash concrete", Cement and Concrete Research, 2004. https://doi.org/10.1016/j.cemconres.2003.09.002

[2] Rafat Siddique, Kushal Kapoor, El-Hadj Kadri, Rachid Bennacer. "Effect of polyester fibres on the compressive strength and abrasion resistance of HVFA concrete", Construction and Building Materials, 2012. https://doi.org/10.1016/j.conbuildmat.2011.09.011

[3] "Waste Materials and By-Products in Concrete", Springer Science and Business Media LLC, 2008

[4] "Advances in Materials Research", Springer Science and Business Media LLC, 2021

[5] Rafat Siddique, Mohammad Iqbal Khan. "Chapter 2 Silica Fume", Springer Science and Business Media LLC, 2011. https://doi.org/10.1007/978-3-642-17866-5_2

[6] Siddique, R."Effect of fine aggregate replacement with Class F fly ash on the abrasion resistance of concrete", Cement and Concrete Research, 2003. https://doi.org/10.1016/S0008-8846(03)00212-6

Recent Advancements in Geotechnical Engineering - NCRAG'21   Materials Research Forum LLC
Materials Research Proceedings **19** (2021) 191-199   https://doi.org/10.21741/9781644901618-24

A Systematic Study on Physical and Mechanical Properties of No-Fine Concrete with Additives

T.S. Mukesh[1,a*], K. Thiru Vignesh[2,b], S. Sri Rama Chandra Pradeep[2,c],
R. Selva Bharathi[2,d]

[1]Assistant professor, Department of Civil Engineering, Kongu Engineering College, Perundurai, Erode, Tamil Nadu, India

[2]Student, Department of Civil Engineering, Kongu Engineering College, Perundurai, Erode, Tamil Nadu, India

[a*]mukesh.sakthivel@gmail.com, [b]vignesh.26.125@gmail.com
[c]sriramachandrapradeeps.17civil@kongu.edu, [d]selvabharathi3992@gmail.com

Keywords: Additives, Porosity, Strength, Fly Ash, RCA, Rice Husk

Abstract. No-fine concrete (also called as pervious concrete or porous concrete) is a lightweight concrete made up of primary binder and coarse aggregates with little or no sand. Due to the reduced amount or absence of fines, it produces large number of voids which improves permeability to greater extent. Hence this type of concrete can be used in pavements and in parking lots. The literature review is carried out to study the physical and mechanical properties of no-fine concrete with additives. Various reports were collected and studied about variation in physical and mechanical properties of pervious concrete with different additives. Additives may be either mineral additives (fly ash, silica fumes, rice husk ash etc..,) or chemical additives (plasticizers, super plasticizers, retarders etc...,). Our project involved the utilization of recycled coarse aggregates, fly ash and rice husk in no-fine concrete. After this study, it was concluded that 'upon the addition of additives, it increases permeability by decreasing its strength and vice-versa'. Balancing its permeability and strength remains challenging.

Introduction
In a recent study, it is revealed that India recycles only 1 percentage of C&D (Construction and Demolition) waste [1]. India produces nearly 150 million tones of construction and demolition waste each year. These wastes often contain materials such as asphalt, gypsum, concrete debris, plastic etc.., Those things cannot be recycled easily because it may heavy, inert and bulk in nature. In addition to these wastes, some non-hazardous wastes are also produced in bulk quantity[2]. Our project involves the utilization of Recycled coarse aggregates, Fly ash and Rice huskin no-fine concrete (also called as pervious concrete or porous concrete). Two goals can be achieved by using those waste materials in concrete mix – Minimizing waste and adding some good properties in concrete [3]. Since the concept of green concrete is dominating now-a-days, it is necessary to utilize waste from all aspects to determine its capability. These alternatives also reduces the usage of natural resources such as sand, rock etc.., which enhances sustainable development to larger extent. Three types of specimen were used in our experiment. First type of specimen utilizes Recycled coarse aggregates (RCA) as a replacement for coarse aggregates. Typical porous concrete mix may consists of 185-360 kg/m^3 of primary binders, 1400-1600 kg/m^3 of coarse aggregates and w/c ratio ranged from 0.27 to 0.45. Usually fine aggregates will not be used in pervious concrete, as it may reduces permeable properties. But usage of little amount of fine aggregates may increases mechanical properties such as compressive strength, flexural strength

Recent Advancements in Geotechnical Engineering - NCRAG'21   Materials Research Forum LLC
Materials Research Proceedings **19** (2021) 191-199   https://doi.org/10.21741/9781644901618-24

etc.., Specimen without RCA and with few percent of RCA were casted and checked for porosity, compressive strength and flexural strength. Recycled concrete aggregates may absorb some amount of water which may results in decrease of workability. So super plasticizer is added for better workability. Second type of specimen utilizes fly-ash as an alternative for cement in concrete mix. Fly ash is a coal combustion product which can be used as a supplementary cementitious material (SCM) [4]. The use of fly ash in concrete has many advantages. It improves performance of concrete in both fresh and hardened state. It also improves workability, strength and durability of hardened concrete [5]. Fly ash is a cost-effective product which may decreases construction cost to some extent. Third type of specimen utilizes Rice-husk as fine aggregate in concrete mix. Rice-husks are the hard protective coverings of rice grains. It contains approximately 40 percent of cellulose, 30 percent of lignin and 20 percent of silica [2]. Presence of lignin and silica enhances strength of concrete. As previously said, usage of fine aggregate may decreases permeability but it increases mechanical properties. Some part of coarse aggregates is replaced by fine aggregates and rice husk and properties were compared with conventional pervious concrete.

Materials
The materials used in our project are Cement, Coarse aggregates, Fine aggregates, Recycled concrete Aggregates, Fly ash, Rice husks and water. Some basic properties of those materials are tested and their results were discussed below.

i) *Cement:* Cement is a primary binder which binds all other ingredients and sets and hardens independently. It is made by heating Calcium Carbonate ($CaCO_3$) with other materials such as clay in a rotating kiln with a temperature of 1723.15K. In this project 53 grade Ordinary Portland cement (OPC) is used and tested for specific gravity, Fineness, Consistency, Initial setting time and Final setting time. The properties obtained are as follows:

Table 2.1: Properties of cement

Description	Test Values of OPC
Specific Gravity	3.13
Consistency	31
Fineness	9.3
Initial setting time	36 minutes
Final setting time	606 minutes

ii) *Coarse aggregates:* Coarse aggregates usually occupies 75 to 80 percent of volume in concrete mix. The crushed stone aggregates passing through 40mm sieve and retained in 20mm sieve are collected and used in our experiment. The properties of Coarse aggregates were evaluated on the basis of procedures given in IS:383-1970 and IS:2386-1963 (Part I, Part II, Part III). The coarse aggregates were tested for specific gravity, Fineness modulus and grade limit and results obtained are as follows:

Table 2.2: Properties of coarse aggregates

Description	Test Values
Maximum size	20mm
Specific gravity	2.47
Fineness modulus	7.2
Grade limit	Single sized aggregates

iii) *Fine aggregates:* Usage of fine aggregates in this type of concrete may improve mechanical properties. Manufactured sand (M-sand) were used. It is produced by crushing hard rocks or stones into small sand sized and angular shaped particles. M-sand is the best alternative for River sand. Aggregates passing through 4.75mm sieve and retained in 2.36mm sieve were used in our experiment. The fine aggregates were tested for specific gravity and fineness modulus. The results obtained are as follows:

Table 2.3: Properties of fine aggregates

Description	Test Values
Maximum size	2.36mm
Specific gravity	2.67
Fineness modulus	3.06

iv) *Additives:* Additives were used to improve the mechanical properties of concrete [6]. Three types of additives were used in three different specimens. They are Recycled concrete aggregates, Fly ash and rice husk. All these materials are tested for specific gravity and results obtained are as follows.

Table 2.4: Properties of additives

Materials	R.C.A	Fly ash	Rice husk
Specific Gravity	2.71	2.8	2.13

Fig 2.1: Concrete mix

Testing of specimens:
Various types of cube and prism specimen were casted with standard sizes and with suitable materials. The size of cube is 150mm x 150mm x 150mm and that of prism is 500mm x 100mm x 100mm. The cube specimen were tested for compressive strength and porosityand prism specimen were tested for flexure strength. The calculated amount of cement, coarse aggregates, fine aggregates and additives were mixed with suitable water cement ratio and specimen were casted with proper damping. After casting, the specimen were demouldedand curing was done for 28 days using curing tank. After 28 days of curing the specimen were tested for compression, flexure and porosity. The properties of various specimen were studied and compared.

Fig 3.1: Cube specimen

Recent Advancements in Geotechnical Engineering - NCRAG'21
Materials Research Proceedings **19** (2021) 191-199

Materials Research Forum LLC
https://doi.org/10.21741/9781644901618-24

Fig 3.2: *Prism specimen*

Compressive strength: Compressive strength of a specimen is the capacity of a concrete to withstand loads tending to reduce size, as opposed to which withstand loads tending to elongate. As per BIS:516-1959 cubes of standard dimension 150mm x 150mm x 150mm are tested in compressive testing machine of 3000 kN.The results obtaines are shown in Table 3.1 .Compressive strength can be calculated by using the formula

$$\text{Compressive strength} = \frac{Maximum\ load\ applied\ to\ the\ specimen\ in\ kN}{Area\ of\ the\ specimen\ in\ mm^2}$$

Table 3.1: *Compressive strength test results*

S.No	Additive used	Weight of cement (kg)	Weight of Coarse aggregates (kg)	Weight of Fine aggregates (kg)	Percentage of additives	Weight of additive (kg)	Load (kN)	Compressive strength (N/mm^2)
1.	None	2	6	0	-	-	226	10.04
2.	None	2	4.8	1.2	-	-	231	10.27
3.	R.C.A	2	5.7	0	5	0.3	224	9.96
4.	R.C.A	2	5.4	0	10	0.6	228	10.13
5.	R.C.A	2	5.1	0	15	0.9	227	10.09
6.	R.C.A	2	4.8	0	20	1.2	225	10.0
7.	Fly ash	1.9	6	0	5	0.1	225	10.0
8.	Fly ash	1.8	6	0	10	0.2	227	10.09
9.	Fly ash	1.7	6	0	15	0.3	228	10.13
10.	Fly ash	1.6	6	0	20	0.4	226	10.04
11.	Rice Husk	2	4.8	1.14	5	0.06	230	10.22
12.	Rice Husk	2	4.8	1.08	10	0.12	228	10.13
13.	Rice Husk	2	4.8	1.02	15	0.18	226	10.04
14.	Rice Husk	2	4.8	0.96	20	0.24	224	9.96

Fig 3.3: *Compression test*

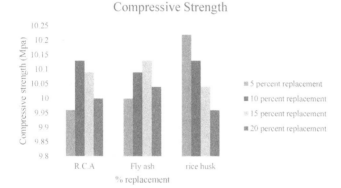

Fig 3.4: *% replacement vs Compressive strength chart*

Inference: The compressive strength test of specimens revealed that upon the addition of additives suitably, there is an improvement in compressive strengths than conventional concrete. Over usage of additives in concrete mix decreases compressive strength. It is appreciable to replace 10 percent of coarse aggregates by RCA and 15 percent of cement by fly ash and just 5 percent of fine aggregate by rice husk to yield better compressive strength which will be higher than conventional porous concrete.

Flexural strength: Flexural strength is a property of a material which is defined as the stress in a material just before it yields in a flexure strength. Concrete is strong in compression but weak in tension. Prism specimen of dimensions 500mm x 100mm x 100mm were casted and tested in flexural strength testing machine. Flexural strength can be calculated by using the formula

Flexural strength = $(P \times L)/(B \times D^2)$, where
P=Load applied in kN
L=Length of the specimen in mm
B=Breadth of the specimen in mm
D=Depth of the specimen in mm

Fig 3.5: *Flexural test*

The results obtained are shown in Table 3.2

Table 3.2: *Flexural strength test results*

S.No	Additive used	Weight of cement (kg)	Weight of Coarse aggregates (kg)	Weight of Fine aggregates (kg)	Percentage of additives	Weight of additive (kg)	Load (kN)	Flexural strength (N/mm^2)
1.	None	3.125	9.375	0	-	-	2.1	1.05
2.	None	3.125	7.5	1.875	-	-	2.3	1.15
3.	R.C.A	3.125	8.906	0	5	0.469	1.9	0.95
4.	R.C.A	3.125	8.438	0	10	0.937	2.2	1.1
5.	R.C.A	3.125	7.969	0	15	1.406	2.0	1.0
6.	R.C.A	3.125	7.5	0	20	1.875	1.7	0.85
7.	Fly ash	2.969	9.375	0	5	0.156	2.0	1.0
8.	Fly ash	2.812	9.375	0	10	0.313	2.2	1.1
9.	Fly ash	2.656	9.375	0	15	0.469	2.3	1.15
10.	Fly ash	2.5	9.375	0	20	0.625	2.1	1.05
11.	Rice Husk	3.125	7.5	1.781	5	0.094	2.0	1.0
12.	Rice Husk	3.125	7.5	1.687	10	0.188	1.8	0.9
13.	Rice Husk	3.125	7.5	1.594	15	0.281	1.6	0.8
14.	Rice Husk	3.125	7.5	1.5	20	0.375	1.3	0.65

Recent Advancements in Geotechnical Engineering - NCRAG'21   Materials Research Forum LLC
Materials Research Proceedings **19** (2021) 191-199   https://doi.org/10.21741/9781644901618-24

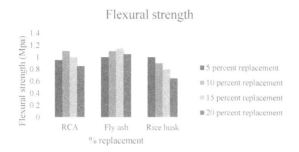

Fig 3.6: % replacement vs Flexural strength chart

Inference: The flexural strength test of specimens revealed that upon the addition of additives suitably, there is an improvement in flexural strengths than conventional concrete. Over usage of additives in concrete mix decreases flexural strength. As similar to that of compressive strength results it is also appreciable to replace 10 percent of coarse aggregates by RCA and 15 percent of cement by fly ash and just 5 percent of fine aggregate by rice husk to yield better flexural strength which will be higher than conventional porous concrete.

Porosity: Porosity is the measure of the void spaces in a concrete specimen, and it is the ratio of volume of voids to total volume. It is expressed in percentage and varies from 0 percent to 100 percent. Cube specimen of dimensions 150mm x 150mm x 150mm were used in porosity test. The specimens were immersed in known volume of water in a container for about 24 hours. By measuring the variation in water level before and after immersion, the volume of water replaced by the sample (V_r) can be calculated. Subtracting V_r from bulk volume (V), volume of open pores can be found. Hence porosity can be calculated by the formula

$$\text{Porosity percentage} = \frac{V_r - V}{V_r} \times 100$$

Fig 3.7: Porosity test

The results obtained are shown in Table 3.3

Table 3.3: Porosity test results

S.No	Additive used	Weight of cement (kg)	Weight of Coarse aggregates (kg)	Weight of Fine aggregates (kg)	Percentage of additives	Weight of additive (kg)	Porosity %
1.	None	2	6	0	-	-	39.6
2.	None	2	4.8	1.2	-	-	37.4
3.	R.C.A	2	5.7	0	5	0.3	37.1
4.	R.C.A	2	5.4	0	10	0.6	36.2
5.	R.C.A	2	5.1	0	15	0.9	34.8
6.	R.C.A	2	4.8	0	20	1.2	33.7
7.	Fly ash	1.9	6	0	5	0.1	38.5
8.	Fly ash	1.8	6	0	10	0.2	37.2
9.	Fly ash	1.7	6	0	15	0.3	35.9
10.	Fly ash	1.6	6	0	20	0.4	34.3
11.	Rice Husk	2	4.8	1.14	5	0.06	32.6
12.	Rice Husk	2	4.8	1.08	10	0.12	31.4
13.	Rice Husk	2	4.8	1.02	15	0.18	29.7
14.	Rice Husk	2	4.8	0.96	20	0.24	28.1

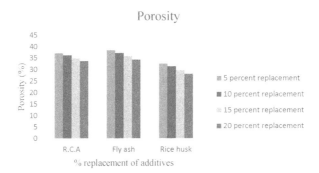

Fig 3.8: % replacement vs Porosity chart

Inference: The variation in porosity results were studied for pervious concrete with different additives. It is concluded that the porosity decreases even with the addition of small quantity of additives. Only the conventional porous concrete possess good porosity results. Replacement of coarse aggregates by RCA nearly maintains the porosity. Addition of finer particle additives like fly ash and rice husk arrests the voids in porous concrete which in turn decreases porosity. But decrease in voids content due to addition of additives will increase mechanical properties like compressive strength and flexural strength. It is also concluded that porosity is inversely proportional to percentage of additives added.

Materials Research Forum LLC
https://doi.org/10.21741/9781644901618-24

Conclusion and results:

The addition of various types of additives in porous concrete yields different results. Anyhow, the results obtained are in accordance with the acceptable limits. These type of concrete can be used in parking lots to improve ground water level. The pores in this concrete arrests the rain water run-off. In addition to this, the following conclusions are made.

1. The conventional pervious concrete possess high percentage of porosity when compared to those with additives. Adding additives decreases voids which in turn decreases porosity. But conventional porous concrete has low compressive and flexural strength comparatively.
2. Adding small amount of fine aggregates in a concrete mix decreases porosity by increasing its strength.
3. Replacing coarse aggregate by recycled concrete aggregate upto 10 percent gives good mechanical properties, but decreases porosity.
4. Replacing cement by fly ash upto 15 percent yields good mechanical properties (not greater than recycled concrete aggregates). This replacement also decreases porosity.
5. Replacing fine aggregates by rice husk does not improve mechanical properties and porosity. Hence this type of concrete cannot be used in heavy load applications due to its low strength.

References

[1] "Effects of rice husk ash and fibre on mechanical properties of pervious concrete pavement"-S Hesami, S Ahmadi, M Nematzadesh-Construction and building materials,2014.

[2] "Effects of Rice Husk ash on properties of pervious concrete"-S Talsania, J Pitroda,C M Vyas. 2015.

[3] "Properties of pervious concrete containing fly ash"- Y Aoki, R Sri Ravindrarajah-materials and pavement-2012.

[4] "Studies on the properties of pervious fly ash-cement concrete as a pavement material"-UM Muthaiyan, S Thirumalai- Cogent Engineering-2017.

[5] "Properties of pervious concrete containing recycled concrete block aggregate and recycled concrete aggregate"- Y Zaetang, V Sata, A Wongsa-Construction and building materials-2016.

[6] "Sustainable Design of Pervious concrete using waste glass and Recycled concrete aggregates"- J X Lu, Xyam, P He, C S Poon,Journal of cleaner production, 2019.

[7] "Influence of recycled aggregate replacement and fly ash content in performance of Pervious concrete mixes"-G L Vieira, J Z Schiavon, P M Borges, S R da Silva,Journal of cleaner production-2020.

Recent Advancements in Geotechnical Engineering - NCRAG'21
Materials Research Proceedings 19 (2021) 200-207

Materials Research Forum LLC
https://doi.org/10.21741/9781644901618-25

Experimental Study on Soil Stabilization Using Fibres

B. Priyadharshini[1,a*], Boopathiraj[1,b], P. Eshanthini[1,c]

[1]Department of civil engineering, Sathyabama Institute of Science and Technology, Chennai, India

[a*]dharspriya@gmail.com, [b]boopathiraj1964@gmail.com, [c]eshaindia14@gmail.com

Keywords: Bearing Capacity, CBR Test, Fine-Grained Soil, Fibres, Stabilization, Unconfined Compression, Unreinforced Sample

Abstract. For pavement constructions such as runway and highway construction, fine-grained soils are not suitable because of their undesirable properties such as grading of particle size, low bearing capacity, and more plasticity, and its ability to swell. To improve these soil properties various soil stabilization methods are needed. The stabilization is done by adding various stabilizing materials with the fine-grained soil. Fibres are one of the materials used in soil stabilization. This experimental study has been carried over to improve the bearing capacity of soft soil (from Sholinganallur, Chennai) by using Natural and Artificial fibres. During this study, the soil samples which has been stabilized with various fibres was prepared i.e., soil with Natural fibres (jute fibre) and soil with artificial fibres. In this experimental study, index properties and engineering properties of soft soil or unreinforced samples and stabilized soil samples with fibres are determined. Samples are subjected to various soil tests which have been used to determine the engineering properties of soil. The soil tests such as the standard proctor compaction test, unsoaked California Bearing Ratio (CBR) test, and Unconfined Compression (UCC) test had been done to determine the characteristics of the samples. To determine the properties of the reinforced materials, the fibres also have undergone various geosynthetic laboratory tests. The results of the study show that the bearing capacity of Shollinganallur fine-grained soil can be improved subsequently and water absorption by soil has been reduced significantly by using fibres.

Introduction
The fine-grained soils have low strength and high compressibility, building highways and runways over them is one of the most common civil engineering problems encountered in various parts of the world. [1]. So, Roads should be constructed on strong native soil deposits and the behaviour of the road surface depends upon the strength of the base material and the subgrade below it or the fine-grained soils are needed to be stabilized to attain a required strength of pavement [2]. Fine-grained soil is described as soil with a California Bearing Ratio (CBR) of less than 8% and an Unconfined Compressive Strength (UCS) of less than 48 kPa that requires stabilization, especially in pavement applications, to improve its properties. The standard method for building a highway or runway on fine-grained soils is to excavate the soft soil layer and then substitute it with a stabilizing material such as geosynthetics, crushed rock, or other similar materials., The high cost of transporting soil makes higher authorities establish the alternate solution of construction of structures on fine-grained soils and new techniques of stabilization [3]. Stabilization is important to increase the strength of the base layer based on that the base course gravel layer can be constructed. Stabilization is being used for many engineering works, the common application being in the construction of pavements such as road and airfield pavements, where the aim is to increase the bearing capacity or strength of fine-grained soil and to reduce the construction cost [4][5]. The pavement is supported by subgrade soil and which helps the foundation to carry a load

Recent Advancements in Geotechnical Engineering - NCRAG'21   Materials Research Forum LLC
Materials Research Proceedings **19** (2021) 200-207   https://doi.org/10.21741/9781644901618-25

and for this purpose, an appropriate value of California bearing ratio (CBR) is required for subgrade soil to ensure required strength to support the imposed load came from traffic, regardless adverse conditions such as high rainfall and flooding. Some of the subgrade soils are not able to meet these criteria because of lower and inappropriate CBR values [6]. The geosynthetics which have been most commonly used in the construction field are geosynthetic clay liners, geomembranes, geogrids, fibres, geonets, geocomposite drainage materials, erosion control blankets, and materials [7]. The word 'Geo synthetics' has two parts in it, the 'geo' indicates an increase in the stability of civil engineering works including earth or ground or soil and the 'synthetics' indicates the man-made products. synthetic polymers are used to manufacture geosynthetics which are commonly derived from crude petroleum oils, rubber [8]. Sometimes other materials apart from the oils, rubber is also used for the manufacturing of geosynthetics. The major functions of geosynthetic materials, related to civil engineering are drainage reinforcement, separation, filtration, and acting as a liquid barrier. Fibres is one of the geosynthetic materials used to improve the stability of soil [9]. Fibres are used in flexible pavement systems for separation and reinforcement purposes which have been obtained from planar polymeric materials and for many years, the fibres are used in the construction of road works, which has been acting as a separator in the area of stabilization [10][11]. This is the major application of fibres. Natural and synthetic (artificial) fibres are usually graded based on their material composition. Natural fibres such as jute fibre (Geojute) and coir nets are widely used and biodegradable, whereas synthetic fibres are made from synthetic polymer materials and are not biodegradable. Geojute is produced from jute plants that have been pollinated by bees [13]. Synthetic fibres are used in between the subgrade for two purposes. One is to improve the bearing capacity of subgrade and another one is to improve the efficiency of drainage. The main purpose is to the addition of these materials in soil are, the fabric reinforcement has to stay in the soil, for the entire life span of structure and also to separate the various layers or grades of soil [12]. An increase in fibre content will increase the tensile strength of the soil along with the maximum dry density and reduce the water content[15].

Materials and Methodology
This experimental study was aimed to use natural and synthetic fibres for improving the bearing capacity in fine-grained soil. Fine-grained soil samples were obtained from ponniamman temple street nearby Shollinganallur, Chennai. In this study, the fine-grained soil has alone undergone all the tests which are used to find out the soil properties. The laboratory tests such as particle size analysis, Specific gravity, Atterberg limits, Unconfined compression (UCC) test were performed on a fine-grained soil sample which is taken from the above location and shown in Table.1. Then natural fibres have been added to the soil to find out the variation in the engineering properties of soil with the use of the following tests as Direct shear test, Standard proctor compaction test, California bearing ratio (CBR) test. Again, the same procedure was repeated for synthetic (artificial) fibres. All three tests were conducted on three different samples. Results obtained from all three conditions are compared and the experiment was concluded based upon the effect of material that is used to improve the properties of soil in that fine-grained soil.

Table 1. Properties of unreinforced soil

S No	Test	Characteristics	Unit	Result
1	Sieve test	Sand	%	86.8
		Fine	%	13.2
2	Direct shear test	Ultimate shear angle	Degree	'0'(for cohesive soil)
3	Atterberg limits	Liquid limit (LL)	%	32.20
		Plastic limit (PL)	%	51.35
		Plasticity index (Ip)	%	19.15
4	Soil classification	USCS	-	SC (Clayey sand)
5	Specific gravity Test	G_s	-	2.65
6	Standard proctor Test	Optimum moisture content	%	12
7	Compaction Test	Maximum dry density (d_{max})	g/cc	1.894
8		For 2.5mm Penetration	%	2.26
	California			
9	Bearing ratio test	For 5.0mm Penetration	%	2.92

Stabilizing materials are namely natural and synthetic fibres were obtained from home and industry respectively. Synthetic fibres are light grey. Table 2 shows the properties of natural and synthetic fibres from Mahuyu Ghosh et.al.,(2014) [14]

Table 2. Properties of fibres(after Mahuya Ghosh 2009)

Type of fibres	Properties	Unit	Result
Natural fibres	Thickness	Mm	4.0
	Tensile strength	Kn	8.0
	Bursting strength (Mass/unit area test)	kg/cm^2	0.375
Synthetic fibres	Thickness	Mm	0.7
	Tensile strength	kN	4.20
	Bursting strength (Mass/unit area test)	kg/cm^2	8.50

Results and Discussion

Particle Size Analysis
The particle size distribution analysis was conducted to classify the soil sample which has been taken for experiment purpose. From the result of sieve analysis and based on the Unified soil classification system, the soil was classified as Clayey sand (SC), (refer to table-1).

Specific gravity
The specific gravity of a soil sample was determined with the use of a pycnometer. The weight of the pycnometer with various conditions are observed and the values are substituted in the specific gravity formula. The specific gravity soil sample is tabulated in table 1. The specific gravity of clayey soil is between 2.65 to 2.67.

Atterberg Limits
According to ASTM D4318, the Atterberg limits tests were carried out on samples, which is "Standard Test Methods for Plastic Limit (PL) and Liquid Limit (LL) of Soils". The results were obtained and the values are tabulated in Table 1.

Soil Classification
Using the result obtained by various tests such as Atterberg limits and sieve test (particle size analysis), the group symbol, i.e., According to ASTM D2487 the sample was classified from "Standard Practice for Classification of Soils for Engineering Purposes (Unified Soil Classification System)". The results were obtained are tabulated in Table 1. The classification shows that the soil sample which has been carried over from Ponniamman temple street fine-grained soil is SC (clayey sand)

Unconfined compressive strength test (UCC)
This test is used to determine the compressive strength and cohesion of the soil sample, normally it is used for cohesive soil (Fine-grained soils), during the test the lateral confining pressure is equal to zero. The UCS value indicates the compressive stress at which the cylindrical sample fails. The maximum value which was observed during the test was marked as compressive strength. For UCS test specimens (diameter greater than 30 mm and height to diameter ratio between 2 to 2.5), half of the value of compressive stress at failure is denoted as the cohesion of the sample. The UCS test was performed on an unreinforced soil sample and values were tabulated in Table 3 and plotted in Fig 1. The UCS value at the failure of a sample from the graph is 0.34 N/mm^2 and the cohesion will be half of this value which is 0.17 N/mm^2.

Table 3. Compressive strength and cohesion of unreinforced soil

Properties	Unconfined compressive strength at failure (q_u) (N/mm^2)	Cohesion (C) (N/mm^2)
Unconfined compression test	0.34	0.17

Recent Advancements in Geotechnical Engineering - NCRAG'21   Materials Research Forum LLC
Materials Research Proceedings 19 (2021) 200-207   https://doi.org/10.21741/9781644901618-25

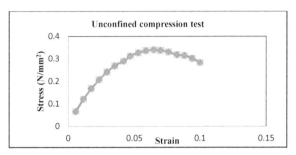

Fig 1. *Compressive strength and cohesion of unreinforced soil*

Standard Proctor Compaction test

According to Method A of ASTM D1557, the standard Proctor compaction tests were carried out on different samples. The fibres were laid with three layers with a soil sample to improve the stabilization. The result of these tested samples is to be used in sample preparation for the California bearing ratio tests. The results were tabulated in Table 4. The maximum dry density of the samples of the soil increases with the addition of fibres and the optimum moisture content varies between 12% and 10% [14]. The gradual decrease in Optimum moisture content indicates that the adsorption of water by the fine-grained soil is reduced. The results were plotted in Fig 2.

Table 4. *Proctor test result of different samples*

Properties of samples	Unreinforced soil	Soil with natural fibres	Soil with synthetic fibres
Optimum moisture content (%)	12	10	10.8
Maximum dry density (g/cc)	1.714	1.780	1.856

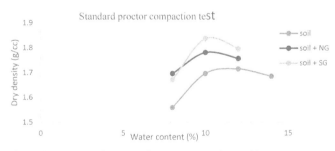

Fig 2. *Relation between dry density and water content obtained by compaction test*

California Bearing Ratio (CBR)

CBR test samples were prepared with a predetermined water content which was obtained from the standard proctor compaction test. CBR test is used to find the bearing ratio of the sample under a gradual increase in pressure. According to ASTM D1883, the test procedure was carried out i.e., "Standard Test Method for CBR (California Bearing Ratio) of Laboratory-Compacted Soils" shown in Fig 3.The samples were placed in three layers with the unreinforced soil and tested. The results of CBR tests carried out in this study are tabulated in Table 5 and plotted in Fig. 4.

Fig 3. *CBR test apparatus and CBR moulds*

Table 5. *Bearing ratios of different samples*

Properties \ samples	Unreinforced soil	Soil with natural fibres	Soil with synthetic fibres
For 2.5mm penetration – CBR (%)	2.26	4.015	2.55
For 5.0mm penetration – CBR (%)	2.92	3.698	3.55

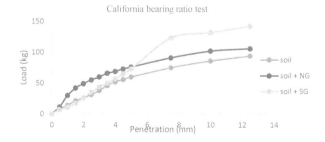

Fig 4. *The load corresponding to penetration of different samples*

Recent Advancements in Geotechnical Engineering - NCRAG'21   Materials Research Forum LLC
Materials Research Proceedings **19** (2021) 200-207   https://doi.org/10.21741/9781644901618-25

Direct Shear Test
This is the simple test that is used to determine the shearing strength of the different soil samples. This test was performed under two conditions are soil with natural fibres and soil with synthetic fibres.In the shear box the sample place in two layers and tested. The results from the shear test were tabulated in table 6 and the results were discussed in Table 6. Fig 5 show the stress difference between normal and shear.

Table 6. *Angle of Shear resistance for different soil samples*

Determination \ samples	Unreinforced sample	Soil with natural fibres	Soil with synthetic fibres
Ultimate shear angle	0^0 0'(for cohesive soil)	$20^0 5$ '	$43^0 9$ '

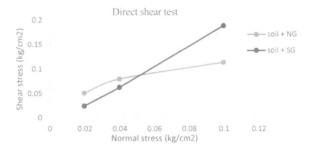

Fig 5. *Relation between Direct shear test resulting graphs of different soil samples*

Conclusion
This experimental study shows the effect of fibres addition on the geotechnical properties of the collected fine-grained soil. According to the results, the conclusion is as follows: Standard proctor compaction test results were obtained from the tests conducted on fine-grained soil by placing fibres sheet gives a reduction in optimum moisture content from 12% without fibres to 10% when carried out with natural fibres and 10.8% when carried out with artificial fibres and the maximum dry density was increasing with the addition of fibres, suggesting that the fibres inclusion is effective in improving soil failure ductility. Fine-grained soil is a cohesive soil that has zero angles of internal friction but when replaced with Natural and Artificial Fibres it possesses an angle of 20 05 ' and 43 09 ' respectively. The CBR values of soil with stabilized samples and soil without stabilized (unreinforced) sample shows that the increment in bearing capacity of the soil and makes it applicable for pavement. The stability of soil has been increased with reduction in optimum moisture when replaced with fibres gives wide applications of civil structures to be raised on fine-grained soil.

Materials Research Forum LLC
https://doi.org/10.21741/9781644901618-25

References

[1] Murat azizozdemiR, Improvement in bearing capacity of a soft soil by addition of fly ash,Procedia Engineering, 143, 2016, 498-505. https://doi.org/10.1016/j.proeng.2016.06.063

[2] Ogundare D.A, Familusi A.O, Utilization of fibres for soil stabilization, American J Eng Research, 7(8), 2018, 224-231.

[3] B.Panigrahi, P.K. Pradhan, Improvement in bearing capacity of a soil by using natural geotextile, Int J Geo Eng, 10(9),2019, 1-12. https://doi.org/10.1186/s40703-019-0105-7

[4] Vivekkakdiya, Pushpendramisha, Soil stabilization using bamboo fibers, Int j Innovative tech, 5(11), 2019,436-440.

[5] Mahdi TaghipourMasoumi, Ali Abdi Kordani, Experimental study of geotextile effect on improving soil bearing capacity in aggregate surfaced roads, Int J Civil and Env Eng, 11, 2017, 43-49.

[6] Ajeet Rathee, Geetshivdasani, Shubham Sharma, Yash Sharma, Study on stabilization of soil using powdered glass, IJRET, 5(5), 2018 pp 1054-1056.

[7] Dhule S.B, Lalit jiremali, Shailesh shejwal, Sana Nasser, Kiran shejwal, Leena wanare, Study on stabilization of soil using stone dust, IJRET, 6(5), 2019, 815-828.

[8] Anjanadevi K.A, Azharrahman A.R, Merine George, Soil stabilization using jute and human hair fiber, IRJET, 6(5), 2019, 5117-5121.

[9] Sunil, Akash batra, Pappu Sharma, Sohanlal, Soil stabilization by using jute fiber, IRJET, 6(3), 2019, 8209-8212.

[10] Ankit Yaduvansh, Ankur tayal, Aman bhatnagar, Varun Aggarwal, Plastic as a soil stabilizer, IRJET 6(4),2019, 4866- 4870.

[11] B.Priyadharshini, M.Kavisri, Utilization of textile sludge in manufacturing e-bricks, Int J Civil Eng and Tech, 9(11), 2018, 2266–2273.

[12] Sridhar Rajagopalaiah, A Review on Improvement of Subgrade Soil Using Coir Geotextile2019, Springer international publishing, 2014.

[13] Mahuya Ghosh, P.K. Choudhury and Tapobrata Sanyal, Suitability of Natural Fibres in Geotextile Applications, IGC 2009, Indian geotechnical society, 2009.

[14] N F Bawadi, N S Ahmad, A F Mansor, S A Anuar1 and M A Rahim, Effect of natural fibers on the soil compaction characteristics, IOP Conf. Series: Earthand Environmental Science 476, 2020 012043. https://doi.org/10.1088/1755-1315/476/1/012043

[15] Jian Li, Chaosheng Tang, Deying Wang, Xiangjun Pei, Bin Shi, Effect of discrete fibre reinforcement on soil tensile strength,J Rock Mech and Geo Eng 6(2), 2014, 133-137. https://doi.org/10.1016/j.jrmge.2014.01.003

[16] Kavisri M,Sathish S, B.Priyadharshini, Experimental Studies on Properties of Self-Compacting Concrete by Partial Replacement of Cement by Industrial Waste Red Mud and Slag, Indian J Env Protection, 39(10),2019, 902–904.

Recent Advancements in Geotechnical Engineering - NCRAG'21   Materials Research Forum LLC
Materials Research Proceedings 19 (2021) 208-214   https://doi.org/10.21741/9781644901618-26

Experimental Study on the Behavior of Tension Member Under Rupture

M. Rajendran[1,a*], V. Gnanasundar[1,b], C. Aravindhan[1,c]

[1]Department of Civil Engineering, Bannari Amman Institute of Technology, Sathyamangalam,Tamil Nadu, India – 638401

[a*]rajendranm@bitsathy.ac.in, [b]gnanasundar@bitsathy.ac.in, [c]aravindhanc@bitsathy.ac.in

Keywords: Tension Member, Hot-Rolled Steel Sections, Rupture Strength, Lap Joint, Bolted Connections, Pitch, Gauge, End and Edge Distance

Abstract. A steel structure is naturally lighter than a comparable concrete construction because of the higher strength and firmness of steel. Nowadays, the growth of steel structures in India is enormous. There are so many advantages in adopting the steel as structural members. Almost all high-rise buildings, warehouses & go-downs are steel structures and even some of the commercial buildings are made of steel. Tension members are the elements that are subjected to direct axial load which tends in the elongation of the structural members. Even today bolted connections play a major role in the connection of hot rolled structural steel members. In this experimental study the behavior of tension members (TM) such as plates, angles & channels have been studied under axial tensile force. There is strong relation between pitch and gauge (with in the specified limit as per IS 800:2007) in determining the rupture failure plane. In this study we intensively tested the behaviour of TM for different fasteners pattern by changing the pitch, gauge, end & edge distance and by adopting the different patterns or arrangements of bolted connection in it.

Introduction

Steel is a structural member which is extensively used in industrial buildings, warehouse, residential buildings as a tensile member. Due to its tensile property, industrial buildings and warehouses are completely constructed with steel. When using steel entirely in buildings, duration of the construction can be significantly reduced [1]. In future, usage of steel in construction is going to be increased. So, we are determining tensile strength [2] of steel by testing the steel as per IS standard with varying connections such as chain pattern, zig-zag pattern, diamond pattern with varying pitch and gauge distance.

Cold-formed structural steel plates of thickness 1.5 mm can be lap joined with bolted connections which are designed as per IS 800-2007[3]. The final load-supporting potential connection considered to feasible failure modes, which includes bearing, give-up tear-out, bolt shear, block shear [4], rupture, etc... fy=550MPa, G300 (fy=300MPa) sheet plates were inspected. From the result we concluded that both the Australian/New Zealand (AS/NZS 4600, "cold-shaped metallic" and the Iron and metallic Institute (AISI, "1996version" 1997) layout requirements cannot be used to expect the failure modes of skinny-sheet-steel bolted connection loaded in shear.

Commonly, the internet-phase fracture is predicted looking at outcomes displayed that bearing distress in the sheet metal is the controlling mode. Likewise, suggestions are made regarding themodern-day method to become aware of the bearing-failure modes [5]. Furthermore, a detailed discussion is equipped with the test data that being used inside the improvement of the AS/NZS 4600 ("cold-shaped steel" 1996) [6]and AISI ("1996edition" 1997) design equations used for connections.Several different types of bolted connections, including shear connections at the ends of coped beams, tension member connections, and gusset plates, can be regulated by a block shear failure [7]. A tension force in the splice causes the flange plates to deform in normal loading conditions [8]. bolted connections are often favoured over other forms of mechanical fasteners, such as split rings [9].

Figure 1.Universal Testing Machine   *Figure 2.Testing of Metal Plate*

Materials Used
1. Thin Metal Sheet of thickness 1.5mm
2. Fastener of size 12.75 mm
3. Driller for holes

Figure 3.Thin Metal Sheet of 1.5mm thick   *Figure 4.Fastener of 12.75mm*

Thin Metal Sheet
Thin metal sheet is used because of its many advantages like it is resistance to corrosion and prone to all weather conditions. The sheet metallic fabrication is idealized for used in today's environment in which various weather and climatic conditions and it is more durable. The sheet metals are sufficient to resist pressures and it is easy to make a drill on it. The thin sheet metals of thickness 1.5mm are designed on the length of 120mm and width of 75mm respectively (Refer with: Figure 3). The thin metal sheet is designed and cut to the required size for the different patterns of bolted arrangements.

Recent Advancements in Geotechnical Engineering - NCRAG'21
Materials Research Proceedings **19** (2021) 208-214

Materials Research Forum LLC
https://doi.org/10.21741/9781644901618-26

Fastener
The fasteners used in this project are the Mild Steel fasteners of diameter 12.75 mm.(Refer with: Figure 4)

Methodology
Preparation of bolted metal sheet -Lap Joint
Initially, the thin metal sheet of thickness 1.5mm are purchased in market and cut for our desired length and width to do our experiment purpose.Then after cutting in suitable size and width, do measures to make the lap joint for the metal plates.To ensure twice it was placed in a current position to make holes in it. The bolt arrangement will play a major role in it.Totally there are nine plates, the pattern consists of zig-zag of 3 sets, diamond of 3 sets and the finally the bolt are arranged as chain pattern.After placing, mark with chalk piece for putting holes to hold the fastener in it.By the help of drillers, we need to drill the hole after tightly fix in a drilling machine then turn on the drilling machine to make the hole. After the drilling was done ensure that the fastener will fix in it and finally place the fastener and tight it as a lap joint connection.

Testing of Bolted Metal Sheet – Lap Joint
After the metal plates with lap joint get ready, it is supposed to test in the lab for identifying the failure modes of the fastener and the bolt arrangement to check where it gets failed, whether it is safe or unsafe and all. The machine used for testing these plates is named as Universal Testing Machine (UTM) (Refer with: Figure 1)which can withstand up to40 tones. Initially, turn on the UTM and push the up bottom or down button to make space to fit the thin metal bolted lap joint sheet in the machine. After got placed in the machine we need to tight it up and down manually (Refer with: Figure 2). Then we are supposed to give load for that particular metal bolted sheet and carefully note the reading when the needle in the meter reaches the value and suddenly get back.We need to take the reading, when the needle starts from the point back to zero. This value is known as the edge value of the bolted connection. Then the same procedures are repeated for the further designed bolted metal plates of lap joint.Then after completing the tests for all the nine plates compare and conclude the value.

Thickness of a Bolt = 15mm
Diameter of a Bolt = 12.7mm
Area of a Single Bolt = 126.61 mm^2
Shear Calculation:
$A_{nb} = 0.8 * A_{sb}$
= 100 mm^2.
Vn_{sb} = 400/√3*(1+100)
= 18.656 KN
End / Edge Distance:
Minimum Distance = 1.5 * d$_o$
=21 mm.
Pitch & Gauge Distance:
Minimum Distance = 2.5 * d$_o$
= 35 mm.
Maximum Distance = 16t.
Single Bolt Value = 16.154 KN
4*Total Bolt Value = 32.308 KN.

Recent Advancements in Geotechnical Engineering - NCRAG'21   Materials Research Forum LLC
Materials Research Proceedings **19** (2021) 208-214   https://doi.org/10.21741/9781644901618-26

Result and Discussion
Provided Edge Distance as per IS 800:2007:

Table 1: Edge distance provided as per IS 800:2007 recommendations.

Provided Dimension and Calculated Value	Obtained Result	Type of Failure
Gross yielding=25.58KN Rupture strength=20.31KN	Result=23KN	RUPTURE FAILURE
Gross yielding=25.56KN Rupture strength =23.39 KN	Result=24.6KN	SHEAR AND EDGE FAILURE
Gross yielding=28.2 KN Rupture strength =20.83 KN	Result=28KN	BEARING FAILURE

The testing is done in Steel Plates with the edge distance as same as codal recommendations. In Chain Patten as per codal recommendations the edge distance is provided as 20 mm, in that a calculated Tensile Strength is 25.58 KN. But, in tested it occurs a failure at 23 KN and a rapture failure is occurred. Next, In Zig- Zag Pattern edge distance is 20 mm, in that a calculated Tensile Strength is 23.34 KN. But, in tested it occurs a failure at 24.6 KN and a Shear and Edge failure is occurred. Next, In Diamond Pattern edge distance is 20 mm, in that a calculated Tensile Strength is 20.81 KN. But, in tested it occurs a failure at 28 KN and a Bearing Failure is occurred (Refer with: Table 1).

Reducing Edge Distance

Table 2: Reduced Edge distance than recommended by IS 800:2007.

Provided Dimension and Calculated Value	Obtained Result	Type of Failure
Gross yielding=27.48KN Rupture strength =22.48KN	Result= 21.8KN	RUPTURE FAILURE
Gross yielding =22.37KN Rupture strength =20.14KN	Result=22.6KN	SHEAR AND EDGE FAILURE
Gross yielding = 25.83KN Rupture strength = 17.513KN	Result=25KN	BEARING AND SHEAR AND EDGE FAILURE

The testing is done in Steel Plates with the reduced edge distance of 15 mm. In Chain Patten the calculated Tensile Strength is 22.48 KN. But, in tested the rapture failure occurred at 21.8 KN and the plates gets a buckled. In Zig- Zag Pattern edge distance is 15 mm, in that a calculated Tensile Strength is 20.14 KN. But, in tested it occurs a failure at 22.6 KN and a Shear and Edge failure is occurred. Next, In Diamond Pattern edge distance is 15 mm, in that a calculated Tensile Strength is 17.51 KN. But, in tested it occurs a failure at 25 KN and a Bearing Failure is occurred (Refer with: Table 2).

Increasing Edge Distance

Table 3: IncreasedEdge distance than recommended by IS 800:2007.

Provided Dimension and Calculated Value	Obtained Result	Type of Failure
Gross yielding= 30.29KN Rupture strength =28KN	Result=20.8KN	RUPTURE FAILURE
Gross yielding=25.14KN Rupture strength =23.14KN	Result=26KN	SHEAR AND EDGE FAILURE
Gross yielding=27.45KN Rupture strength =21.51KN	Result=26.8KN	BEARING AND RUPTURE FAILURE

The testing is done in the Steel Plates with the increased edge distance of 25 mm. In Chain Patten the calculated Tensile Strength is 21.48 KN. But, in tested it occurs a failure at 20.8 KN and a rapture failure is occurred. In Zig- Zag Pattern edge distance is 15 mm, in that a calculated

Tensile Strength is 23.14 KN. But, in tested it occurs a failure at 26 KN and a Shear and Edge failure is occurred. In Diamond Pattern edge distance is 20 mm, in that a calculated Tensile Strength is 21.51 KN. But, in tested it occurs a failure at 26.8 KN and a Bearing and Rupture failure is occurred (Refer with: Table 3).

Conclusion

As the experiment is done in 3 different methods by changing the edge distance from the reducing and increasing and same as the code provided. in that experiment and come to conclusion that by changing the edge distance in increasing the edge distance in zig zag connection obtained a higher strength then the code provided by its failure under a buckling an edge plates is gets a tear and got failure it is not recommended while designing a connection. In other connections are obtaining a strength less than the code provided. So, edge distance provided in code is better for designing a connection.

References

[1] Huajie Wen, Hussam Mahmoud, Simulation of block shear fracture in bolted connections, Journal of Constructional Steel Research, 2017, Volume 134, pg 1-17. https://doi.org/10.1016/j.jcsr.2017.03.006

[2] IS 800-2007 Indian Standard GENERAL CONSTRUCTION IN STEEL – CODE OF PRACTICE (Third Revision).

[3] Matthew D. Elliott, Lip H. The, Aziz Ahmed, Behavior and strength of bolted connections failing in shear, Journal of Constructional Steel Research, Volume 153, February 2019, pg 320-329. https://doi.org/10.1016/j.jcsr.2018.10.029

[4] Bo Yang, Kang Hai Tan, Experimental tests of different types of bolted steel beam–column joints under a central-column-removal scenario, Engineering Structures 54 (2013), pg 112-130. https://doi.org/10.1016/j.engstruct.2013.03.037

[5] Lip H. The, Mehmet E. Uz, Effect of loading direction on the bearing capacity of cold-reduced steel sheets, Journal of Structural Engineering, Volume 140, Issue 12, December 2014. https://doi.org/10.1061/(ASCE)ST.1943-541X.0001107

[6] AS/NZS 4600:1996, Dec 2005, cold-formed steel structures.

[7] Jagdish R. Dhanuskar, Laxmikant M. Gupta, Experimental Investigation of Block Shear Failure in a Single Angle Tension Member, International Journal of Steel Structures, 2020, pp 847-859

[8] S. Willibald, J. A. Packer, R. S. Puthli, Experimental study of bolted HSS flange-plate connections in axial tension, J. Struct. Eng., 2020, Volume 128, pp 328-336. https://doi.org/10.1061/(ASCE)0733-9445(2002)128:3(328)

[9] N. Gattesco, I. Toffolo, Experimental study on multiple-bolt steel-to-timber tension joints, Materials and structures, 2004,Volume 37, pp 129-138. https://doi.org/10.1617/13724

Recent Advancements in Geotechnical Engineering - NCRAG'21
Materials Research Proceedings 19 (2021) 215-221

Materials Research Forum LLC
https://doi.org/10.21741/9781644901618-27

Feasibility Study on the Utilization of Manufactured Sand as a Partial Replacement for River Sand

Dr. B. Vijaya[1,a*], Dr. S. Senthil Selvan[2,b]

[1]Associate Professor, Department of Civil Engineering, Dr. M.G.R. Educational and Research Institute, Chennai, Tamilnadu, India

[2]Professor in Civil Engg, S.R.M. Institute of Science and Technology, Kattankulathur, Chennai, Tamilnadu, India

[a]bvijayasuresh@gmail.com, [b]senthils10@srmist.edu.in

Keywords: River Sand, Manufactured Sand, Soundness Test, EDAX, Modulus of Elasticity, Pull Out Test

Abstract. Continuous extraction of sand is having a huge impact on the natural river beds which has resulted in lowering of water table and a decrease in the amount of sediment supply. Despite the quantity of sand used in our day-to-day activities, our dependence on sand is significantly increasing. The use of manufactured sand as a fine aggregate in concrete draws the attention of many investigators and researchers. The present investigation includes the study of soundness and EDAX .The test results depicted that for M-sand substituted concrete the loss of weight, when subjected to alternate cycles of freezing and thawing when tested with magnesium and sodium sulphate solution was found to be less when compared with natural sand. The important observation is that the inclusion of manufactured sand in concrete reduces the pores present in concrete resulting in matrix densification and makes the concrete impermeable and substantially reduces the rate of oxygen diffusion and reduces the corrosion process as well. This paper also focuses on the effect of manufactured sand as a fine aggregate in the elastic and bond characteristics of concrete.

Introduction

Natural sand tends to be round due to the cumulative effect of multiple collisions and abrasion. Manufactured sand are the product of rock crushing, which creates grains with distinctive particle shapes that depend upon the parent rock composition fracture mode coordination number during crushing, and the reduction ratio. The crushing process tends to produce angular sharp edged particles [1]. The shape and texture of crushed sand particles results in the enhancement of the strength of concrete due to better interlocking between particles[2].However, for the same water content the angular fine aggregate produces mortar of lower workability than spherical sand [3-5],and for the same volume of cement paste [5-7]. Additional water is often incorporated into cement mixtures to enhance the workability, yet higher water content decreases strength, even though there is increase in the inter particle shear resistance[8].

Washing of the micro-fines according to the Chinese national standard JTG F 30-2003 limits the amount of micro-fines to 5% [9], and it is not feasible to eliminate a portion of them. With the depletion in the river sand supply by over 80%, the necessity for the use of manufactured sand is increasing and is well defined under clause 2 in IS 383-1970 [10].

The bond between concrete and steel enables tensile forces (which concrete has a very low ability to resist) to be transferred to the reinforcement. This steel-concrete bond can be assessed through the bond strength. Bond strength measures the effectiveness of the bond between the

Recent Advancements in Geotechnical Engineering - NCRAG'21   Materials Research Forum LLC
Materials Research Proceedings **19** (2021) 215-221   https://doi.org/10.21741/9781644901618-27

concrete and the embedded steel. The bond strength is determined by the pull-out test conforming to IS: 2770 (Part I) -1967 [11]. The design accuracy of concrete will depend on the modulus of elasticity of concrete and it was determined as per IS 516-1959 [12].

Sodium sulphate soundness test as per AS 1141.24

The sodium sulphate and magnesium sulphate soundness test was one of the earliest tests adopted for testing the resistance of aggregates to weathering action. This soundness test was conducted as per AS 1141.24. (1997) [13] to determine the percentage loss of the aggregate which is subjected to a chemical attack. The obtained results of soundness test are presented in Table 1. The aggregate sample preparation is depicted in Figure.1.

Figure. 1   *Aggregate Sample Preparation for Sodium and Magnesium*
Sulphate Soundness Test

Table 1 *Soundness Test*

Sample	Test conducted	Result (%)	Remark
River sand	The average loss of weight after 5 cycles of freezing and thawing when tested with Sodium Sulphate solution. (in percentage)	5.79	The aggregate values shall not exceed 10% and 15% (5cycles) by weight respectively for aggregate when tested with sodium sulphate and magnesium sulphate solution as per IS 383 -1970 [10].
Manufactured sand		1.6	
River Sand	The average loss of weight after 5 cycles of freezing and thawing when tested with Magnesium Sulphate solution. (in percentage)	7.64	
Manufactured sand		2.0	

Recent Advancements in Geotechnical Engineering - NCRAG'21   Materials Research Forum LLC
Materials Research Proceedings **19** (2021) 215-221   https://doi.org/10.21741/9781644901618-27

Presence of impurities such as silt, clay in river sand makes it inferior to soundness test when it is subjected to alternate cycles of freezing and thawing when tested with magnesium and sodium sulphate solution and hence the average loss of weight was found as more when compared with M-sand. M-sand as it is manufactured from VSI crusher it is free from deleterious impurities such as silt and clay and hence the loss of weight when is subjected to alternate cycles of freezing and thawing when tested with magnesium and sodium sulphate solution was found to 1.6 and 2 percentage respectively. The percentage loss of weight for M-sand is very less when compared to natural sand. This proves that M-sand is a good and durable material and M-sand may be used for concrete construction works.

EDAX analysis
EDAX is an energy dispersive analysis done with the help of X-ray which depicts the elemental composition of individual crystals. EDAX is an X-ray system used to identify the basic organization of materials. Peak positions and intensities associated with the pattern are analysed using computers to enable the qualitative analysis. The EDAX shows the various mineral elements present in normal sand and manufactured sand.

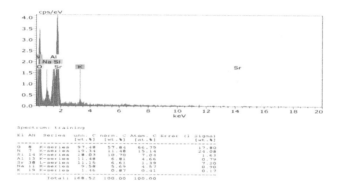

Figure. 2 EDAX Results of River Sand

Figure. 2 shows the EDAX results of river sand. The EDAX of river sand shows the strong peaks for aluminium, silicon, oxygen and weak peaks for strontium, sodium, and potassium. The EDAX seems to have agglomerated expansive gathering of particles of silicon, strontium, oxygen, nitrogen and aluminium. The EDAX clearly shows that there are no traces of iron and calcium particles in river sand but M-sand possesses strong peaks of iron and calcium particles. River sand contains nitrogen, aluminium and potassium elements which are not present in M-sand. There are some regions which appear flattened showing less hydration process. A tangled web of flake-like crystal structure appears due to excess hydration process. The minerals present in river sand form hydrated compounds which give better workability to river sand when compared to M-sand.

Materials Research Forum LLC
https://doi.org/10.21741/9781644901618-27

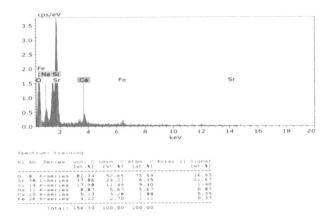

Figure. 3 *EDAX Results of Manufactured Sand*

Figure.3, shows the EDAX results of manufactured sand. The EDAX of manufactured sand shows the strong peaks for silicon, strontium, oxygen and weak peaks for calcium, iron, sodium. The EDAX seems to have agglomerated expansive gathering of particles of silicon, strontium, oxygen, calcium Iron etc. The extent of coverage is substantial. There are some regions where no hydration had taken place and there is the absence of deposition of hydration products. Some regions illustrate that the hydration process had taken place and there is a change in the appearance of the peaks. There are some regions which show an abundance of hydration products which changes the appearance from small isolated particles to a tangled web of flake-like crystals. The calcium present in M-sand reacts with alumina and oxides and produces tricalcium aluminate which allows early setting and thereby reduces the workability when compared with river sand.

Experimental Investigation

In the experimental investigation, ordinary Portland cement of 53 grade confirming to IS 12269:2013 [14] and river sand confirming to Zone II of IS 383: 1970 [10] was used. Mix design was carried out based on IS 10262:2009 [15] for M30 grade with 0.45 W/C and ratio 1:1.70:2.70. From the experimental results, the increase in the percentage of manufactured sand increases the compressive strength up to 60% substitution of manufactured sand for river sand, beyond which there is a decrease in compressive strength and it was concluded that the optimum percentage of substitution of manufactured sand is taken as 60% [16,17]. The modulus of elasticity and the bond strength behaviour were dertermined for 60% M-sand substituted concrete.

Bond Strength

Twenty eight cylindrical specimens of size 300mm in length and 150mm in diameter were cast with embedded high strength deformed (HYSD) bar of 16mm in diameter placed at the centre to determine the bond strength behaviour of concrete. Figure 4.shows the casting ,curing and testingof the specimens for the bond strength.

Recent Advancements in Geotechnical Engineering - NCRAG'21   Materials Research Forum LLC
Materials Research Proceedings **19** (2021) 215-221   https://doi.org/10.21741/9781644901618-27

Table 2 *Average Bond Strength Values of Conventional and M-Sand Concrete*

Sl.No	Mix Identification	Average Bond Strength (MPa)
1	M30-Conventional	7.82
2	M30 –M-sand (60%)	9.72

Figure 4 *Casting ,curing and testing of the Specimen for the Bond Strength Test*

From the Table 2, it is proved that the average bond strength tends to increase with respect to the inclusion of M-sand in concrete. The proper gradation of M-sand obtained through the VSI crusher, the angular nature of the M-sand particles and the rough surface texture improves the inner friction within the mix and creates better interlocking between the M-sand particles and the rebar which increases the bond characteristics.

Modulus of Elasticity

Modulus of Elasticity is a necessary parameter to determine the stresses in materials and structures. Even though concrete has nonlinear stress-strain behaviour, modulus of elasticity is important material property to design and analyse concrete structures. The design accuracy of concrete will depend on the modulus of elasticity of concrete and it was determined as per IS 516-1959 [12] by subjecting a cylindrical specimen of size 150 mm in diameter and 300 mm in height to uniaxial compression in server control UTM. The deformations are measured by means of dial gauges fixed between certain gauge length. The strain is measured by dividing the dial gauge reading with the gauge length and the applied load divided by the area of cross section of the cylindrical specimen will give the corresponding stress.This change in stress with respect to the elastic strain gives the modulus of elasticity of concrete. The experimental values of E were obtained from the slopes of the corresponding stress-strain curves. The theoretical values of E were calculated as per IS 456: 2000 [18].The calculated values of E are compared with the experimental values and are tabulated in Table 3

Table 3 shows the E values of control concrete and 60% M-sand concrete. As the percentage substitution of manufactured sand is increased, the value of modulus of elasticity also increased. The experimental investigation showed that the M30 grade concrete with 60% M-sand substitution has the higher modulus of elasticity value than the conventional The modulus of elasticity increased by 11.92% for the M30 grade of concrete when replaced with 60% M-sand. The experimental values of E were found to be more than the theoretical values by 6.53 % and 4.53% for M30 control concrete and for 60% manufactured sand substituted concrete respectively. From the experimental investigation, it was found that the experimental values of E is more than the theoretical values for control concrete and manufactured sand substituted concrete. It was clear from the results that the addition of M-sand had improved the modulus of elasticity of concrete.

Table 3 *The average Characteristic Compressive Strength and Modulus of Elasticity of Concrete incorporating M-sand*

Sl.No	Mix Identification	Characteristic Compressive Strength (MPa)	Modulus of elasticity, E (MPa)		
			Experimental	Theoretical	Expt./ Theo.
1	M30- Conventional	36.12	32149.87	30049.95	1.06
2	M30 –M-sand (60%)	47.20	35982.26	34351.12	1.04

Conclusion

- Incorporation of manufactured sand improves the bond characteristics of concrete. The proper gradation of M-sand obtained through the VSI crusher, the angular nature of the M-sand particles and the rough surface texture improves the inner friction within the mix and creates better interlocking between the M-sand particles and the rebar which increases the bond characteristics.

- The soundness test results for river sand and manufactured sand are within the permissible limits as specified in IS 383-1970.
- The EDAX results of river sand shows that the minerals present in river sand forms hydrated compounds which gives good workability for river sand when compared with M-sand.

- It was also concluded that the development length of the rebar can be reduced, when M-sand is used in construction, which consequently reduces the economy in construction.

- The modulus of elasticity increase with the addition of M-sand in concrete due to the rough surface nature and the angular particles of manufactured sand creates better bonding between the hydrated cement paste and the aggregate.

- In general manufactured sand can be used as an efficient and effective alternative for river sand in concrete.

References

[1] H.Donza,O. Cabrera, E.F. Irassar, High-strength concrete with different fine aggregate , Cement and Concrete Research 32 (11) (2002) 1755-1761. https://doi.org/10.1016/S0008-8846(02)00860-8

[2] P. Quiroga, D. Fowler, The effects of aggregates characteristics on the performance of Portland cement concrete, International center for aggregates research 104-1F .

[3] S.Jamkar, C.Rao, Index of aggregate particle shape and texture of coarse aggregate as a parameter for concrete mix proportioning, cement and concrete research 34 (11) (2004) 2021-2027. https://doi.org/10.1016/j.cemconres.2004.03.010

[4] M.Westerholm, Rheology of the mortar phase of concrete with crushed aggregate, Department of chemical engineering and Geosciences, Licentiate, vol.198, Lulea University of technology, Stockholm, 2006.

[5] F.I. Mel'nikov, calculation methods for determining compositions of refractory concretes, refractories and industrial ceramics 11 (1970) 591-595. https://doi.org/10.1007/BF01290553

[6] H.Jarvenpaa, Quality characteristics of fine aggregates and controlling their effects on concrete, department of materials science and rock engineering, Helsinki University of technology, Doctor of Thechnology, vol.243, 2001.

[7] M.F. Kalpan, Flexural and compressive strength of concrete as affected by the properties of a coarse aggegrates,American Concrete Institute 55 (1959) 1193 – 1208.

[8] JTG F 30-2003, Technical specification for construction of highway cement concrete pavements. Beijing; Ministry of transport of the People's Republic of China: 2003.

[9] Ahn N, Experimental study on the guidelines for using higher contents of aggregate micro fines in Portland cement concrete . Ph.D.Thesis. University of Texas.

[10] IS: 383 (1970, Reaffirmed: 2002), Code of Practice: Specification for Coarse and Fine Aggregates from Natural Sources for Concrete, Bureau of Indian Standards, New Delhi.

[11] IS: 2770 (Part I)-1967 "Methods of testing bond in reinforced concrete," BIS, New Delhi.

[12] IS:516-1959, Recommended guidelines for concrete mix, Bureau of Indian Standards,New Delhi.

[13] AS 1141.24, (1997) "Methods for sampling and testing aggregates-Aggregate soundness," Evaluation by exposure to sodium sulfate solution.

[14] IS 12269 : 2013 Code of Practice: Ordinary Portland Cement, 53 Grade – Specification

[15] IS:10262-1982, Recommended guidelines for concrete mix, Bureau of IndianStandards, New Delhi.

[16] Vijaya. B and Senthil Selvan.S,Comparative Study on the Strength and Durability Properties of Concrete with Manufactured sand, Indian Journal of Science and Technology, (2015), 8(36),.1-7. https://doi.org/10.17485/ijst/2015/v8i36/88614

[17] Vijaya, B and Senthil Selvan. S.,Experimental Investigation on the strength and Durability properties of concrete using Manufactured sand," International Journal of Applied Engineering Research , International Journal of Applied Engineering Research, (2015), 10 (68), 109-114.

[18] IS 456 (2000), - Code of Practice for Plain and Reinforced Concrete, Bureau of Indian Standards, New Delhi.

Recent Advancements in Geotechnical Engineering - NCRAG'21
Materials Research Proceedings **19** (2021) 222-230

Materials Research Forum LLC
https://doi.org/10.21741/9781644901618-28

Influences of Welding Parameters on Friction Stir Welding of Aluminum and Magnesium: A Review

Boopathi Sampath[1,a] *, V. Haribalaji[2,b]

[1]Department of Mechanical Engineering, Muthayammal Engineering College, Rasipuram, Tamil Nadu 637408, India

[2]Department of Mechanical Engineering, Narasu Sarathy Institute of Technology, Salem. Tamil Nadu 638401, India

* [a]boopasangee@gmail.com, [b]harimechnsit@gmail.com

Keywords: Aluminum, Magnesium, Friction Stir Welding, Joining Factor, Welding Quality, Defect-Free

Abstract. Friction stir welding (FSW) is an important joining process wherein two dissimilar metals and alloys are welded together using frictional heat produced in a revolving tool and workpiece. FSW is playing an important role in dissimilar material joining of Magnesium (Mg) and Aluminum (Al) materials due to the increasing demand for their industrial applications. In this review article, the research background of FSW processes, and influences of joining factors on tensile strength, micro-hardness, and microstructures of FSW of Al-Mg alloy materials have been studied. The effects of joining factors for example axial force, tool revolving speed, tool incline, speed, and offset on welding characterizes have been enlightened to make defect-free FSW of aluminum and magnesium alloys. The microstructural behaviors of intermetallic formation and material drift in FSW zones of Al-Mg were also studied to find the scope to improve the welding quality.

Introduction and background
Friction stir welding (FSW) is an essential metal welding technique that was invented in 1991 by The Welding Institute (TWI). It had been first applied to join the two dissimilar alloys and metals by the application of frictional heat produced by a rotating tool and two metals [1,2,6]. The FSW process has been applied in the joining of non-ferrous materials such as Aluminum, Magnesium, and Copper alloys with high strength weight ratio. In a product assembly section of production industries, the welding of dissimilar alloys is challenging to improve the physical properties of joints in naval, aerospace, automotive, and various precision applications [24]. Tool revolving speed, tool feed rate, force applied and the tilting angle of FSW is general process parameters of the FSW of dissimilar Al-Mg components[24]. Banglong Fu et al. stated that the toughnessof welded joints was increased while locating Mg on the leading edge and offsetting tool of dissimilar metals (AA6061 and AZ31B) and it was reduced while placing Al on the leadingside and tool offsetting due to reducing heat absorption[11]. M. Azizieh et al. attempted to weld 3mm thickness of plates (AA1100 and AZ31 Mg). Mg was either on the leading side or tailing side and the five modes of tool offset positions center line to 2.5mm towards both Al and Mg sides. It was concluded that the quality welding was obtained from processes of advancing side and tool pin offset towards magnesium side; the hardness and tensile strength were also improved by the process in Al side [3]. Uday kumar et al. experimented that the 6 mm thickness Al 6061-T6 and AZ31 dissimilar alloy plates are welded using 600 rpm tool rotation speed, 0.5mm/s to 1mm/s of tool travel speed, 1o tool tilting angle, and 16mm diameter shoulder in the FSW. The

microstructures of welding characteristics have been analyzed to find the effects of the Mg and Alleading side and top of the weld. The welds nugget zones, intermetallic compound Al12Mg17, and Al3Mg2, and Al-Mg Alloy intermixing region were also investigated [16].

Very recently, Dharmalingam et al. testified from FSW experiments of Al-Mg that the maximum tool revolving speed and minimum tool feed rate were applied to improve the micro-grain structure and tensile strength while welding AA8011 and AZ31 Alloys [10]. H. H. Jadav et al. Co2 and compressed air were applied to cool the welding zone of dissimilar Al-Mg. the tensile capacity and hardness of the Al-Mg joints had been enhanced by the application of the Co2 cooling method. In this process, 545 rpm tool revolving speed, 31.5mm/min of tool feed rate, 2 degreesof tool tilt, and 2mm tool offsetting to advancing side Magnesium alloy [12]. A H Baghdadi et al.[4] revealed from FSW that the uniform distribution of microstructure grain size in the joining zone and improved tensile capacity of FSW junction were observed from the post-weld heat-treatment process. A.Bandi et al. concluded that the intermetallic joining layer and the intermetallic mixture of AA6061-T6 and AZ31B-H24 magnesium plates were presented. It was also observed that Al3Mg2 was obtained in the Aluminium side and a major Eutectic mixture of Al12Mg17 was derived in the Magnesium side [5].

It is observed from the above literature survey the major parameters for dissimilar FSW joining are tool revolving speed, tool travel feed, tool geometry, and axial forces are playing a major contribution in Al-Mg weld processes. Dissimilar material mixing and flow of intermetallic layers were influenced by the geometry of tool and pin length. In this paper, the impacts of joining parameters, microstructural characteristics, and mechanical behaviors of FSW joints Al-Mg alloys were elucidated.

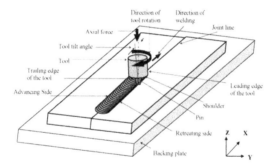

Figure 1. Schematic diagram of FSW [14]

FSW experimentation

The schematic experimental setup for FSW is shown in Figure 1. The work materials' size and shape were prepared based on the type of fixtures used in the FSW machine. Before the welding process, Aluminum and Magnesium plates were well cleaned by steel brush and acetone to remove the dust on the workpieces[9,21]. Locating these plates on the fixture is essential to joint dissimilar metals welding. The aluminum was connected to leading edge and the Magnesium was connected to tailing side to improve material flow and quality of welding joints.[13].The tool design is playing a significant role in uniform temperature distribution, the flow of welding metal, and the quality of intermetallic layers [21].

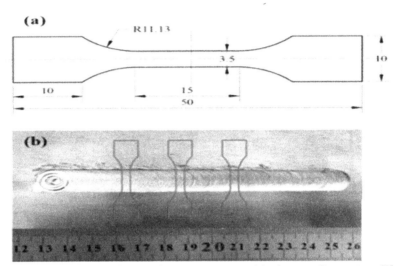

Figure 2. ASTM E8/E8M-09 Tensile testing specimens: (a) schematic (b) experiment[9]

After the FSW process, the hardness was observed on all three sides of welded specimens. Vickers hardness test for dissimilar Al-Mg joints was stirring zone as a center point and the hardness level was tested from center point to Al side or Mg Side. Before tensile testing, the weld samples were machined by EDM with ASTM E8/E8M-09 Standards as displayed in Figures 2 (a) and (b). The ultimate tensile, yield stress and amount of deformation of FSW weld specimens were measured by a universal testing machine. The welded parts were transversely cut from plates as per standard shape and size. The metallographic samples were polishing with different grade emery papers and the area of the part was chemically cleaned by a solution from acetic acid, ethanol, picric acid, and distilled water[8,13]. The macrostructure of weld joints was inspected by a laser microscope and the microstructure of weld zone like stir zone (SZ), Heat affected Zone (HAZ), and thermo mechanically affected zone (TMAZ) are performed by Transmission electron microscope (TEM) and scanning electron microscope (SEM). Aluminum and magnesium phase composition was detected by Energy dispersive spectrometer (EDS) and X-ray diffraction (XRD) methods[8,13].

FSW - Al-MG alloy: characterization analysis
Analysis of Microstructure
From this macrostructure analysis, the defects of the welding joint were examined by varying joiningfactorssuch as tool revolving speed, tool feed rate, and pin position.The cross-sectional morphologies of weld joints were examined the material flow and identify the defect formation in the weld zones[20]. Defects were found when the offset of the toolalong with the Aluminum plate and desired weld quality was recorded while tool offsetting onthe magnesium plate [19]. Material flow and IMCs were the two key features leads to defects in FSW welds. Friction between the tool and the aluminum alloy was generated more heat than Mg alloy. Tool offset towards aluminum side leads to more formation of IMCs and it produces hot cracking defects[26,27]. The

intermetallic distribution is directly related to the peak temperature, the ratio between tool rotation and travel speed. The material flow rate is higher at high rotational speed by excessive liquation and is lower at a very low speed of rotation[3]. The good quality of weld joints between Al-Mg dissimilar alloys is attained by placing magnesium alloy on the advancing side [7].

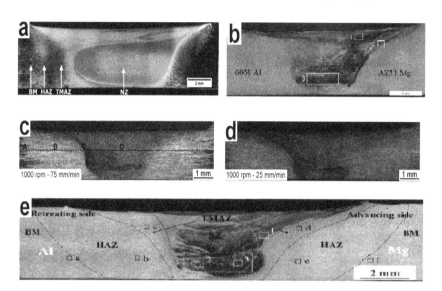

Figure 3. Macrostructure of FSW zone of Al-Mg[8,9,17,23]

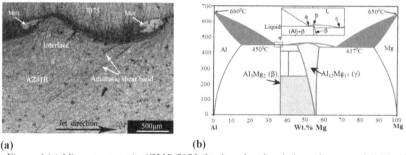

(a)   (b)

Figure 4.(a) Microstructure in AZ31B/7075 (b) shear band and phase diagram of Al-Mg alloys [15]

In the FSW region of the Al-Mg welded joint, the material flow and IMCs were examined by SEM and EDS images. The intermetallic layer and bonding of Al-Mg joints were shown in Figures 3(a),(b), (c), (d) and (e). The four different weld zones like SZ, TMAZ, HAZ, and BM were analyzed with the help of microstructural images. While FSW operation, a particular volume of metal was debris in the intermediate zone of Al-Mg and intermixed material was finally settled down in SZ. In the IMCs phases, Al12Mg17 and Al3Mg2 were formed across the Al-Mg zone pictures are displayed in Figure 4 (a) and the concentration distribution of Al-Mg atoms was formed as displayed in figure 4(b) [15].

A typical SEM image and EDX images are shown in Fig.4 (a & b). Nugget zones are further classified into three different zones to examine the Al-Mg intercalated structure and the formation of the intermetallic eutectic structure of $Al_{12}Mg_{17}$ and Al_3Mg_2. Moreover, IMCs Al-Mg solid solutions were indicated by XRD patterns[11]. Instead of the conventional FSW process, the ultrasonic-assisted FSW was found to enhance the IMC stream thickness as a maximum of58% was reported with peak vibration condition. The acoustic assistance had considerably improved the material deform and intermixing of dissimilar Al-Mg. From the ultrasonic-assisted FSW process, the interconnected zone of the joints was significantly modified [15].

After microstructure analysis of the PWHT method, the grain size of SZ increased several hundred microns and this phenomenon was the instability of the microstructure of the joining phase [4].

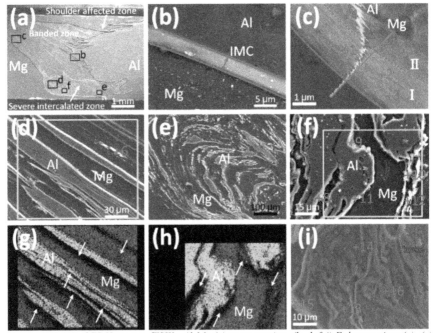

Figure 5. SEM and EDX image ofFSW - Al-Mg (a) cross-section, (b, d–f, i) Enlarges views(a), (c) EDX line of interface, (g) EDX mapping of zone (d), (h) EDX mapping phase[11]

From this microstructure analysis of the FSW process, the material intermixing, heat affected the weld zones and the intermixing of Al-Mg alloy were analyzed to enhance the weld properties.

It has been gathered that the IMCs stream and grain structure of the FSW process was improved than the conventional welding process.

Analysis of Microhardness

The hardness was obtained on three area zone of the weld specimens. Vickers hardness test for dissimilar Al-Mg joints was stirring zone as a center point and the hardness level was tested from center point to Al side or Mg Side. In dissimilar Al-Mg alloys welding process, the hardness was 86 Hv for Mg alloy set near the leading edge and 89 Hv for Mg alloy set on the trailing edge, this small modification on hardness value was due to material flow and IMC stream of Al and Mg [20]. The internal heat was reduced when increasing the tool offset to the Mg plate and the morphology of IMCs was distributed more homogeneous and the hardness value was declined[18]. The strong ultrasonic vibration can break the IMCs into fragments and enhance the finer grain size compared to conventional FSW and the mean hardness value of NZ was significantly increased[19]. At the area of the Nugget zone, a sharp connection line was identified and the hardness value reduced rapidly at the Al side. Hardness variation was decreased at NZ and the total hardness was enhanced due to grain resettlement of the revolving tool point[22]. The hardness in that zone is decreased when referred to as HAZ and TMAZ. Thus, the hardness of the PWHAZ was significantly enhanced while comparing with the existing FSW process [4]. The hardness value of the weld zone was improved by low weld speed and decreased while the increase in feed rate.

From this study of hardness analysis for dissimilar Al-Mg welding, the hardness was decreased at weld zones when compared to base metals of Al-Mg alloys. Instead of the conventional FSW process, the average hardness value was increased in ultrasonic-assisted FSW and post-weld heat treatment processes due to the fine grain structure of IMCs layers of the weld zone. The SEM and EDX images of FSW : Al-Mg are displayed in Figures 5(a), (b), (c), (d), (e), (f),(g) and (h).

Analysis of Tensile strength

In the FSW Al-Mg, the tensile capacity of the FSW joint in Mg placed on the advanced side of FSW was obtained as 172.3 MPa and the Al on the advanced side was found 156.25 MPa because of the formation of IMCs in dissimilar welds[20]. The tensile property of welded joints was reduced by 38% while comparing with base metals due to coarse grain size in Heat-affected zone and the tensile strength was increased by 15% by the post-weld heat treatment process[4]. The average tensile strength has been improved to contain the level of welding speed. Further increasing speed, the strength is reduced. The highest strength value of 477MPa was obtained from the mean welding velocity and the highest tool revolving velocity. The worst tensile properties were found in the highest welding speed due to the loose bonding structure[17]. The maximum tensile strength for dissimilar Al-Mg alloys was observed from maximum tool revolution speed and lower feed rate. It is also obtained from the cylindrical tool than the straight square profile of the tool pin[10]. It was also found that the great tensile property (143MPa) was attained from the highest tool revolving speed (1400 rpm) and lowest tool travel rate(100 mm/min), and the joint efficiency is nearly equivalent to 72%[25]. The maximum elongation was found from 500 rpm of tool revolving velocity and moving feed of 20mm/min[3].

It was revealed from the literature that the weld parameter of high revolving speed and low tool feed were found to highest tensile strength and the highest percentage of deformation of Al-Mg alloy joining processes.

Summary

- In this article, FSW of Aluminium and Magnesium alloy was considered to understand the influences of various joining factors on tensile strength, microhardness, and microstructure of welding zone by various Al-Mg alloys researchers.

- The defects-free friction-stir-welding have been found from macrostructure analysis and optimal quality weld joints have been attained by changing the factors such as tool revolving speed, travel feed, tilt angle, and tool offset.

- IMCs layer and material flow of FSW from various research activities have been summarized with the evidence of the SEM and EDX images. IMCs growth was found by providing an additional cooling system during the FSW process. The welding zone grain structure and enhance weld strength have been enhanced by the PWHT method.

- The tensile property and microhardness of FSW Al-Mg joints were improved in ultrasonic-assisted FSW than conventional FSW process.

References

[1]   R. Allen, T. Thomson, Friction welding, Chinese Patent., (1986).

[2]   R. V Arunprasad, G. Surendhiran, M. Ragul, T. Soundarrajan, S. Moutheepan, S. Boopathi, Review on Friction Stir Welding Process, Int. J. Appl. Eng. Res. ISSN., 13 (2018) 5750–5758.

[3]   M. Azizieh, A. Sadeghi Alavijeh, M. Abbasi, Z. Balak, H.S. Kim, Mechanical properties and microstructural evaluation of AA1100 to AZ31 dissimilar friction stir welds, Materials Chemistry and Physics., 170 (2016) 251–260. https://doi.org/10.1016/j.matchemphys.2015.12.046

[4]   A.H. Baghdadi, Z. Sajuri, M.Z. Omar, A. Rajabi, Friction stir welding parameters: Impact of abnormal grain growth during post-weld heat treatment on mechanical properties of Al–Mg–Si welded joints, Metals., 10 (2020) 1–18. https://doi.org/10.3390/met10121607

[5]   A. Bandi, S.R. Bakshi, Effect of Pin Length and Rotation Speed on the Microstructure and Mechanical Properties of Friction Stir Welded Lap Joints of AZ31B-H24 Mg Alloy and AA6061-T6 Al Alloy, Metallurgical and Materials Transactions A: Physical Metallurgy and Materials Science., 51 (2020) 6269–6282. https://doi.org/10.1007/s11661-020-06020-8

[6]   S. Boopathi, A. Kumaresan, N. Manohar, R. Krishna Moorthi, Review on Effect of Process Parameters-Friction Stir Welding Process, International Research Journal of Engineering and Technology (IRJET)., 4 (2017).

[7]   G. Buffa, D. Baffari, A. Di Caro, L. Fratini, Friction stir welding of dissimilar aluminium–magnesium joints: Sheet mutual position effects, Science and Technology of Welding and Joining., 20 (2015) 271–279. https://doi.org/10.1179/1362171815Y.0000000016

[8]   W. Chen, W. Wang, Z. Liu, D. An, N. Shi, T. Zhang, M. Ding, Microstructure evolution mechanism of Al/Mg dissimilar joint during friction stir welding, Metallurgical Research & Technology., 117 (2020) 311. https://doi.org/10.1051/metal/2020012

[9]   W. Chen, W. Wang, Z. Liu, X. Zhai, G. Bian, T. Zhang, P. Dong, Improvement in tensile strength of Mg/Al alloy dissimilar friction stir welding joints by reducing intermetallic

compounds, Journal of Alloys and Compounds., (2020) 157942.
https://doi.org/10.1016/j.jallcom.2020.157942

[10]   S. Dharmalingam, K. Lenin, P. Navaneetha Krishnan, Comparative analysis of cylindrical
thread and straight square profile pin on ultimate tensile strength of AA8011/AZ31B in friction stir
butt welding, Materials Today: Proceedings., 21 (2020) 523–526.
https://doi.org/10.1016/j.matpr.2019.06.661

[11]   B. Fu, G. Qin, F. Li, X. Meng, J. Zhang, C. Wu, Friction stir welding process of dissimilar
metals of 6061-T6 aluminum alloy to AZ31B magnesium alloy, Journal of Materials Processing
Technology., 218 (2015) 38–47. https://doi.org/10.1016/j.jmatprotec.2014.11.039

[12]   H.H. Jadav, V. Badheka, D.K. Sharma, G. Upadhyay, Effect of pin diameter and different
cooling media on friction stir welding of dissimilar Al-Mg alloys, Materials Today: Proceedings.,
(2020). https://doi.org/10.1016/j.matpr.2020.09.553

[13]   S.A. Khodir, T. Shibayanagi, Dissimilar friction stir welded joints between 2024-T3
aluminum alloy and AZ31 magnesium alloy, Materials Transactions., 48 (2007) 2501–2505.
https://doi.org/10.2320/matertrans.MRA2007093

[14]   K. Kumar, S. V. Kailas, The role of friction stir welding tool on material flow and weld
formation, Materials Science and Engineering A., 485 (2008) 367–374.
https://doi.org/10.1016/j.msea.2007.08.013

[15]   S. Kumar, C. Wu, Suppression of intermetallic reaction layer by ultrasonic assistance
during friction stir welding of Al and Mg based alloys, Journal of Alloys and Compounds., 827
(2020) 154343. https://doi.org/10.1016/j.jallcom.2020.154343

[16]   U. Kumar, U. Acharya, S.C. Saha, B.S. Roy, Microstructure and mechanical property of
friction stir welded Al-Mg joints by adopting modified joint configuration technique, Materials
Today: Proceedings., 26 (2019) 2083–2088. https://doi.org/10.1016/j.matpr.2020.02.450

[17]   Y. Li, H. Yan, J. Chen, W. Xia, B. Su, T. Ding, X. Li, Influences of welding speed on
microstructure and mechanical properties of friction stir welded Al-Mg alloy with high Mg
content, Materials Research Express., 7 (2020). https://doi.org/10.1088/2053-1591/ab9854

[18]   H. Liu, Y. Chen, Z. Yao, F. Luo, Effect of tool offset on the microstructure and properties
of AA6061/AZ31B friction stir welding joints, Metals., 10 (2020) 1–9.
https://doi.org/10.3390/met10040546

[19]   Z. Liu, X. Meng, S. Ji, Z. Li, L. Wang, Improving tensile properties of Al/Mg joint by
smashing intermetallic compounds via ultrasonic-assisted stationary shoulder friction stir welding,
Journal of Manufacturing Processes., 31 (2018) 552–559.
https://doi.org/10.1016/j.jmapro.2017.12.022

[20]   S. MD, A.K. Birru, Mechanical and metallurgical properties of friction stir welded
dissimilar joints of AZ91 magnesium alloy and AA 6082-T6 aluminium alloy, Journal of
Magnesium and Alloys., 7 (2019) 264–271. https://doi.org/10.1016/j.jma.2018.09.004

[21]   J. Mohammadi, Y. Behnamian, A. Mostafaei, H. Izadi, T. Saeid, A.H. Kokabi, A.P.
Gerlich, Friction stir welding joint of dissimilar materials between AZ31B magnesium and 6061
aluminum alloys: Microstructure studies and mechanical characterizations, Materials
Characterization., 101 (2015) 189–207. https://doi.org/10.1016/j.matchar.2015.01.008

[22]   B.L. Prasad, G. Neelaiah, M.G. Krishna, S.V.V. Ramana, K.S. Prakash, G. Sarika, G.P.K. Reddy, R. Dumpala, B.R. Sunil, Joining of AZ91 Mg alloy and Al6063 alloy sheets by friction stir welding, Journal of Magnesium and Alloys., 6 (2018) 71–76. https://doi.org/10.1016/j.jma.2017.12.004

[23]   O.S. Salih, N. Neate, H. Ou, W. Sun, Influence of process parameters on the microstructural evolution and mechanical characterisations of friction stir welded Al-Mg-Si alloy, Journal of Materials Processing Technology., 275 (2020) 116366. https://doi.org/10.1016/j.jmatprotec.2019.116366

[24]   Y.S. Sato, S.H.C. Park, M. Michiuchi, H. Kokawa, Constitutional liquation during dissimilar friction stir welding of Al and Mg alloys, Scripta Materialia., 50 (2004) 1233–1236. https://doi.org/10.1016/j.scriptamat.2004.02.002

[25]   I. Shigematsu, Y.J. Kwon, N. Saito, Dissimilar friction stir welding for tailor-welded blanks of aluminum and magnesium alloys, Materials Transactions., 50 (2009) 197–203. https://doi.org/10.2320/matertrans.MER2008326

[26]   Y.B. Yan, Z.W. Zhang, W. Shen, J.H. Wang, L.K. Zhang, B.A. Chin, Microstructure and properties of magnesium AZ31B-aluminum 7075 explosively welded composite plate, Materials Science and Engineering A., 527 (2010) 2241–2245. https://doi.org/10.1016/j.msea.2009.12.007

[27]   Y.K. Yang, H. DongG, S. Kou, Liquation Tendency and Liquid-Film, Welding Journal., 87 (2008) 202–211.

Keyword Index

About the Editor

Dr. Soundara Balu is a Professor in the Department of Civil Engineering, Bannari Amman Institute of Technology, Tamilnadu, INDIA. She has obtained BE in Civil Engineering from Alagappa Chettiar College of Engineering and Technology, Karaikudi, India in 2002, Masters in Soil Mechanics and Foundation Engineering from College of Engineering Guindy, Anna University in 2004, and Ph.D in Geotechnical Engineering from IIT Madras in 2010. After working for about 2 years in UAE, she has joined as Assistant Professor and HoD at SKR Engineering College Chennai (2012-15) and then joined BIT in 2015. Her research interest includes study on the behaviour of problematic soils, various ground improvement methods and Physical modelling of geostructures. She has received Grants from various government funding agencies like AICTE, DST NIMAT, SERB, and TNSCST and was the recipient of the Early Career Research Award from Science and Engineering Research Board in 2016. She has published around 30 peer-reviewed journal papers, 35 conference papers, 3 book chapters and filed 3 patents. She is an active reviewer in 5 leading journals, and chaired technical sessions in 3 International conferences. She has guided 2 Ph.D scholars and guiding 8 members, at present. She is a professional member of American Society of Civil Engineers, International Society for Soil Mechanics and Geotechnical Engineering, Indian Geotechnical Society and Indian Society for Technical Education.

Dr. M. Vasudevan is currently working as Assistant Professor and Head of the Department of Civil Engineering at Bannari Amman Institute of Technology Sathyamangalam, Tamil Nadu, India with a teaching experience of 6 years. He obtained his bachelor's degree in Agricultural Engineering from Kerala Agricultural University, India in 2007, followed by master's degree (M.Tech.) in Environmental Engineering from Motilal Nehru National Institute of Technology Allahabad, India in 2009. He completed his Ph.D. from Indian Institute of Technology Madras in 2015 in the area of Environmental Engineering. He has published about 45 research papers in peer-reviewed international journals and 70 international/national conferences. He has also authored 8 book chapters and co-edited 2 books. He is a professional member of Indian Geotechnical Society and Indian Society for Technical Education and Indian Water Works Association.

Mr. V. Jeevanantham is Assistant Professor in the Department of Civil Engineering, Bannari Amman Institute of Technology, Tamilnadu, INDIA. He has obtained BE in civil engineering from Thanthai Periyar Government Institute of Technology, Vellore, INDIA in 2013, masters in Geotechnical Engineering from Government College of Technology, Coimbatore, INDIA in 2015. He started his professional carrier as assistant professor and presently with 6 years of experience in teaching. His research interest includes study on the behaviour of problematic soils and various ground improvement methods. He has published around 8 peer-reviewed journal papers, 9 conference papers and filed 1 patent. He is extending his service to the society as Soil Consultant, carrying out field tests for commercial building construction at his working locality. He is a professional member of Indian Geotechnical Society, Coimbatore Chapter.

Mrs. V. Preetha is Assistant Professor in the Department of Civil Engineering, Bannari Amman Institute of Technology, Tamilnadu, INDIA. She obtained BE in Civil Engineering from Kongu Engineering College, Erode, INDIA in 2006, masters in structural engineering from Bannari Amman Institute of Technology, Erode, India in 2009 and pursuing her Ph.D in structural engineering from Anna University. Having worked for about 1 year in Jain Housing and Construction as Quantity surveyor, she joined Larsen and Toubro Pvt Limited, ECC division, Headquarters, Manapakkam Campus as Senior Design Engineer during 2009 to 2011 and then joined BIT in 2012. Her research interests include earthquake engineering, steel concrete composite structures and structural design. She has published around 15 peer-reviewed journal papers, 20 conference papers, 1 book chapters and filed 2 patents. Her service includes field studies in the area of concrete technology and non-destructive testing methods as consultancy projects. She is a professional member of Institution of Engineers India, Indian Geotechnical Society and Indian Society for Technical Education.

CPSIA information can be obtained
at www.ICGtesting.com
Printed in the USA
BVHW010319280921
617490BV00013B/19